THE ROOTS OF MOLECULAR MEDICINE

Speakers at the Orthomolecular Medical Society symposium
in honor of Linus Pauling,
and officers of the society (*left to right*):
(*first row*) Michael Lesser, Irwin Stone,
Linus Pauling, Michael Rosenbaum, Richard Kunin;
(*second row*) John Catchpool, Richard Huemer,
Bernard Rimland, Robert Cathcart, Jeffrey Bland;
(*third row*) Crellin Pauling, Emile Zuckerkandl,
Stephen Levine, Melvin Greenblatt;
(*fourth row*) Carl Ebnother, Jerzy Meduski, Denham Harman;
(*fifth row*) Rob Krakovitz, Richard Jones, Jonathan Rothschild.

THE ROOTS OF MOLECULAR MEDICINE

A TRIBUTE TO
Linus Pauling

Based on a collection of papers
presented at a symposium of
the Orthomolecular Medical Society
in San Francisco, May 7–8, 1983,
with revisions and additional papers

Edited by
Richard P. Huemer, MD

W. H. Freeman and Company
New York

Library of Congress Cataloging-in-Publication Data
Main entry under title:

The Roots of molecular medicine.

Based on a symposium presented on May 7–8, 1983 in San Francisco by the Orthomolecular Medical Society.
Includes bibliographies and index.
1. Orthomolecular therapy—Congresses. 2. Molecular biology—Congresses. 3. Pauling, Linus, 1901– —Congresses.
I. Pauling, Linus, 1901– . II. Huemer, Richard P.
III. Orthomolecular Medical Society (U.S.)
[DNLM: 1. Biochemistry—congresses. 2. Medicine—congresses.
3. Molecular Biology—congresses. WB 100 R783 1983]
RM235.5.R66 1986 610 85-29376

ISBN 0-7167-1761-1
ISBN 0-7167-1762-X (pbk.)

Printed in the United States of America

1 2 3 4 5 6 7 8 9 0 M 4 3 2 1 0 8 9 8 7 6

CONTENTS

viii **Preface** RICHARD P. HUEMER
xi **Foreword** BERNARD RIMLAND

PART I The Biochemistry of Disease

1 **CHAPTER ONE**
Toward a Molecular Biology of Predisposition to Disease: The Case of Cancer
EMILE ZUCKERKANDL

28 **CHAPTER TWO**
Functional Properties of Abnormal Human Hemoglobins
RICHARD T. JONES and DANIEL T.-B. SHIH

48 **CHAPTER THREE**
Scurvy, the Cosmic Connection: An Ancient Supernova and the Practice of Medicine in the Twentieth Century
IRWIN STONE

57 **CHAPTER FOUR**
Lipid Peroxidation-Induced Diseases: A Model of Molecular Disease
JEFFREY BLAND

75 **CHAPTER FIVE**
The Aging Process
DENHAM HARMAN

88 **CHAPTER SIX**
Antioxidant Biochemical Adaptation: A Unified Disease Theory
STEPHEN A. LEVINE and PARRIS M. KIDD

113 **CHAPTER SEVEN**
Photon Counting in Nutritional Biochemistry
J. W. MEDUSKI, J. D. MEDUSKI, KHASHAYAR KHAKMAHD, AKBAR AZAD, CLAUDE CRUZ

PART II Nutrition and Health

133 CHAPTER EIGHT
Vitamin C and Cancer Cachexia: The Carnitine Connection
EWAN CAMERON

140 CHAPTER NINE
Nitrites, Nitrosamines, and Vitamin C
MELVIN GREENBLATT

144 CHAPTER TEN
Nutrients and the Immune System
MICHAEL ROSENBAUM

172 CHAPTER ELEVEN
Hormones, Formones, and Gormones
JOHN E. MORLEY and ALLEN S. LEVINE

180 CHAPTER TWELVE
Orthomolecular Psychiatry
RICHARD A. KUNIN

214 CHAPTER THIRTEEN
The Role of Phospholipids in Neurological Function
JONATHAN E. ROTHSCHILD

PART III The Scientist as Citizen

227 CHAPTER FOURTEEN
The Evolution of a Scientist's Social Conscience
JOHN F. CATCHPOOL

235 CHAPTER FIFTEEN
The Lysenko-Pauling-Sakharov File
IRVING S. BENGELSDORF

243 CHAPTER SIXTEEN
Linus Pauling and the Medical Revolution
RICHARD P. HUEMER

249 CHAPTER SEVENTEEN
The Future of Orthomolecular Medicine
LINUS PAULING

254 **CHAPTER EIGHTEEN**
The Twenty-five Most Cited Publications of Linus Pauling
ZELEK S. HERMAN

260 **The Authors**

271 **Index**

PREFACE

This book began as spoken words. It grew out of a symposium presented in May 1983 by the Orthomolecular Medical Society to honor Linus Pauling. This special meeting was not to celebrate Dr. Pauling's birthday or the anniversary of a special achievement or any of the other usual occasions. We just decided it was our turn to honor this man who had done so much to raise public awareness of nutrition and health and whose orthomolecular concept had guided our society and given it its name.

As president of the Orthomolecular Medical Society at that time, I had the privilege of organizing the meeting and inviting the speakers. This was no easy task, since through his long career Linus Pauling had known and worked with many people and had made many friends. Alexander Rich and Norman Davidson, who had edited a festschrift for Dr. Pauling in 1968,* very kindly provided names and addresses of significant people in his life. To that list I added the names of others who were working in areas of interest to Dr. Pauling.

I originally had in mind a sort of "This Is Your Life, Linus Pauling," but it was not to be. I learned that Linus Pauling's intellectual edifice had many rooms, with doors through which Dr. Pauling passed with ease, but other occupants of this mansion felt more comfortable in their own chambers. So I did not succeed in enticing any of his earlier colleagues, pure chemists and crystallographers, to our medical gathering. As I became more familiar with Dr. Pauling's remarkably varied career, I thought of Oliver Wendell Holmes's lines about the chambered nautilus:

> Year after year beheld the silent toil
> That spread his lustrous coil;
> Still, as the spiral grew,
> He left the last year's dwelling for the new.

The speakers were invited, the members of the Orthomolecular Medical Society were notified, and everyone gathered in San Francisco on May 7 and 8. Displaying no jet lag despite having just returned from speaking engagements in Europe, Dr. Pauling listened to each presentation with evident relish and attended the Saturday evening reception at Dick Kunin's elegant home. The program went off without a hitch.

*Rich, A, Davidson, N: *Structural Chemistry and Molecular Biology.* San Francisco, Freeman, 1968.

The society planned right from the beginning to make the proceedings of the meeting into a book, a festschrift for Dr. Pauling. However, what you see in these pages is not exactly what was presented at the meeting. Some speakers have extensively revised their papers, and two invitees who could not attend sent excellent manuscripts that I have included. Other speakers did not submit manuscripts for publication. We began to see the purpose of the book as different from that of the meeting. Whereas the symposium was intended as a tribute to a great man, the book would do double duty as both tribute and text. We perceived the book, more and more, as a means of communicating the essentials of orthomolecular medicine to our friends in other fields of practice. Thus, four chapters have been added to draw a clearer and more comprehensive picture of orthomolecular medicine.

Although Dr. Pauling's work for peace and social justice is not obviously connected to orthomolecular medicine, I cannot see that it is any less important than his scientific work. I am not even sure that it can be separated from his scientific work. As discussions of it were part of our original tribute, I have included the subject in this volume.

In editing this collection, I have tried to preserve the intimacy and spirit of the spoken presentations wherever I could. Thus, I have left mostly intact the authors' personal reminiscences and comments about Dr. Pauling. I have also retained the extemporaneous remarks presented by Pauling at the end of the symposium, thereby scoring a first in publishing history: Dr. Pauling has contributed to his own festschrift! But some things cannot be set in type: emotions, such as our delight at Crellin Pauling's account of growing up with his famous father, or the comradery we felt, or our awe at viewing hemoglobin A in color and three dimensions—an ancient microlandscape that evokes feelings you might experience in Monument Valley.

Vitamin C buffs will not be disappointed by this volume, but orthomolecular medicine encompasses far more than vitamins. Practicing physicians will find particularly relevant the chapters with extensive reviews of immunology and orthomolecular psychiatry. I must admit to having been unprepared in 1983 for the emphasis placed on free-radical biology by many of the symposium speakers. Three years later it seems very appropriate and well within the mainstream. Dr. Pauling, of course, had written on free radicals back in the 1930s.

I have enjoyed editing this book. The authors were usually prompt and were always tolerant of suggestions for improvement. (Fully a third of the authors, by the way, are current or former members of the Orthomolecular Medical Society.) But I edited Irwin Stone's contribution with great sadness, for Dr. Stone died from an accident in May 1984, a year after our symposium. I hope that, in polishing his words, I have not made less luminous the message he had for us.

I would like to thank some people. In the early stages of this project, Ralph Buchsbaum and Ted Melnechuk provided valuable advice on book production to the neophyte editor. Gerard Piel gave the green light for publication at W. H. Freeman, and Jim Dodd took the book through its first steps. Our project editor, Susan Moran, coordinated everything, kept everyone on schedule, and did it all with good humor and tact. I thank my wife Gloria for transcribing tapes and retyping manuscripts, and my son Peter for the frontispiece photograph. Thanks are also due to the OMS headquarters staff, and particularly Ruth Cammack, for typing and symposium coordination.

Most of all, I thank the contributors to this volume for giving me the opportunity to become thoroughly familiar with a wealth of fascinating information. There is something to be said for Keats's assertion that truth is beauty; there is much beauty in the truths of science, and I trust that those who read these pages will see it behind the technical words. Similar thoughts have been well expressed by Albert Szent-Gyorgyi. He was not able to come to our symposium in 1983, but in declining the invitation he wrote, in part,

> As [with] most scientific ideas of Linus, his idea of orthomolecularity has its deeper philosophical meaning, which involves the idea that the natural condition is the most perfect one and cannot be improved on. We can reach the maximum of health and well-being by guarding this natural condition, maintaining it as far and as perfectly as we are able.

That message nicely summarizes the pages that follow.

Richard P. Huemer, MD
Westlake Village, California
January 1986

FOREWORD

Like most important ideas, the concept behind orthomolecular medicine is simple. Orthomolecular medicine is the pursuit of good health and the treatment of disease by providing the patient with the optimum concentration of substances *normally* present in the body. Although our esteemed mentor and colleague Linus Pauling had used the term *orthomolecular medicine* earlier, its first widely publicized use was in Pauling's now famous article in *Science* (April 19, 1968). The prefix *ortho* implies correct or proper; Pauling was calling for "the right molecules in the right amounts."

The basic idea is an ancient one, expounded by great thinkers in many cultures. It was well expressed in the twelfth century by the physician Maimonides: "Let nothing which can be treated by diet be treated by other means." It fell to Pauling, however, to state the concept explicitly and provide the theoretical basis for it.

Pauling's *Science* article concentrated on the psychiatric implications of the concept: his paper was titled "Orthomolecular Psychiatry." It referred, in some depth, to the pioneering work of Abram Hoffer and Humphry Osmond on the use of vitamin B_3 and vitamin C in the treatment of schizophrenia. Since Linus lived near me in San Diego at the time, I had the opportunity to ask him how he had become interested in the use of megavitamins. He recalled visiting a friend's home a few years earlier and noticing some Hoffer and Osmond books and papers on a table. Out of curiosity, he began reading these materials. He was astonished to learn of the extraordinary success Hoffer and Osmond were reporting, in controlled studies, in the treatment of schizophrenia, a virtually untreatable disorder. Could a treatment as safe and simple as giving a few vitamins in large amounts really be as helpful as Hoffer and Osmond claimed? If so, why were the patients of other psychiatrists being given years of psychotherapy or electroshock or harmful drugs?

Characteristically, Linus did not let the matter rest. Visits to the library produced more evidence favoring Hoffer and Osmond, but he could find no studies contradicting their efforts. Also characteristically, the medical establishment was rewarding the unconventional efforts of Hoffer and Osmond by ignoring them. Here was a challenge for Pauling's curious and insightful mind: What mechanisms could account for the need for gram amounts of certain vitamins, when the rest of us require only milligrams? How could the scientific and medical establishments be induced to take off their blinders and see what he, and a few others, could see so clearly?

Linus's paper received wide coverage in the press. Well-known psychiatrists were interviewed in the *New York Times* and elsewhere. The consensus of their remarks: "When a scientist of the stature of Linus Pauling speaks, we must take him seriously. Very often in the past he has challenged the beliefs of the authorities and he has been proven right. But I still don't believe what he says about vitamins and schizophrenia."

One outcome of the increased attention focused on the megavitamin issue by Pauling's article was the publication in 1973 of the American Psychiatric Association's Task Force Report on Megavitamin Therapy in Psychiatry. The task force report roundly criticized the work of Hoffer and Osmond and declared megavitamin therapy to be of no value. Suffice it to say that the chairman of task force had been bitterly opposed to megavitamin therapy long before he was assigned the chairmanship. (I witnessed a heated debate between him and Hoffer in 1971.) The other committee members were no friendlier. One task force member was quoted as saying, "Even if every other psychiatrist in the country believes in megavitamin therapy, I still will not." Although the Academy of Orthomolecular Psychiatry, an organization of psychiatrists who had successfully replicated Hoffer and Osmond's work, had been formed several years earlier, and its officers were members in good standing of the American Psychiatric Association, not one of the AOP psychiatrists was consulted by the task force, nor was any AOP member permitted to review the report before it was circulated. And circulated it was! It was mailed to every major newspaper and magazine and was heavily covered. The report was riddled with misstatements and inaccuracies, but the press knew and cared little about them. Hoffer and Osmond's careful and well-documented rebuttal received very little attention from the press.

It may or may not be true that nothing is as powerful as an idea whose time has come, but the orthomolecular concept has been found to be at least strong enough to survive the APA Task Force (and many similar) attempts to destroy it.

On February 15, 1975, a group of interested physicians and researchers met in San Diego to form the Orthomolecular Medical Society, the organization that sponsored this festschrift for Linus Pauling. The founding members present at that first meeting were Linus Pauling, John Catchpool, Richard Kunin, Michael Lesser, Elizabeth Rees, Julian Whittaker, and myself. Michael Lesser became the first president of the Orthomolecular Medical Society, succeeded in turn by Richard Kunin, Richard Huemer, Michael Gerber, and Michael Rosenbaum.

As the evidence favoring the orthomolecular concept continues to accumulate, and as the costs, risks, and failures of traditional medicine become increasingly apparent, reasonable people everywhere will recognize the wisdom of invoking health by filling the body's needs, rather than by distorting its functioning with drugs. That day is coming, and its arrival will be due in no small part to the herculean efforts of Linus Pauling.

Bernard Rimland, PhD
San Diego, California
November 1985

THE ROOTS OF MOLECULAR MEDICINE

CHAPTER ONE

TOWARD A MOLECULAR BIOLOGY OF PREDISPOSITION TO DISEASE: THE CASE OF CANCER

EMILE ZUCKERKANDL, PhD

It is a fallacy to think that a disease is unavoidable because it is genetically conditioned. Every change in an organism, whether perceived as avoidable or unavoidable, is controlled both genetically and environmentally, and the two types of control are closely intertwined. Genes are not genes without their cellular and extracellular environments, but merely special chemicals with no meaning in terms of life. Nonetheless, in actual experience, the inheritance of genetic disease factors results all too often in a fatality. The fact that there is no fatality in principle is of little help to victims of their genes. As part of a better future, can we develop methods for accurately predicting the chances of an individual's falling victim to a particular disease, for example, cancer?

A "bad" gene that is expressed not at the inception of an organism's life but later, or a "good" gene that is expressed initially but the active product of which is critically reduced later, embody a "predisposition" to a disease. Predisposition (susceptibility) or, inversely, resistance to disease is a measure of an organism's chances of developing a certain disease in the future. It is not easy to arrive at a rational concept of predisposition, especially in the case of cancer, let alone to arrive at an accurate way of measuring it.

The focus of this chapter will be on cancer. It is important to be able to determine predisposition to cancer, yet determining predisposition remains an exceptionally difficult, albeit fascinating, biological problem.

Factors affecting predisposition to cancer can be divided into two groups: those that favor the formation of a malignant cell in the organism and those that favor the elimination of a malignant cell once it is formed. I shall address the issue of predisposition to cancer primarily in relation to the pathway of molecular changes that leads to the malignant state. (It seems probable that we should speak of pathways in the plural, although they are as yet barely understood.)

The group of factors that favor elimination of malignancy include the cellular immune system and the DNA repair system. The likelihood of a potentially carcinogenic mutation in a cell being handed down to subsequent cell generations—i.e., a predisposition to cancer—depends on the effectiveness of the DNA repair system. This is dramatically illustrated by the heritable disease ataxia telangiectasia. In this disease, the DNA repair system is damaged, leaving affected individuals prone to develop cancers of various kinds.

When the DNA repair system fails, the cellular immune system can eliminate malignant cells. Whether it does depends in part on genetic and in part on environmental control of the number and state of suppressor T-cells, macrophages, natural killer cells, and others. In regard to environmental control, stress and immunosuppressants as well as acquired immunodeficiencies are known to increase the incidence of cancer. Nutritional deficiencies also must be considered.[1]

This theme will not be further developed here. Those topics that I shall discuss will remain simply overviews illustrated by some examples.

SOME BACKGROUND TO THE GENETIC STATUS OF CANCER

In speaking about genetic predisposition, we need to refer to an organism's or a cell's mutational state. We define the mutational state as the totality of characters of DNA sequence of a genome. Through sequence analysis of the DNA, the mutational state of a cell could in principle be completely defined, though the cell would not survive the process. The mutational state of an *organism* can only be referred to loosely, because within a given tissue secondary changes in the mutational state of some cells are likely to occur over an individual's lifetime (somatic mutations). In addition, in some organisms, the mutational state of certain tissues is typically different from that of other tissues. One example is the chromosomal differences between germ cells and somatic cells in the fly *Sciara.*[2]

The word *mutation* is used here in its most general sense, a sense that includes all types of changes in DNA sequence: point mutations (the substitution in DNA of an individual deoxyribonucleotide by another), insertions (including the insertions of viral genomes), deletions, inversions, transpositions of small DNA segments, translocations of large segments, and duplications or multiplications of different-sized segments of DNA. On the basis of this inclusive definition, linking cancer to the mutational state of the individual's cells provides a comprehensive picture of carcinogenesis, a picture that includes cancers caused by physical, chemical, and viral carcinogens.

In germ cells, the largest number of mutations is retained where their effects do not compromise the viability of the organism, namely outside of the structural genes. Structural genes are the sets of coding sequences of DNA that control the structure of the gene product, a polypeptide chain. A polypeptide chain constitutes all or part of a protein. Mutations within a structural gene easily alter the ability of the corresponding protein to function. When the mutations occur outside the structural genes they no longer affect the structure of the gene product, but they may affect the rate of expression of the gene, that is, the rate at which a normal protein is synthesized.

DNA sequences that affect the rate of gene expression combine with relevant macromolecules: proteins or RNAs. Such DNA sequences are therefore receptor sequences for regulator molecules, notably regulator proteins. The structure of each regulator protein is in turn controlled by a structural gene. Mutations thus can occur in structural genes controlling regulator molecules or in noncoding sequences near these structural genes. In either case, the effect may be a change in the ability of the regulator protein to exercise its regulatory function: either the regulator protein is structurally altered or, although structurally normal, it is synthesized at an altered rate.

It is documented that certain cancers run in families, and that there exists a genetic predisposition to cancer.[3-9] The general correlation between mutagenicity and carcinogenicity in turn shows that cancer is controlled at the level of the genes.[10] The understanding of heritable factors in transformation has gained in depth by the discovery of a series of apparently cancer-causing genes, the so-called oncogenes. Oncogenes were originally found in the genomes of carcinogenic retroviruses (RNA viruses). Soon similar genes were found to be present in the cells of all normal organisms investigated.[11] Some were shown to participate in normal developmental processes[12] as well as in the chain of normal molecular actions involved in the processes and control of cell division.[13-17] Heldin and Westermark have said, "Any regulatory component in the chain of events linked to normal growth factor action may have oncogenic properties."[18] Several genes closely related to a given oncogene are sometimes found in the same organism.[19] Oncogenes are evolutionarily stable genes, and this stability suggests that they interact with other evolutionarily stable macromolecules.

Temin[20] has enumerated six ways in which a normal cellular gene can be turned into a cancer-causing gene. Whichever molecular process takes place, transformation of the cell is achieved either through a structural change in the protein that the gene codes for or through an abnormally high rate of synthesis of the normal protein.[21, 22]

Let us consider rate. Transcription of a gene can be up-regulated by any one of at least four methods: (1) through point mutations and, at times, by small insertions or deletions in neighboring noncoding sequences that control transcription, notably the so-called promoter sequences, located close to the coding sequences, (2) through changes in quantity or structure of one or several regulator proteins that combine with the noncoding sequences, (3) by means of the insertion of certain noncoding sequences, such as a promoter stronger than the gene's own, an LTR-like (long terminal repeat) sequence,[23] or a strong enhancer sequence, and (4) via movement of the coding sequences themselves, so that they come to lie next to a stronger promoter or one that is subject to a different regulation in regard to time and place (tissue) of activity.* In addition, a gene can be duplicated or multiplied ("amplified") and its product accordingly doubled or further augmented. Examples of several of these occurrences involving genes linked to carcinogenesis have already been found. Activation of cancer-linked genes through chromosomal translocations is particularly frequent.[27] Chromosomal deletions or the mutational inactivation of a gene also yields a strong predisposition to cancer when the deleted or mutated gene acts as a suppressor of cancer-causing genes, as appears to be the case in retinoblastoma.[28] A decrease in the amount of suppressor protein seems to result in the activation of one or more (as yet unidentified) cancer-causing genes. The direct molecular cause of cancer again seems to be of a quantitative nature, even though a structural alteration of DNA is underlying the quantitative change in the synthesis of critical proteins.

After the threshold of malignancy has been reached, it may again be the over- or underproduction of certain proteins that underlies the progression to cellular states of increased virulence. Thus, the degree of amplification of the *myc* and N-*myc* genes is correlated with increasingly poorer prognosis of some cancers.[29–32]

Just as chromosomal events, such as a specific translocation,[33] may strongly predispose to cancer, there perhaps exists in genomes a predisposition to the mutational events themselves, for example to certain insertions, deletions, or transpositions of segments of DNA. Such predisposition is likely to be inherent in aspects of the preexisting DNA sequences, such as the distribution and number of certain

*Enhancers have been found to contain repeat sequence motifs,[24] which might serve as receptors for specific proteins. A mechanism for the action of enhancers may be tentatively considered. Gene transcription can be inhibited in higher order chromatin structures.[25] These may be stabilized by DNA combining with mutually interacting "transconformational" proteins.[26] Multiple binding sites, probably of low individual sequence specificity and spread over a DNA sector many kilobases long that includes the gene, might be involved. Enhancer sequences may combine preferentially with proteins that interrupt the putative pattern of cooperative interaction in which the transconformational protein is engaged. Such interference may decrease the stability of a higher order deoxyribonucleoprotein (DNP) structure of chromatin. Hence, DNP structure in the region close to the enhancer (whether the latter be located upstream or downstream to the coding sequences) may be destabilized, and the region of the nearby promoter and coding sequences brought into a configuration favorable to transcription.

repetitive sequences. A predisposition to structural changes in DNA may be linked with predisposition to cancer via local trends to certain DNA sequence modifications in somatic cells, including insertion of viral genomes. Thus, predisposition to cancer may in part depend on sequence characters at a number of genomic sites within noncoding regions. DNA with unknown functions, which has been called "junk DNA," might thus play a role in predisposition.

The participation in human carcinogenesis of those oncogenes so far identified has not been established.[34] The status of some candidates for major carcinogenesis genes is currently being investigated.[35, 36] In addition, a number of genes may be involved in malignant transformation, each in a minor way. They would be cancer "polygenes," to use an old terminology, and would represent the genetic background for the transformation processes. Collectively, they would be important for assessing predisposition. The existence of such minor cancer genes has not been extensively documented, unless some or all known oncogenes were to be considered minor cancer genes themselves. Their striking effectiveness may indeed have resulted from the already transformed character of the cells in which they were usually tested, mouse NIH 3T3 fibroblasts.[37] An example of a minor yet sometimes significant cancer gene may be the gene coding for ferritin, which plays a role in development of hepatitis B and hepatic cancer.[38]

Cancer appears to be primarily an abnormality in the regulation of certain gene activities; in other words, it is in large measure a disease of gene regulation. This generalization is probably correct, although some cancer-causing mutations occur in the coding parts of structural genes, and are expressed as changes in the amino acid sequence of the polypeptides under the control of these genes. Such cancer-causing mutations in structural genes imply that some cancers, or most cancers to some extent, are molecular diseases in the classic sense of the term.[39] On the other hand, a causal link between changes in the rate of production of a normal protein and carcinogenesis implies that cancer is a controller gene disease.[40] Controller gene diseases may be considered molecular diseases in a wider sense. They involve mutations in noncoding sequences or, as in classic molecular disease, in coding sequences that determine the structure of a regulator protein controlling the rate of synthesis of another protein. In both situations the result is a quantitative change in a protein. The carcinogenic effect of a structurally altered protein may often involve a change in the regulation of a series of genes whose products are coded for normally, but are present in abnormal amounts or are secondarily modified.

Because a number of mutational events may be involved in a complete malignant transformation (see below), a single cancer may express a mixture of several molecular diseases *sensu stricto* and of several controller gene diseases. If we take the expression *molecular disease* in its extended sense, we may state that each cancer is in fact several molecular diseases in one.

REMARKS ON THE RELATION BETWEEN HERITABLE AND ENVIRONMENTAL EFFECTS IN CANCER

If predisposition to any disease, including cancer, depends on the mutational state of the genome, it also depends on the quantities of certain nuclear and cytoplasmic factors. The genome controls the structure and quantities of these factors. They in turn play a role in translating the DNA potential into an actual state of the cell and into actual alternatives between developmental pathways. The question is whether the quantities of the factors are exclusively determined by the mutational state of the cell or whether their quantities, if changed through some environmental effect, are a "given" that in turn sometimes controls quantitative aspects of the genome's expression in a heritable way.

The processes of differentiation and the heritability over a number of cell generations of a particular state of differentiation suggest that there may be heritable alterations in gene regulation that are not due to modifications in a cell's mutational state, but are due to changes in ratios of certain proteins to certain genes—changes that are brought about nonmutationally by a shift in cellular concentration of the proteins in their active state. Such changes could be environmentally controlled or accidental, if one counts among accidents, for instance, an uneven distribution of certain factors between daughter cells at cell division. If these factors, notably regulator proteins, are not present in active form in certain concentrations at certain phases of the cell cycle, differentiation might not occur, might follow a different course, or might not be maintained. In particular, the cell might take a step toward malignant transformation. Environmental agents may prevent a regulator protein from being present in sufficient concentration in its functional form at the critical time, or cause it to be present in excessive amounts. For example, environmental agents may change the concentration of some effector molecule that combines with the regulator or may bring about a secondary modification of a gene product involved with regulation of gene expression. The effect may be heritable, if it is expressed in a certain constellation of protein-DNA complexes. Such complexes indeed appear to be replicated from cell generation to cell generation, until a new transmissible change in these complexes occurs. In short, if one adds to a cell a further amount of a certain regulator protein or subtracts from its amount, the system of mutual control of DNA over protein synthesis and of protein over DNA transcription might possibly be shifted in a heritable way.

The effects of carcinogens demonstrate that heritable cellular changes can be induced by the environment. The interpretation of this observation is not straightforward, however. It is often assumed that all environmental effects that lead to malignant transformation act through changes in the mutational state. To use an accepted phrase, it is assumed that they are all genotoxic. This is not necessarily so. Some steps in transformation (namely of heritable cellular changes in the direction of malignancy) are clearly brought about by agents that are not genotoxic, such as the so-called tumor promoters, of which phorbol esters are the best known example. Yet promoters cannot bring about the malignant state, except when they act on cells that have already been subjected to a genotoxic agent, the so-called initiator. Initiators presumably modify the mutational state of cells. It is doubtful that nongenotoxic agents alone can bring about malignant transformation. On the other hand, the malignant state can be reversed, in some cases, by appropriate environmental influences. Such observations are compatible with, although do not necessarily imply, the view that malignant transformation does not always depend on changes in the mutational state. Examples of a reversion of the malignant state through environmental influences have been found in experiments with murine cells. Sachs and associates[41] injected myeloid leukemic cells into mouse embryos in utero and observed that the apparently healthy adult mice developing from these embryos had granulocytes containing a marker derived from the leukemic cells. Earlier, Illmensee and Mintz[42] had injected mouse teratocarcinoma cells into mouse blastocysts and had obtained adult chimeras composed in part of the mouse's own cells and in part of differentiated, normal cells that were the descendents of the cancer cells. These former cancer cells contributed normal cells to many tissues and organs of the developing mouse.

These striking observations may indicate reverse mutations occurring, for instance, through the loss of an insertion sequence that determines the malignant state.[43] If this were generally so, malignant transformation would be entirely determined by a cell's mutational state.

The observations of Ossowski and Reich[44] on environmentally induced changes in properties of highly malignant human epidermoid carcinoma are hardly compatible with this interpretation. They found that *all* cell clones experienced a progressive loss of tumorigenicity when the cells were cultured in vitro, and they progressively recovered tumorigenicity when the cells were subsequently exposed to in vivo conditions in chick embryos. Thus, the possibility that not only mutations but also environmental and accidental effects may redirect the developmental alternatives of a cell should be taken seriously. The probability of any of the possible alternative states of the cell actually occurring is to be equated with predisposition to that state. Predisposition thus evolves constantly during an organism's development. The action of the environment in this regard hinges on the cell's position in a tissue, the activity of other tissues and the substances that they release into the bloodstream, the physiologic reaction of the organism to "situations" (e.g., to stress), and physical and chemical components of the external milieu. Cancer cells themselves can determine the environment for adjacent nonmalignant cells, making them malignant. The active agent transferred from cell to cell does not appear to be viral in all cases. The effect has been observed across species, between human and mouse tissues.[45]

Even though a cell in a normal state of differentiation cannot be switched to any other state of differentiation—for instance no one to my knowledge has observed the transformation of a macrophage into a nerve cell—transformation in the direction of malignancy might remain an option open to all cells capable of division. We repeatedly find the ability to transform to the malignant state when transformation to many other cellular states is excluded. This observation suggests that malignant transformation is few steps away from a state shared by all cells that undergo division.

Terminal differentiation and cell division tend to be mutually exclusive. Interestingly, malignant cells have something in common with normal cells that are some distance away from terminal differentiation, namely with cells at early developmental (embryonic or fetal) stages. Syrian hamster embryo cells from the early gestation period and at early passage in tissue culture are more frequently transformed than cells from a later gestation period and from later tissue culture passages, when lack of postconfluence inhibition of cell division and anchorage independence of growth are used as transformation criteria.[45] Thus, at early stages and at early passage, cells in general may have a greater predisposition to malignant transformation than they would have later. This seems to imply that early cells are fewer steps away from the malignant state than those in late development.

In fact neoplastic cells are known to generate fetal gene products, such as α-fetoprotein, carcinoembryonic antigen, and many other "oncodevelopmental antigens."[47, 48] Also, there is an apparent resurgence of fetal isozyme patterns in cancerous cells,[49] although these malignant cells might derive from individual cells that remained at an earlier developmental stage, i.e., stem cells. Often true dedifferentiation is more likely.[47] A number of the oncodevelopmental proteins have been observed in regenerating nonmalignant tissue in the adult.[47] Any local stimulation of cell proliferation may offer an opportunity for malignant transformation, provided that a predisposition to such transformation has been inherited or acquired. In chemical carcinogenesis the predisposition is created or enhanced by the so-called initiator, and cell proliferation is brought about in a subsequent step by promoter substances whose action leads to malignancy.[50]

The effect of physical and chemical environmental agents can mimic the effect of mutations. This observation is important in biology, and is exemplified in phenocopies. To give some examples of relevance, normal fibroblasts in the presence of 20 percent fetal calf serum and 10 μg/ml of hydrocortisone will grow without anchorage to their substratum, just like transformed fibroblasts that have undergone a heritable change.[51] Certain tumor promoters will induce reversible changes in cells that mimic those observed in transformed cells. Thus, an increase in saturation density, stimulation of glucose uptake, loss of microfilament and fibronectin, and increase of ornithine decarboxylase activity and of plasminogen activator are among the changes that phorbol esters induce in cultured cells.[52] Apparently, in cell populations subjected to tumor promoters a mutation can ultimately occur that has the same effects as the environmental agent. There is a clear equivalence between mutations and environmental effects. Moreover, there appears to be a predisposition to mutations in certain oncogenes[37] and it has not been excluded that this predisposition can be influenced by environmental effects.

Conversely, after a mutation has occurred, an action or circumstance in the environment can prompt the mutated cell to mimic the nonmutated state—a general basis for palliative treatments that eliminate the symptoms of genetic defects. For instance, the cell-surface protein fibronectin is generally decreased on the surface of malignant cells. Therefore, any innate or somatically acquired but heritable reduction in the synthesis of this protein could be a step—though probably not a sufficient step—toward malignancy. Fibroblasts producing less fibronectin may have an increased predisposition to cancer. By an "environmental" intervention, the experimenter can recoat the surface of transformed cells with purified fibronectin. This can partially restore in the malignant cell a number of normal characteristics, namely, normal morphology, adhesiveness to culture substrata, decreased microvilli and ruffles, decreased cell overlapping, and organization of intracellular, cytoskeletal elements, notably the organization of actin and myosin into microfilament bundles.[53]

Mimicry is only mimicry. In these cases a mutation is required in order to render heritable any state that the environment is able to induce. It is likely that this always applies to some step or steps of the malignantly transformed state. Yet there are two further processes to be considered that would be important if they were established. One is that a cellular state induced by the environment somehow predisposes the cell to a mutation that renders that state hereditary in the absence of the environmental stimulus that brought it about;* the other is that the environment or an accident can induce a heritable change in cells that is not linked to a sequence change in DNA. Experimental approaches for evaluating these possibilities are available.

*If it could be shown that an increase in transcription rate leads to an increase in mutation rate in the transcribed gene, one would establish the existence of directional effects of environmental factors on the genome and a link between acquired and heritable characters (in the present case the passage from cell proliferation controlled by tumor promoter to uncontrolled constitutive cell proliferation). Special opportunities for mutations that mimic the environmental effect would be provided by such a linkage between transcription rate and mutation rate.

PRIMAL VERSUS CURRENT PREDISPOSITION TO DISEASE

In considering predisposition to disease, it is best to forget neither genes nor environment. Better understanding of this rather complex situation might be reached by looking at predisposition in two ways—either taking into account an individual's history of environmental effects or not doing so. The distinction is between germ-line, primal predisposition, on the one hand, and current predisposition, on the other hand.

We may define primal, germ-line predisposition to disease as the predisposition inherent in the mutational state of germ-line DNA in combination with the qualitative and quantitative distribution of cellular factors in the fertilized egg. As Tracy Sonneborn pointed out many years ago, the cellular factors and DNA determine each other's activities in an unresolvably circular relationship. Thus, in this definition, the environment of the genes is not dropped from consideration—it must not be—but the basic predisposition is established at a time when the history of the individual has not yet begun. Both a trend toward formation of malignant cells and a trend relating to their control, in particular through the immune system, are included in the definition of primal predisposition.

Even if primal predisposition could be determined through analysis of all the components that enter into its definition, the prediction of disease would be only a rough approximation. In many cases such an approximation would be meaningless in terms of what a given individual is actually to expect. In extreme cases, on the other hand, the likelihood of the disease occurring would appear very high on the basis of primal predisposition alone. Hereditary retinoblastoma and hereditary adenomatosis of the colon and rectum are examples.

Even in extreme cases of genetic predisposition, the choice of which of two or more possible developmental paths will be followed by a cell depends in part on environmental factors. Predisposition to disease, even strong predisposition, is an individual's chances of developing the disease in a natural or cultural environment that is "normal." If the environment changes, for instance because the individual starts ingesting some particular substance in sufficient amounts, even a strong predisposition to cancer might weaken, and even a developmental pathway already taken by a cell might be switched in the cell's progeny.

When referring to environmental changes we begin considering the individual's life history. Thus, our best estimates of predisposition must deal with current predisposition. Let us define current predisposition as resulting from both the mutational state and environmental effects on rates of gene expression integrated over the total duration of the individual's life. This integration is accomplished automatically by the present state of a cell, as defined by the totality of sequence characters and quantitative characters of the informational macromolecules (DNA,

RNA, protein) that it contains. Current predisposition and primal predisposition coincide only for the fertilized egg and differ from there onward, with primal predisposition remaining constant and current predisposition changing.

Strictly speaking, both primal predisposition and current predisposition may be destined to remain mere concepts, nontranslatable into measurements. In order to measure primal predisposition most accurately, one would have to destroy the fertilized egg. Likewise, in order to reach full knowledge of current predisposition, one would ideally have to analyze separately each cell of an organism—an absurd proposition—and, in contrast to the case of primal predisposition, presumably not just all the DNA of each cell, but the quantities of many proteins and RNAs. In practice, however, it is possible to refer to significant aspects of primal predisposition and current predisposition.

Something more would be learned about current predisposition if a sample from each tissue of an organism were taken and analyzed. Besides being unfeasible, this procedure would not necessarily give us a picture of the most transformed cells, which are the ones of greatest interest to us.

A further station on this retreat is to measure current predisposition in just one tissue, one easily accessible for analysis, such as skin fibroblasts. This may strike many as a strange idea. Fibroblasts, they will say, should be an adequate material if we wish to evaluate predisposition to the malignant transformation of fibroblasts. How could fibroblasts inform us about predisposition to a disease that is to develop in another tissue, say pancreatic cancer? Perhaps fibroblasts cannot tell us much about predisposition specifically to pancreatic cancer. Yet they may well, at the very least, tell us something about an individual's predisposition to cancer in general. I shall outline the theoretical reasons that make it worthwhile to explore such an approach to the evaluation of predisposition to disease and to various abnormalities.

DETERMINING PREDISPOSITION TO DISEASE IN A TISSUE NOT INVOLVED IN THE DISEASE

A mutation affecting one given gene can lead either to a structural modification of the protein controlled by this gene or to a quantitative change in the production of this protein. In either case it is possible that the mutation will be reflected by changes in rate of expression (not in structure) of a number of other genes.[54] A mutation leading to disease in tissue A because it affects a given protein *a* may be expressed by quantitative characteristics of certain proteins in tissue B, including protein *a*. The chances of protein *a* being expressed in tissue B are perhaps greatest for tissues that are embryologically related, namely those that are of common ectodermal, mesodermal, or endodermal origin.

Furthermore, the protein products of many genes are expressed in all tissues; many others are expressed in several tissues to varying extents; yet others are expressed in one or few tissues only. The last circumstance offers limited opportunity for discovering predisposition markers from a single, arbitrarily chosen tissue. However, genes closely linked to the one in question and expressed in that tissue may, by quantitative characteristics of their expression, serve as markers for the unexpressed gene. For many genes, quantitative characteristics of gene expression probably vary from individual to individual, from haplotype to haplotype. (A haplotype is defined by the mutational state of one out of the two similar genetic units of every kind that cells of higher organisms contain.)

Diseases that appear at certain defined stages in life—childhood, adolescence, adulthood, or old age—may be viewed as the expression of a developmental process. The concept of development is often used in a limited way, as though development were confined to early embryonic and later fetal stages. Yet some developmental changes continue in organisms after birth, and give rise to universal "normal" landmarks, such as sexual maturity and menopause, in humans. Some of the changes associated with old age may be considered developmental. All developmental processes must be assumed to be characterized by changes in ratios of rates of gene expression. Diseases linked to defined periods in life are probably the expression of, or favored by, the crossing of certain thresholds by certain gene activities. These changes in gene activities lead either to overproduction or to underproduction of certain gene products. Though a trend toward either over- or underproduction of gene products may proceed over a number of years, and perhaps over a whole lifetime, it is only as a threshold is passed by one or several proteins that disease would become manifest. Yet the quantities per cell of the proteins involved may, before the appearance of the disease, be markers for predisposition to the disease.

Changes in ratios of gene expression may lead to disease in one given tissue because of certain threshold values for gene expression in that particular tissue. Different, though correlated, changes in these ratios in other tissues may not produce pathological consequences. An example of correlated changes of this kind is offered by certain enzymes called isozymes, which are controlled by different but closely related genes. They are often found in different relative and absolute amounts per cell in different tissues. The data of Ferris and Whitt[55] show that, as evolution proceeds—the organisms compared are species of fish—a quantitative change in the production of an isozyme in one tissue attributable to mutations is likely to be reflected in other tissues, although not to the same extent. This is expected on theoretical grounds.[54]

Findings in the literature support the notion that a genetic abnormality that causes a pathological process in one tissue can be detected in another, apparently unaffected tissue. Wilson's disease involves a defect in copper metabolism. Though in Wilson's disease the metabolic disturbance affects a number of organs (the principal pathological symptoms being generated in the liver and in the brain), fibroblasts do not appear to be "diseased." Whether as a direct or an indirect effect, the genetic abnormality is nevertheless expressed in fibroblasts, as witnessed by their increased copper content.[56] In both Alzheimer's and Parkinson's diseases it was found that peripheral blood lymphocytes—a cell type not implicated in the manifestations of the diseases—are more sensitive to X rays than lymphocytes from normal subjects.[57] Such a difference is likely to be linked to some difference(s) in proteins. Similarly, in Huntington's chorea, a degenerative disease of the central nervous system, abnormalities in cell membrane protein have been found in erythrocytes.[58] Recently it has been found that patients with a major affective disorder—one therefore not considered to be located in their skin—had a higher density of cholinergic receptors on skin fibroblasts than did controls.[59]

Thus, as data accumulate they seem to fit with expectation. In the case of familial predisposition to adenomatosis of the colon and rectum (ACR), the approach advocated here has in fact already been successfully applied. Kopelovich[7] found, in particular, that actin cables tend to be depolymerized in cultured fibroblasts from carriers of the ACR gene.

DEGREES OF TRANSFORMATION AND PREDISPOSITION

The possibility cannot be excluded that in some cases a single mutation will bring a cell from the normal to the malignant state. The normal state of a cell cannot be defined rigorously, however, and when a single mutation suffices for rendering a cell malignant, it can be said that the cell probably was already partly transformed; in other words, that its current predisposition to malignant transformation was above the ill-defined baseline positioned at the largest achievable distance from the malignancy threshold. There are difficulties inherent in the use of the word *distance.* The baseline in question may be intrinsically at different levels for different tissues of the same organism. It may also be at different levels for different organisms, such as mice and men. It may be generally closer to the malignancy threshold in organisms with a shorter rather than longer life span and/or in organisms with a greater intensity of oxidative metabolism. The difficulty of malignant transformation in human cells, compared with the ease of malignant transformation in rodent cells, may indeed be expected to reveal some generalizable underlying difference.

The concept of stepwise neoplastic development through different stages has been proposed by Foulds.[60] Knudson[61] proposed that at least two mutational events are necessary for tumor formation. More than two heritable cellular events appear in fact to be required.[60]

It is a now classic finding that the mechanism of tumor induction by chemical carcinogens involves at least two distinct steps: *initiation* by a carcinogen and *promotion* by certain substances that alone will not cause cancer. It has been shown, however, that two steps of heritable cell modifications do not always bring about malignant transformation. Two oncogenes acting together are not necessarily sufficient.[62] Furthermore, a germ-line mutation that predisposes to cancer does not necessarily imply a great enough predisposition for effective promotion to malignancy by tetradecanoylphorbol acetate, a powerful promoter. This was demonstrated in tissue culture of fibroblasts from individuals with different germ-line mutations, including a dominant mutation leading to colorectal cancer, the cancer-predisposing xeroderma pigmentosum mutation, and yet other cancer-predisposing mutations.[63] Malignant transformation did not follow exposure of the cells to the promoter, although some heritable transformation probably did take place. On the other hand, the genetically predisposed cells are more susceptible to virally induced malignant transformation than cells from normal individuals.[64]

At least two heritable steps are required for malignant transformation in normal rodent embryonal fibroblasts. They cannot be fully transformed by a single oncogene, but are transformed by two oncogenes belonging to different complementation groups.[65, 66] Furthermore, hamster fibroblasts, which are more "normal" than mouse NIH 3T3 fibroblasts (though less resistant to transformation than human fibroblasts) do not, in contradistinction to 3T3 cells, become malignant on transfer into them (transfection) of the c-Ha-*ras* oncogene from a human bladder carcinoma line. By contrast, the transfection of the gene does lead to malignant transformation if the hamster fibroblasts have first been "immortalized" by a carcinogen.[67]

The immortalization of cells and their malignant transformation represent another important distinction between two major steps in carcinogenesis. The somewhat whimsical term *immortalization* designates the potential of a cell for indefinite division in culture. Normal, nontransformed cells, if they divide at all in culture, will do so only a limited number of times. Immortalization and malignant transformation are separable phenomena. Certain viral genomes (e.g., herpes virus II) localize their ability to induce immortalization in a specific viral DNA region. Malignant transformation occurs only when an additional, different viral fragment is transfected into the recipient rodent cells.[68–71] However, the ability of cells to proliferate indefinitely in culture is not a general precondition for their tumorigenicity.[7]

A number of observations suggest that carcinogenesis may frequently involve more than two steps, at times as many as seven.[60, 72] Two major correlates of malignancy, as observed in vitro, are deformed actin-containing cables in the cell and decreased amounts of fibronectin on the cell surface. As mentioned above, skin fibroblasts from carriers of the ACR mutation, the mutation predisposing to adenomatosis of the colon and rectum, display a disrupted organization of actin fibers.

Yet they are indistinguishable from normal cells with respect to their ability to express fibronectin.[7] Thus, these two properties are separable. On the other hand, fibroblasts from carriers of the ACR mutation, when treated with a nitrosoguanidine derivative, acquire a prolonged life span—not yet immortality, but delayed senescence.[73] This is a state intermediate between normal senescence and immortality, and it appears to be heritable.

A continuum of mouse fibroblast lines with decreasing growth regulation has been found in particular by Penman and associates.[74] Their observations suggest that a series of mutational steps can progressively lead toward malignant transformation, though the same end result might be achieved with fewer steps. A further observation along these lines is that tumor promotion by the phorbol ester TPA can be dissected into at least two stages.[75]

All of the foregoing findings support the impression that malignant transformation encompasses a series of discrete steps. Tumorigenicity may be the outcome of various possible mixtures of heritable changes, affecting processes that need to be carried to a certain threshold value; but there may be trade-offs among these processes. In that case the same type of cancer could be based on a more or less original cocktail of more or less effective heritable changes in a number of distinct genes.

We conclude that the mutational distance between the nontransformed and the malignant state can probably be covered by different numbers of mutations (Figure 1.1). The number of mutations may not vary only between different cell types of an organism, but even for different cells of the same type.

Many changes in cell morphology and behavior—and probably in profile of gene expression—can be coordinated, as demonstrated by the action of temperature-sensitive mutant virus.[76] This may be the case either because "master" regulatory genes are involved that regulate a certain number of genes under their jurisdiction, or, if genes are involved that are not specifically regulatory, they may nevertheless have indirect effects on rates of expression of other genes. A likely example of the latter situation is mutation in the β-actin coding sequences,[77] which lead to a change in cell shape and are thereby expected[74] to change the regulation of cell growth. This should be reflected in a change of rates of expression of a certain number of other genes. Coordinated quantitative changes in certain proteins have actually been found in the presence of mutant β-actin gene.[78, 79]

If a regulatory master switch or switches are involved in the transformation process, the threshold number of mutations for malignancy may vary from one, if the switch gene itself is involved, to several, if the switch gene is intact but individual genes under its command are separately and successively involved.

Coordinated changes in gene expression may be only apparent, if they result at the cellular level from rapid, independent, successive mutations.

Genetic switches, starting from a master switch, may function in a tree-like structure of command, implying a series of switches of different hierarchical rank.

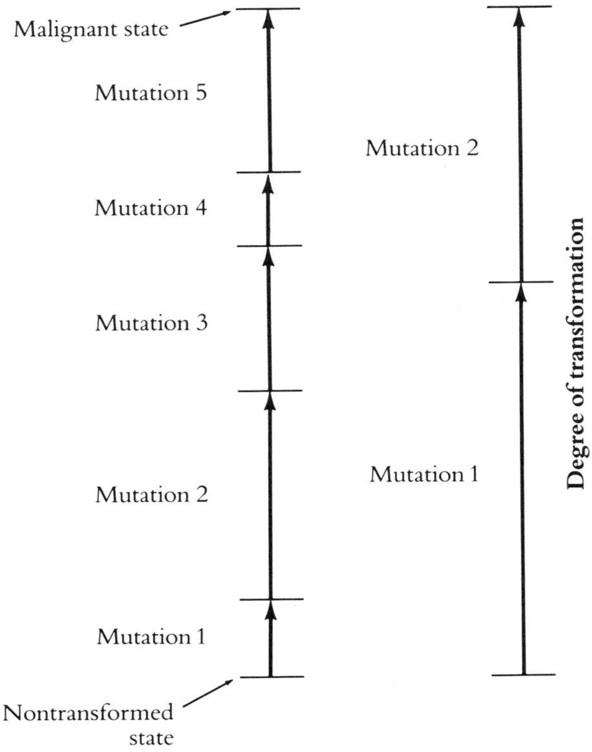

Figure 1.1 The mutational distance between the nontransformed and the malignant state can probably be covered by different numbers of mutations.

If activity or inactivity of the master switch (depending on whether it produces an activator or a repressor) were induced by mutation, a single mutational event could suffice for malignant transformation. If the master switch were not affected, at least two mutations in two distinct genes would be required for malignant transformation, and more if only switches of yet lower rank were involved. A similar end result would be reached with between one and a number of mutations, according to the hierarchical level of the switches hit. On the basis of this view, the malignancy threshold may be reached by different numbers of mutations in different cases.

Other hypotheses have it that there might be more than one independent "tree" of gene command, and there might be stretches of unbranched cascades of command. These are unresolved questions.

The number of mutations necessary to reach the malignant state will also vary with the states of the cells used for experiments in malignant transformation. Figure 1.2 illustrates the fact that the initial degree of transformation may differ for cell lines that are not usually considered to be transformed. Mouse 3T3 fibro-

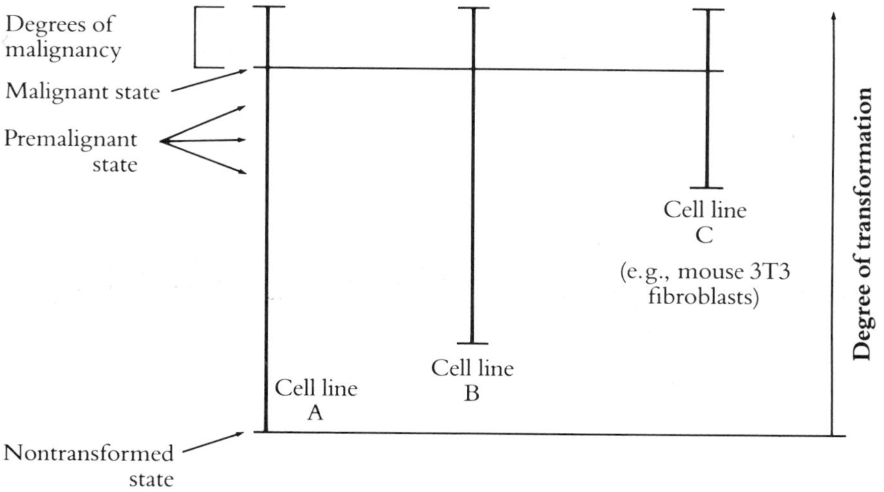

Figure 1.2 Degrees of transformation of cell lines that are putatively normal or close to normal. The initial degree of transformation may differ for cell lines not usually considered transformed.

blasts are already transformed in the sense of being immortalized, but they have not yet reached the threshold of malignancy. This is manifested by the absence of tumorigenicity, by density-dependent growth inhibition, by anchorage dependence, and by a rather normal cell morphology.

In different types of cells of the same organism a given informational macromolecule involved in carcinogenesis, say a protein, is generally produced at different rates or present at different steady-state concentrations. Its concentration is likely to be various distances from the malignancy threshold in different tissues. Moreover, this threshold itself may vary as a function of other proteins and RNAs. There are two implications. One is that there are independent degrees of predisposition to cancer in different tissues, with the highest cancer risk lodged specifically in one tissue. This has been observed. For example, in a certain strain of mice treated with X rays or urethane, 90 percent of the induced tumors were in the lung, and this proportion was maintained in untreated offspring, in which tumor incidence was increased.[80] The second implication is that a protein that is transforming in one tissue may not be so in another. In fact, the *c-fos* oncogene can under certain conditions transform rodent fibroblasts, in which it is normally expressed at a very low level. It does not transform amnion cells, in which it is normally expressed at high levels.[81] Thus the pathways to transformation may include different genes in different tissues.

If gene products are present in varying amounts in different tissues, it follows that in different tissues there is a varying probability that a particular mutation will push a cell over the malignancy threshold. Thus, when the cell is in a state in which the malignancy threshold can be reached in a single step, different genes in different tissues would be most likely to be linked to cancer. In fact, certain oncogenes are characteristically effective in certain tissues and apparently not in others.[82, 83] On the other hand, there also are oncogenes that are not tissue specific.

The amounts of some critical informational macromolecules—and therefore the distance from malignancy—might be altered as a consequence of aging, by somatic mutations brought about by physical or chemical agents, by viruses, or by some other accidental event. As the concentrations of such macromolecules approach the threshold of malignancy, the amount of aging or the number of somatic mutations necessary for cancer probably decrease. This view may at least occasionally explain why a tumor develops in one tissue rather than in another.

Furthermore, the rate of chemical transformation of carcinogen precursors into active carcinogens or the uptake of active metabolite may vary from tissue to tissue.[84] Such differences may also contribute to variation among tissues in predisposition to cancer. We would expect different tissues to respond diversely, even if the cells were exposed to identical doses of active carcinogen.

Some proteins that change in quantity with age[85] may be involved in transformation. Individual differences in regulatory status of certain genes are expected to bring about variations in predisposition to cancer and other diseases. Thus, one individual with a large amount of a protein early in life will have more time until the protein is decreased to a threshold level than another individual whose cells are closer to that threshold level from the start. More or less aging may be required for a malignancy to appear. A quantitative change with age in the availability of the active form of certain proteins may in part explain the intimate connection between aging and cancer.

VALUE OF ESTIMATING PREDISPOSITION TO CANCER

Predisposition to cancer can be assessed as the time span within which a given individual may develop a malignancy, as estimated by marker analysis. In general, the likelihood of a cancer appearing is greater with increasing time, although the opposite is true for childhood cancers from a certain age on.

Possible environmental effects on degree of predisposition are of great practical import. The likelihood of a cancer appearing may differ in virally infectious and noninfectious environments. Second wives of men whose first wives had cervical cancer, which can be viral, are at increased risk of developing cervical cancer.[86] This is an environmental, not a genetic, circumstance.

Genes are important here nevertheless. Even if the second wife were virally infected she might not develop cervical cancer; she may be resistant to cancer, particularly through her immune system. If an analysis of her blood, urine, or cells suggests that she has a good resistance to cancer, accidental environmental developments may not be significant.

On the other hand, an indication of moderate resistance—or its inverse, a moderate predisposition—would not be an accurate prediction aid. The actual fate of such individuals will depend on unforeseeable environmental developments. In the case of high predisposition to cancer, many different environmental developments may lead to cancer; a statement about high predisposition again would be significant.

The most meaningful estimates of predisposition, in terms of what an individual may expect, are therefore estimates of high or low predisposition. Intermediate predisposition is associated with an uncertain future. Intermediate values for predisposition could become usefully predictive only if it were possible to define predisposition in regard to a normal environment, one in which the probability of coming into contact with carcinogenic physical and chemical agents and cancer-causing viruses were constant for most individuals most of the time. It is hard to find such environments.

Moderate predisposition to cancer presumably is more meaningful in dealing with those forms of cancer that increase in incidence with age. The incidence of 70 percent of cancers appears to be an exponential function of age,[86] so that a moderate chance of developing cancer in middle age may become quite high in old age.

AN EXPERIMENTAL APPROACH: THE MEASUREMENT OF LEXOTYPIC CHANGE

The genotype of an organism or cell designates specific sequence characteristics of its genes. Let us call lexotype (from *lexis,* way of expression) the profile of expression of a cell's genes, notably with respect to the *quantitative* aspects of this expression. It is one facet—one that deserves to be given particular consideration—of the so-called phenotype, which represents the set of overt characters of an organism generated by both the structure of the genes and the factors of the environment.

The profile of quantitative expression of a cell's genes can be measured either in terms of RNAs or of proteins. Protein profiling has become a widespread and powerful technique, thanks to the method of two-dimensional electrophoresis of proteins in special gels, introduced by O'Farell in 1975. In the last few years it has become possible to quantitate effectively the individual protein spots that appear in the gels by the hundreds (sometimes over a thousand), thanks to the efforts notably of Peter Geiduschek's and Nguyen Xuong's groups at the University of California in San Diego, of Norman and Lee Anderson at the Argonne National Laboratory near Chicago, and of Jim Garrels and his group at the Cold Spring Harbor Laboratory in Long Island, New York. More recently it has also become possible to measure conveniently the amino acid composition, for purposes of identification, of protein spots in situ, on the basis of a method developed at the Linus Pauling Institute, Palo Alto, by Gerald Latter, Steve Burbeck, and John Leavitt.

It is likely that measurements of differences in protein lexotype will become a major tool for studying predisposition to disease. Perhaps it will to some extent become possible in the future to express in quantitative terms the distance that separates the state of a given cell line from malignancy, and even that of individual cells. Such measurements may determine the amount of change in gene regulation that is required to reach the malignant state.

Would one obtain a measure of the distance between the observed state of a nonmalignant cell and the threshold of malignant transformation by considering percentages of quantitative changes in key proteins required for the malignancy threshold to be reached? There may well be a host of different constellations and balances in the participation of key genes. In principle, the distance from malignancy might still be measured by the length of the shortest route. It is unlikely that this could be done routinely, although as a research project, exploring different pathways from a given state of a cell clone to malignancy would be of great interest, especially if means were available for comparing the different pathways in quantitative terms.

Quantitation of the length of pathways, however, is fraught with another difficulty. Changes in key genes leading to malignant transformation are not limited to quantitative changes in gene expression. A structural change in a key protein present in normal amounts can so alter its functional properties as to make the protein ineffective, or effective in a wrong way. One could estimate the amounts of a protein with partially impaired function that would be required to make up for the loss of function, and formulate this amount in terms of percent increase in steady-state concentration required. A larger number of defective enzyme molecules can give the same amount of product per unit time as a smaller number of the normal enzyme molecules. However, for a totally nonfunctional protein, the compensatory amount required would be infinite, and for a protein that has become actively counterproductive, there is no compensatory amount. The possibilities of describing the effects of structural changes in proteins in terms of equivalent quantitative changes are thus limited.

Also, the threshold of the malignant state depends, in addition to factors already considered, on characteristics of the test for malignancy. The current test is tumor formation in an organism into which the cells to be investigated have been inoculated. One important variable is cell number injected. For higher degrees of malignancy the number of cells required for a tumor to develop is smaller. What is to be considered the threshold of malignancy is thus linked to the conditions of the test for malignancy. It becomes clear that in relation to cancer neither the normality of a cell nor its malignancy can be measured, except by reference to conditions of measurement, the definition of which cannot fail to be in part arbitrary.

Finally, numerous distinct lexotypes are probably represented in the same tissue. In order to quantitate the protein profile of a cell with the purpose of measuring its distance from the malignancy threshold one would have to destroy it, as I have already pointed out. The result, furthermore, may not be exactly applicable to the next cell, and not at all applicable to some cells.

Formulating the difficulties inherent in quantitating predisposition to cancer at the molecular level is perhaps a vain exercise. However, the attempt throws some further light on the complexities of transformation.

ELIMINATING THE EFFECTS OF PREDISPOSITION

The attempt to counteract predisposition to disease leads to one of three situations. Predisposition may be kept in check by adding a substance from the environment (e.g., predisposition to skin cancer or mammary cancer in mice can be counteracted by administering large doses of vitamin C[87, 88, 89]) or by withholding a substance from the environment (e.g., predisposition to phenylketonuria can be counteracted by withholding phenylalanine from the diet). There are, third, the cases in which neither adding nor subtracting an environmental component seems to be effective.

This last category in part expresses our temporary ignorance. The tendency for red cells to sickle in individuals homozygous for a well-known amino acid substitution in the human hemoglobin β chain is so strong that no one speaks of predisposition: one has sickle cell anemia or one does not. One has it when one has a double dose of the mutated gene for the hemoglobin β chain. Yet substances may be discovered that effectively inhibit sickling. One recently found is cetiedil, an amine ester of acetic acid.[90] Such a substance, if administered continuously, might eliminate sickling permanently, just as ingesting vitamin C regularly eliminates scurvy permanently.

There may, however, be genetic diseases the manifestations of which, short of genetic engineering, cannot be precluded by the addition or withholding of chemicals. Yet, if the right substances—direct or indirect gene products, which all are orthomolecular substances—could be brought to the right site of action at the right time and in the right amounts, many fewer genetic diseases would be manifest.

Predisposition relates to diseases or disorders that in spite of some untoward characteristics of the mutational state of an individual's genome may or may not occur. The quantitative assessment of the individual's lexotype, through protein profiling, is going to permit identification of many of those gene products that are "outliers" with respect to the normal range of their cellular concentration. Such determinations should make it possible to deduce what kinds of diseases or insufficiencies the individual is likely to develop. The assessment of lexotypes thus has great potential for public health. But much more work is required before this potential is realized.

The field of cancer research has been plagued by the fact that there are nearly always alternative explanations for any causal mechanism proposed. One is reminded of the alternative explanation proposed by the woman who said, after giving birth to twins for the tenth time—and who therefore may well have been predisposed to having twins—"Just close the windows and leave everything dark when you go to bed. They come out twins every time" (*San Francisco Chronicle,* June 1984). In cancer research we are now moving away from the period in which this woman was to some extent representative, and into a period where causality can be demonstrated or excluded.

ACKNOWLEDGMENTS

This work was supported by the Japan Shipbuilding Industry Foundation, Tokyo, and in part by the Koret Foundation, San Francisco. I express my special thanks, for exceptional services, to Mrs. Ruth Reynolds and Mrs. Corinne Gorham.

REFERENCES

1. Jain VK, Chandra MD: Does nutritional deficiency predispose to acquired immune deficiency syndrome? *Nutrition Res* 1984; 4: 537–543.

2. Metz CW: Chromosomal differences between germ cells and soma in *Sciara. Biologisches Zentralblatt* 1931; 51: 119–124.

3. Heston WE: Genetics of neoplasia, in Burdette WJ (ed): *Methodology in Mammalian Genetics.* San Francisco, Holden-Day, 1963, pp 247–268.

4. Knudson AG Jr: Genetic predisposition to cancer: origins of human cancer. *Cold Spring Harbor Conferences on Cell Proliferation* 1977; 4: 45–52.

5. Skolnick M: Genetic epidemiology of cancer. *Am J Hum Genetics* 1982; 34(6): A16.

6. Marks PA: Distinguished address: genetic predisposition to cancer. *Surgery* 1981; 90: 132–136.

7. Kopelovich L: Genetic predisposition to cancer in man: in vitro studies. *Intern Rev Cytol* 1982; 77: 64–87.

8. Mulvihill JJ: Clinical genetics of human cancer. *International Agency for Research on Cancer Scientific Publication* 1982; 39: 107–117.

9. Murata M, Kuno K, Fukami A, et al.: Epidemiology of familial predisposition for breast cancer in Japan. *J Natl Canc Inst* 1982; 69: 1229–1234.

10. Echols H: SOS functions, cancer and inducible evolution. *Cell* 1981; 25: 1–2.

11. Bishop JM: Cellular oncogenes and retroviruses. *Annual Review of Biochemistry* 1983; 52: 301–354.

12. Muller R, Slamon DJ, Tremblay JM, et al.: Differential expression of cellular oncogenes during pre- and postnatal development of the mouse. *Nature* 1982; 299: 640–644.

13. Waterfield MD, Scrace GT, Whittle N, et al.: Platelet-derived growth factor is structurally related to the putative transforming protein $p28^{sis}$ of simian sarcoma virus. *Nature* 1983; 304: 35–39.

14. Doolittle RF, Feng DF, Johnson MS: Computer-based characterization of epidermal growth factor precursor. *Nature* 1984; 307: 558–560.

15. Downward J, Yarden Y, Mayes E, et al.: Close similarity of epidermal growth factor receptor and *v-erb*-B oncogene protein sequences. *Nature* 1984; 307: 521–527.

16. Burbeck S, Latter G, Metz E, et al.: Neoplastic human fibroblast proteins are related to epidermal growth factor precursor. *Proc Natl Acad Sci USA* 1984; 81: 5360–5363.

17. Robertson M: Message of *myc* in context. *Nature* 1984; 309: 585–587.

18. Heldin C-H, Westermark B: Growth factors: mechanism of action and relation to oncogenes. *Cell* 1984; 37: 9–20.

19. O'Brien SJ, Nash WG, Goodwin JL, et al.: Dispersion of the *ras* family of transforming genes to four different chromosomes in man. *Nature* 1983; 302: 839–842.

20. Temin HM: Oncogenes: we still don't understand cancer. *Nature* 1983; 302: 656.

21. Chang EH, Furth ME, Scolnick EM, et al.: Tumorigenic transformation of mammalian cells induced by a normal human gene homologous to the oncogene of Harvey murine sarcoma virus. *Nature* 1982; 197: 479–483.

22. Rigby PWJ: The oncogenic circle closes. *Nature* 1982; 297: 451–453.

23. Blair DG, Fischinger PJ, McClements WL, et al.: Activation of the transforming potential of a normal cell sequence: a molecular model for oncogenesis. *Science* 1981; 212: 941–942.

24. Boshart M, Weber F, Jahn G, et al.: A very strong enhancer is located upstream of an immediate early gene of human cytomegalovirus. *Cell* 1985; 41: 521–530.

25. Stalder J, Larsen A, Engel JD, et al.: Tissue-specific DNA cleavages in the globin chromatin domain introduced by DNAase I. *Cell* 1980; 20: 451–460.

26. Zuckerkandl E: A general function of noncoding polynucleotide sequences. *Molec Biol Rep* 1981; 7: 149–158.

27. Yunis JJ: The chromosomal basis of human neoplasia. *Science* 1983; 221: 227–235.

28. Murphree AL, Benedict WF: Retinoblastoma: clues to human oncogenesis. *Science* 1984; 223: 1028–1033.

29. Brodeur GM, Seeger RC, Schwab M, et al.: Amplification of N-*myc* in untreated human neuroblastomas correlates with advanced disease stage. *Science* 1984; 224: 1121–1124.

30. Marx JL: Oncogenes amplified in cancer cells. *Science* 1984; 223: 40–41.

31. Marx JL: The N-*myc* oncogene in neural tumors. *Science* 1984; 224: 1088.

32. Robertson M: Progress in malignancy. *Nature* 1984; 309: 512–513.

33. Cairns J: The origin of human cancers. *Nature* 1981; 289: 353–357.

34. Sager R, Tanaka K, Lau CC, et al.: Resistance of human cells to tumorigenesis induced by cloned transforming genes. *Proc Natl Acad Sci USA* 1983; 80: 7601–7605.

35. Leavitt J, Goldman D, Merril C, et al.: Actin mutations in a human fibroblast model for carcinogenesis. *Clin Chem* 1982; 28: 850.

36. Naharro G, Robbins KC, Reddy EP: Gene product of *v-fgr onc*: hybrid protein containing a portion of actin and a tyrosine-specific protein kinase. *Science* 1984; 223: 63–66.

37. Weinberg RA: Oncogenes of spontaneous and chemically induced tumors. *Adv Canc Res* 1982; 36: 159–163.

38. Lustbader ED, Hann HWL, Blumberg BS: Serum ferritin as a predictor of host response to hepatitis B virus infection. *Science* 1983; 220: 423–425.

39. Pauling L, Itano HA, Singer SJ, et al.: Sickle cell anemia, a molecular disease. *Science* 1949; 110: 543–548.

40. Zuckerkandl E: Controller-gene diseases: the operon model as applied to β-thalassemia, familial fetal hemoglobinemia and the normal switch from the production of fetal hemoglobin to that of adult hemoglobin. *J Mol Biol* 1964; 8: 128–147.

41. Gootwine E, Webb CG, Sachs L: Participation of myeloid leukemic cells injected into embryos in haematopoietic differentiation in adult mice. *Nature* 1982; 299: 63–65.

42. Illmensee K, Mintz B: Totipotency and normal differentiation of single teratocarcinoma cells cloned by injection into blastocysts. *Proc Natl Acad Sci USA* 1976; 73: 549–553.

43. Strickland, S: Mouse teratocarcinoma cells: prospects for the study of embryogenesis and neoplasia. *Cell* 1981; 24: 277–278.

44. Ossowski L, Reich E: Changes in malignant phenotype of a human carcinoma conditioned by growth environment. *Cell* 1983; 33: 323–333.

45. Goldenberg DM, Pavia RA: In vivo horizontal oncogenesis by a human tumor in nude mice. *Proc Natl Acad Sci USA* 1982; 79: 2389–2392.

46. Nakano S, Ts'o POP: Cellular differentiation and neoplasia: Characterization of subpopulations of cells that have neoplasia-related growth properties in Syrian hamster embryo cell cultures. *Proc Natl Acad Sci USA* 1981; 78: 4995–4999.

47. Ibsen KH, Fishman WH: Developmental gene expression in cancer. *Biochimica et Biophysica Acta* 1979; 560: 243–280.

48. Sell S: Oncodevelopmental antigens, in Marchalonis JJ, Hanna MG, Fidler IJ (eds): *Cancer Biology Reviews* (vol I). New York, Marcel Dekker, 1980, pp 251–352.

49. Schapira F: Resurgence of fetal isozymes in cancer: study of aldolase, pyruvate kinase, lactic dehydrogenase, and beta-hexosaminidase, in *Current Topics in Biological and Medical Research,* isozymes series. New York, Alan R. Liss, 1981, pp 27–75.

50. Pitot HC: The natural history of neoplastic development: the relation of experimental models to human cancer. *Cancer* 1982; 49: 1206–1211.

51. Peehl DM, Stanbridge EJ: Anchorage-independent growth of normal human fibroblasts. *Proc Natl Acad Sci USA* 1981; 78(5): 3053–3057.

52. Hiwasa T, Fujimura S, Sakiyama S: Tumor promoters increase the synthesis of a 32,000-dalton protein in BALB/c 3T3 cells. *Proc Natl Acad Sci USA* 1982; 79: 1800–1804.

53. Yamada KM, Pouyssegur J: Cell surface glycoproteins and malignant transformation. *Biochimie* 1978; 60: 1221–1233.

54. Zuckerkandl E: Multilocus enzymes, gene regulation, and genetic sufficiency. *J Mol Evol* 1978; 12: 57–89.

55. Ferris SD, Whitt GS: Evolution of the differential regulation of duplicate genes after polyploidization. *J Mol Evol* 1979; 12: 267–317.

56. Chan W-Y, Garnica AD, Owen MR: Abnormal accumulation of copper in cultured fibroblasts as in vitro genetic marker for Wilson's disease. *Pediatr Res* 1979; 13: 418.

57. Robbins JH, Otsuka F, Tarone RE, et al.: Radiosensitivity in Alzheimer disease and Parkinson disease. *Lancet* 1983; 1: 468–469.

58. Butterfield DA, Oeswin JQ, Markesbery WR: Electron spin resonance study of membrane protein alterations in erythrocytes in Huntington's disease. *Nature* 1977; 267: 453–455.

59. Nadi NS, Nurnberger JI, Gershon ES: Muscarinic cholinergic receptors on skin fibroblasts in familial affective disorders. *N Engl J Med* 1984; 311(4): 225–230.

60. Barrett J, Ts'o POP: Evidence for the progressive nature of neoplastic transformation in vitro. *Proc Natl Acad Sci USA* 1978; 75(8): 3761–3765.

61. Knudson AG Jr: Mutation and cancer: statistical study of neuroblastoma. *Proc Natl Acad Sci USA* 1971; 68: 820–823.

62. Cairns J, Logan J: Step by step into carcinogenesis. *Nature* 1983; 304: 582–583.

63. Antecol MH, Mukherjee BB: Effects of 12-0-tetradecanoylphorbol-13-acetate on fibroblasts from individuals genetically predisposed to cancer. *Canc Res* 1982; 42: 3870–3879.

64. Pfeffer LM, Kopelovich L: Differential genetic susceptibility of cultured human skin fibroblasts to transformation by Kirsten murine sarcoma virus. *Cell* 1977; 10: 313–320.

65. Land H, Parada LF, Weinberg RA: Tumorigenic conversion of primary embryo fibroblasts requires at least two cooperating oncogenes. *Nature* 1983; 304: 596–602.

66. Ruley HE: Adenovirus early region Ia enables viral and cellular transforming genes to transform primary cells in culture. *Nature* 1983; 304: 602–606.

67. Newbold RF, Overell RW: Fibroblast immortality is a prerequisite for transformation by EJ c-Ha-*ras* oncogene. *Nature* 1983; 304: 648–651.

68. Jariwalla RJ, Aurelian L, Ts'o POP: Immortalization and neoplastic transformation of normal diploid cells by defined cloned DNA fragments of herpes simplex virus type 2. *Proc Natl Acad Sci USA* 1983; 80: 5902–5906.

69. Rassoulzadegan M, Naghashfar Z, Cowie A, et al.: Expression of the large T protein of polyoma virus promotes the establishment in culture of "normal" rodent fibroblast cell lines. *Proc Natl Acad Sci USA* 1983; 80: 4354–4358.

70. Griffin BE, Karran L: Immortalization of monkey epithelial cells by specific fragments of Epstein-Barr virus DNA. *Nature* 1984; 309: 78–82.

71. Smets LA: Cell transformation as a model for tumor induction and neoplastic growth. *Biochim et Biophys Acta* 1984; 605: 93–111.

72. Emmelot P, Scherer E: Multi-hit kinetics of tumor formation, with special reference to experimental liver and human lung carcinogenesis and some general conclusions. *Canc Res* 1977; 37: 1702–1708.

73. Rhim JS, Huebner FJ, Arnstein P, et al.: Chemical transformation of cultured human skin fibroblasts derived from individuals with hereditary adenomatosis of the colon and rectum. *Int J Cancer* 1980; 26(5): 565–569.

74. Wittelsberger SC, Kleene K, Penman S: Progressive loss of shape-responsive metabolic controls in cells with increasingly transformed phenotype. *Cell* 1981; 24: 859–866.

75. Slaga TJ: Host factors in the susceptibility of mice to tumour initiating and promoting agents. *International Agency for Research on Cancer Scientific Publication* (Lyon, France) 1983; 51: 257–273.

76. Eckhart WR, Dulbecco R, Burger MM: Temperature-dependent surface changes in cells infected or transformed by a thermosensitive mutant of polyoma virus. *Proc Natl Acad Sci USA* 1971; 68: 283–286.

77. Leavitt J, Bushar G, Kakunaga T, et al.: Variations in expression of mutant β-actin accompanying incremental increases in human fibroblast tumorigenicity. *Cell* 1982; 28: 259–268.

78. Leavitt J, Goldman D, Merril C, et al.: Changes in gene expression accompanying chemically-induced malignant transformation of human fibroblasts. *Carcinogenesis* 1982; 3: 61–70.

79. Latter GI, Burbeck S, Fleming J, et al.: Identification of polypeptides on two-dimensional electrophoresis gels by computerized amino acid analysis. *Clin Chem* 1984; 30: 1925–1932.

80. Nomura T: Parental exposure to X-rays and chemicals induces heritable tumors and anomalies in mice. *Nature* 1982; 296: 575–577.

81. Miller AD, Curran T, Verma IM: *c-fos* protein can induce cellular transformation: a novel mechanism for activation of a cellular oncogene. *Cell* 1984; 36: 51–60.

82. Murray MJ, Shilo BZ, Shih C, et al.: Three different human tumor cell lines contain different oncogenes. *Cell* 1981; 25: 355–361.

83. Land H, Parada LF, Weinberg RA: Cellular oncogenes and multistep carcinogenesis. *Science* 1983; 222: 771–777.

84. Hoel DG, Kaplan NL, Anderson MW: Implication of nonlinear kinetics on risk estimation in carcinogenesis. *Science* 1983; 219: 1032–1037.

85. Richardson A, Birchennall-Sparks M: Age-related changes in protein synthesis, in Rothstein M (ed): *Review of Biological Research in Aging,* vol I. New York, Alan R. Liss, 1983, pp 255–273.

86. Doll R: An epidemiological perspective of the biology of cancer. *Canc Res* 1978; 38: 3573–3583.

87. Pauling L, Willoughby R, Reynolds R, et al.: Incidence of squamous cell carcinoma in hairless mice irradiated with ultraviolet light in relation to intake of ascorbic acid (vitamin C) and of D, L-tocopheryl acetate (vitamin E): Proceedings of the 3rd International Symposium on Vitamin C, July 1980, in Hanck A (ed): *Vitamin C: New Clinical Applications in Immunology, Lipid Metabolism and Cancer.* Stuttgart, Hans Huber, 1982, pp 53–82.

88. Dunham WB, Zuckerkandl E, Reynolds R, et al.: Effects of intake of L-ascorbic acid on the incidence of dermal neoplasms induced in mice by ultraviolet light. *Proc Natl Acad Sci USA* 1982; 79: 7532–7536.

89. Pauling L, Nixon JC, Stitt F, et al.: Effect of dietary ascorbic acid on the incidence of spontaneous mammary tumors in RIII mice. *Proc Natl Acad Sci USA* 1985; 82: 5185–5189.

90. Berkowitz LR, Orringer EP: Cetiedil inhibits the Gardos phenomenon: an explanation for the beneficial effect of cetiedil in the treatment of sickle cell anemia. *Clin Res* 1980; 28: 823A.

CHAPTER TWO

FUNCTIONAL PROPERTIES OF ABNORMAL HUMAN HEMOGLOBINS

RICHARD T. JONES, MD, PhD

DANIEL T.-b. SHIH, PhD

My career owes a lot to Dr. Pauling.* Because of him I went to the California Institute of Technology for my undergraduate studies and again later for graduate studies. Because of his advice I became interested in the structure, function, and genetic control of hemoglobins. He did such a good job counseling me that I am still studying hemoglobin, 26 years later.

Studies of the oxygen-binding properties of abnormal human hemoglobin can be used to better understand the relationship between molecular structure and biological function of normal hemoglobins. Studies of mutants permit the mapping of the hemoglobin molecule. This mapping has helped in the identification of regions of the molecule that are important, not important, or only indirectly important for normal function.

This discussion on hemoglobin is divided into three parts. The first part offers four views of three-dimensional computer models of hemoglobin, as prepared by Dr. Richard J. Feldman of the National Institutes of Health from X-ray data obtained from Dr. Max Perutz of Cambridge, England. The second part outlines the measurement of the oxygen-hemoglobin equilibrium and factors that influence it. The final part describes results of some of our studies on functional properties of abnormal hemoglobins, which illustrate how certain important parts of the molecule influence oxygen binding.

*The personal reminiscences are those of Dr. Jones, who presented the oral version of this paper.

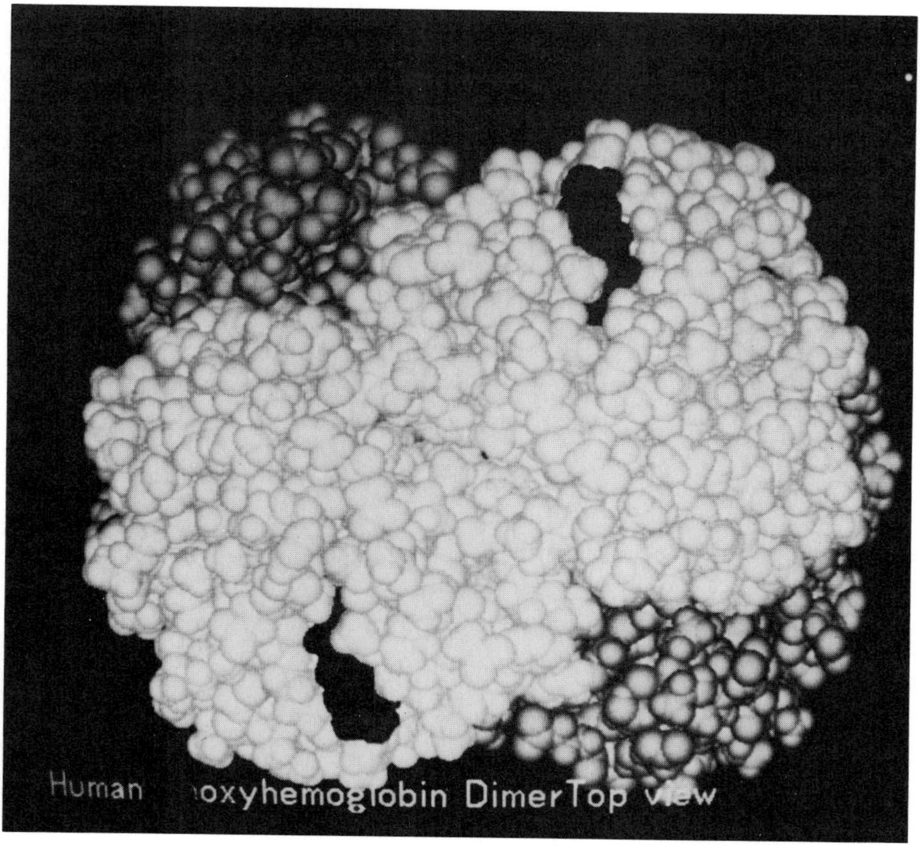

Figure 2.1 Model of human oxyhemoglobin looking along axis of symmetry (y axis) with white α chains in foreground and light gray β chains behind. The heme groups are dark gray.

STRUCTURAL FEATURES OF HEMOGLOBIN

Figure 2.1 shows the hemoglobin model, as viewed from the top of the molecule. The lightest parts represent the two identical α chains. The dark gray parts are the heme groups in each α chain. The light gray parts are the β chain not covered or in contact with the α chain. There is a symmetry to the molecule that can be seen by rotating it 180° around an axis through the center of this model. Although this model does not show oxygen molecules bound to the hemes, they would be tucked down between the heme groups and the polypeptide chain on the side facing the outside of the molecule. This is the oxyhemoglobin configuration of the molecule

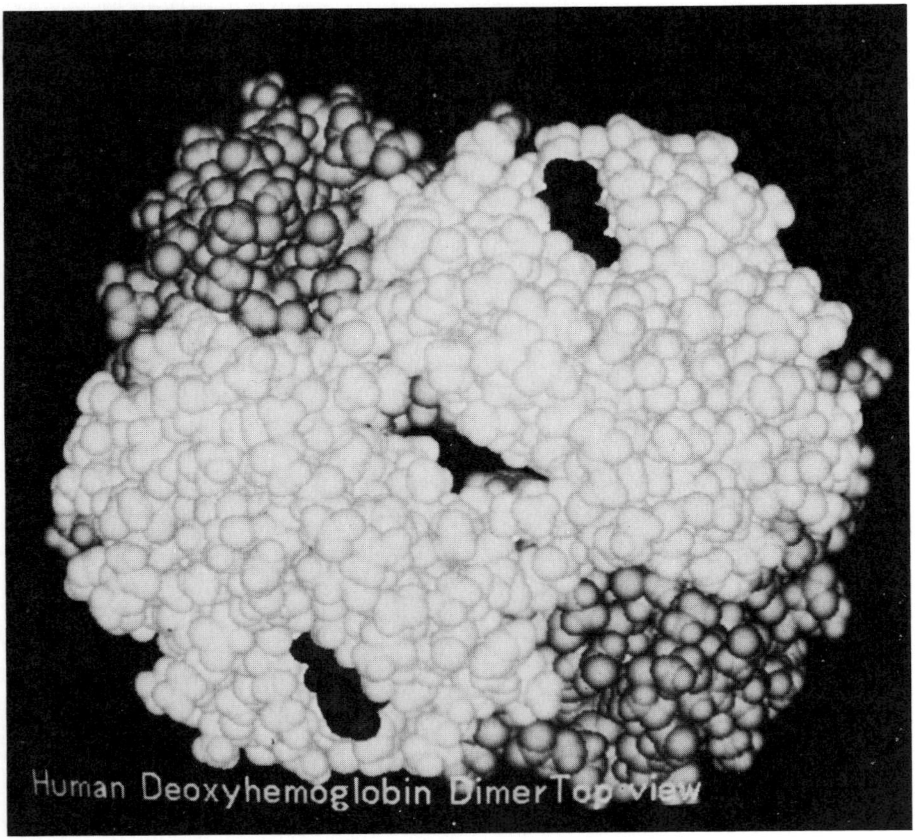

Figure 2.2 View of deoxyhemoglobin model. For description of components, see legend to Figure 2.1.

because it is compact, especially near the center of the molecule. This oxy configuration is the same for carbon-monoxy hemoglobin. Although there is a depression or hollow at the center of the outer surface of the white α subunits, there is no hole through the molecule in its oxy conformation.

Figure 2.2 is another top view of the hemoglobin molecule, now in the deoxy conformation. A space can be seen between the two white α chains. The molecule is more open in the deoxy configuration than in the oxy configuration.

Figure 2.3 shows the model of deoxyhemoglobin turned upside down. The molecule is still viewed along the same axis but now the β chains, in the light gray, are in front and the α chains, in white, are to the sides and behind. Dark gray heme groups are sandwiched into crevices in each β chain. The position of the hemes in the β chains is analogous to that in the α chains. The open space in the center of the molecule can be seen with what appears to be a hole all the way

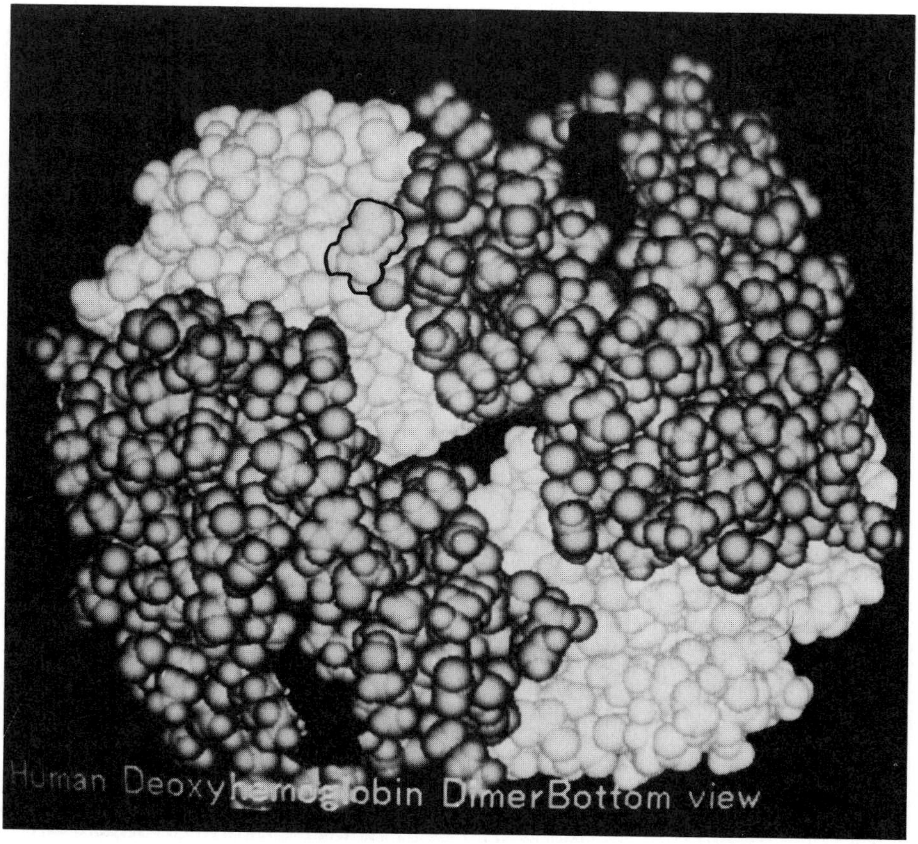

Figure 2.3 Deoxyhemoglobin model as viewed from direction opposite that of Figures 2.1 and 2.2. The light gray β chains are in the foreground and the white α chains are behind. The group outlined in black is the C-terminal histidyl residue of one of the β chains. The central cavity between the two β chains is open and available to bind 2,3-diphosphoglycerate.

through. One molecule of 2,3-diphosphoglycerate (DPG), a physiological regulator, can react with one molecule of deoxyhemoglobin by fitting into this space between the light gray β chains. Also shown on the upper-right β chain in this model is a group of atoms that are outlined in black. These atoms represent the normal histidyl residue, which is at the carboxyl terminal end of the β chain. One of the mutants, to be described later, has a leucyl residue substituted for this histidyl group. The oxygen-binding properties of this mutant are abnormal, even though this histidyl group is not in direct contact with the heme group that actually binds the oxygen molecules.

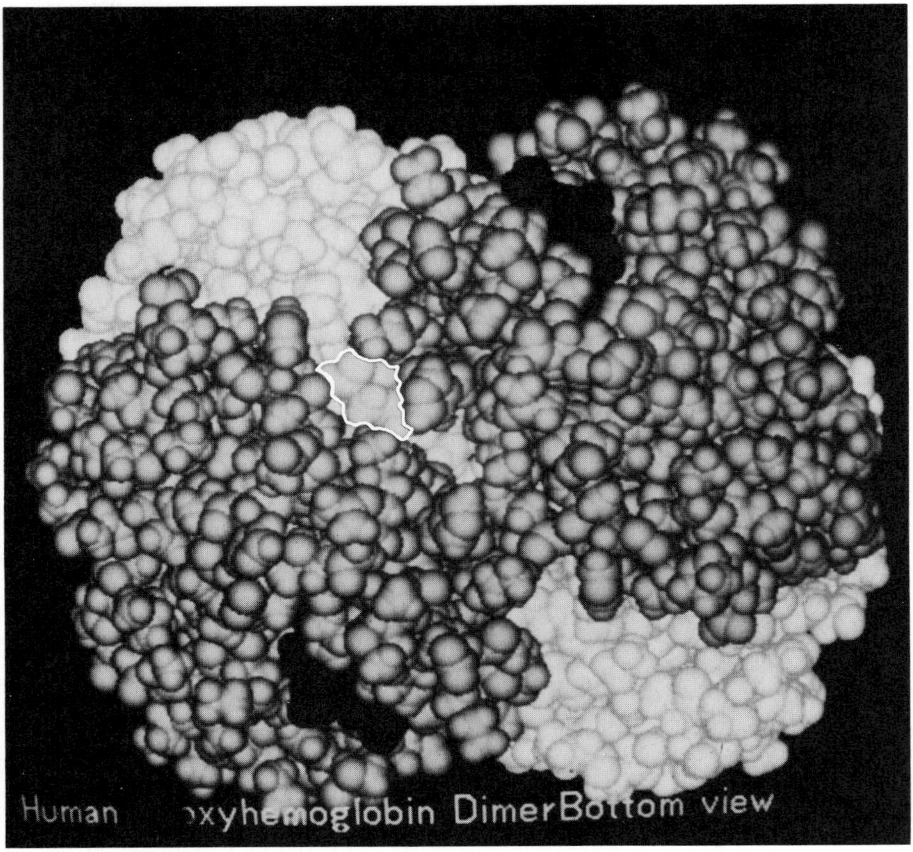

Figure 2.4 Bottom view of oxyhemoglobin model. Note the decrease in the central cavity between the β chains. For description of components, see legend to Figure 2.3.

Note in Figure 2.4 that the central cavity area of the deoxyhemoglobin molecule and the histidyl residue shown in Figure 2.3 have shifted. The molecule becomes more compact when it changes to the oxy or carbon-monoxy configuration. Most of the space between the β chains is obliterated by these chains moving toward each other. Also the C-terminal histidyl group (outlined in white) has moved down into the central cavity region.

In summary, these four models illustrate the following about normal hemoglobin:

1. Hemoglobin is made up of four protein subunits, two α chains and two β chains associated together in space as a tetrahedron.
2. The α and β chains are similar to one another in overall structure.

3. There are four hemes per molecule, one sandwiched into a crevice in each subunit.
4. There is a symmetry to the molecule because it is made up of two identical half molecules. It can be rotated 180° around its axis of symmetry to give the same arrangement in space.
5. There is a change in conformation of the molecule between the deoxygenated and oxygenated states. The subunits move toward one another on oxygenation and apart on deoxygenation. Thus the molecule can be viewed as "breathing." However, the change is in the opposite sense compared to the expansion and contraction of lungs and chest cavity.

FUNCTIONAL STUDIES OF HEMOGLOBIN

Hemoglobin changes color from a bluish red to bright red when it reacts with oxygen. Therefore, the equilibrium reaction between hemoglobin and oxygen can be followed by measuring changes in the color of a hemoglobin solution subjected to different partial pressures of oxygen.

Figure 2.5 is a diagram of the system used in our laboratory to measure hemoglobin-oxygen equilibria of normal and abnormal bloods and hemoglobin solutions. It is modeled after one described by Imai.[1] At the bottom, left center is the reaction chamber in a spectrophotometer. Monochromatic light at an appropriate wavelength is passed through the sample and the light absorbance is recorded on the y axis of the x-y recorder shown at the top, right of center. The percent saturation or fraction of oxygenated hemoglobin can be calculated from this spectrophotometric signal.

Also in the cuvette shown in light gray is an oxygen electrode by which the oxygen concentration or partial pressure can be measured. The signal from this oxygen electrode is sent to the x axis of the x-y recorder after proper amplification. Thus we can obtain simultaneous recordings of the percent saturation of the hemoglobin with oxygen and the oxygen partial pressure that exist in the cuvette at any time while we gradually change the oxygen tension over our sample by introducing various gas mixtures. The measuring system is also attached to a computer in which we can store the data from the experiment and then later analyze and transform them into the conventional saturation curve. For normal hemoglobin we can measure as low as 0.1 percent oxygenation and as high as 99.9 percent saturation.

Figure 2.6 shows the more conventional saturation curve for normal hemoglobin under physiological conditions on the right, and a simulated curve for myoglobin on the left. The shapes of these two curves are quite different. Myoglobin has the shape of a simple rectangular hyperbola, reflecting the presence of a single

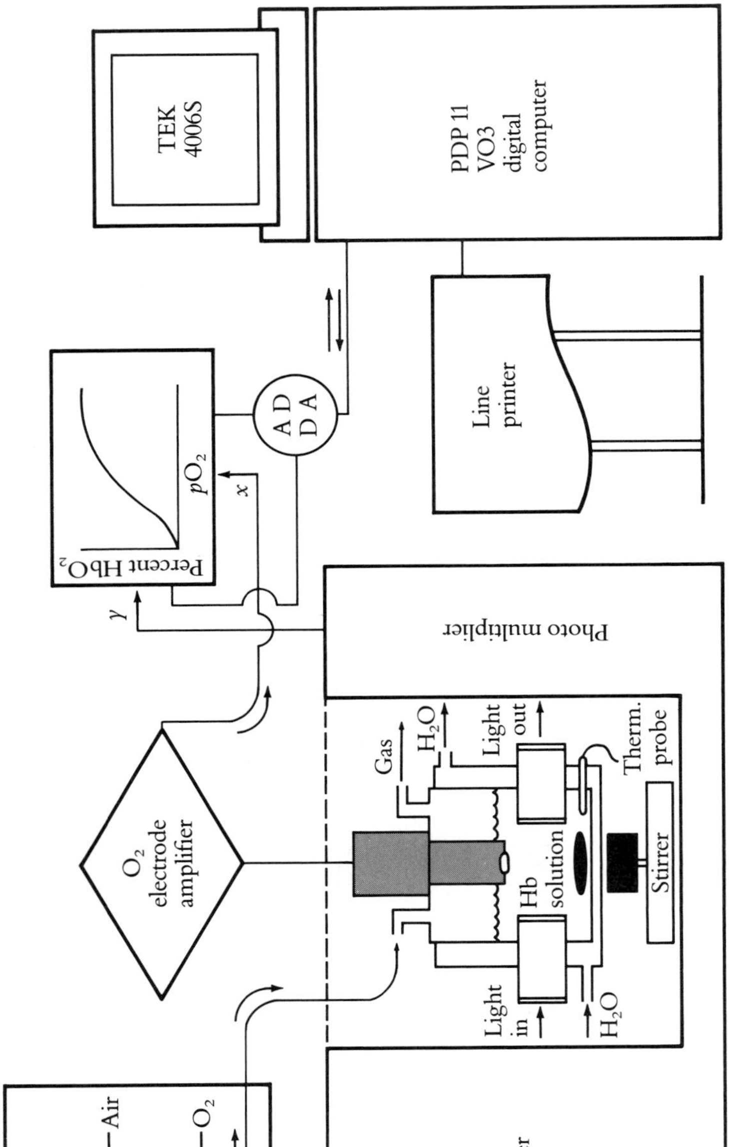

Figure 2.5 Diagram of the automatic oxygen-hemoglobin equilibrium measurement system. See text for description of parts.

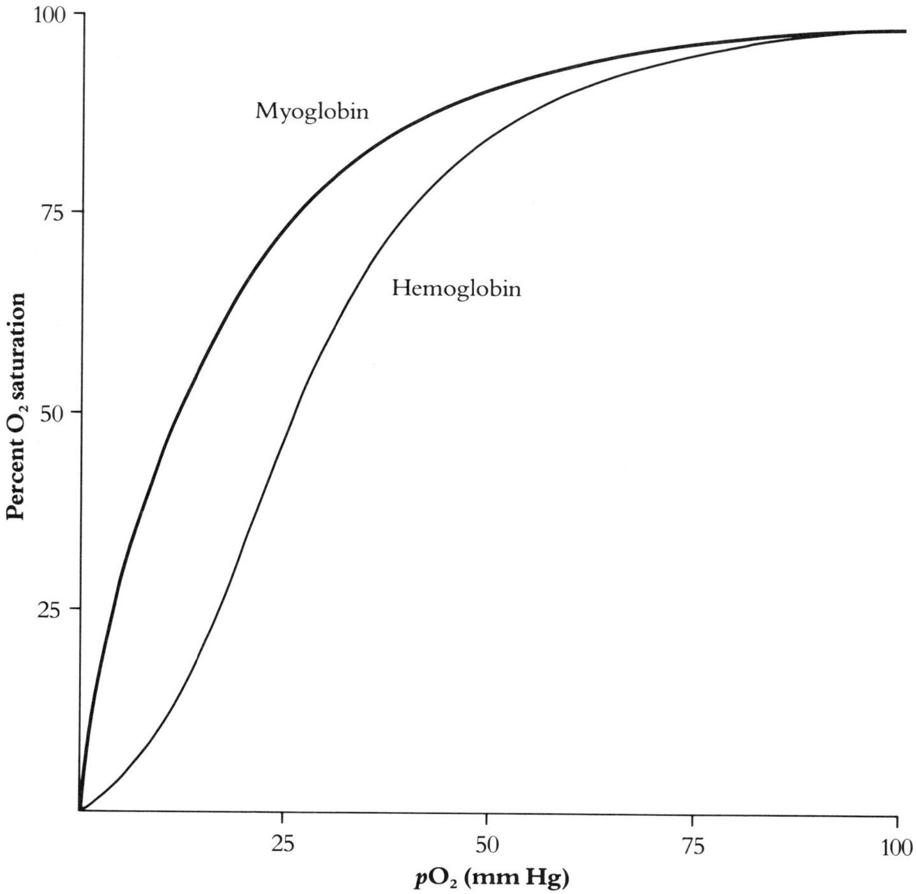

Figure 2.6 Representative saturation curves of hemoglobin (right) and myoglobin (left).

oxygen-binding site, whereas hemoglobin has the familiar sigmoid curve that Dr. Pauling many years ago suggested is due to an interaction between the four heme binding sites in this protein.[2]

Figure 2.7 shows the Hill plot of the oxygen-hemoglobin equilibrium reaction. This is a logarithmic representation of the equilibrium reaction. The ordinate is the log of the fraction of oxyhemoglobin, y, divided by the fraction of deoxyhemoglobin or $1-y$. The abscissa is the log of the partial pressure of oxygen. The curved line represents the Hill plot of normal hemoglobin at pH 7.4. The point at which this line crosses the horizontal line is the point at which half of the heme sites are saturated with oxygen. The pressure at this half saturation point is called

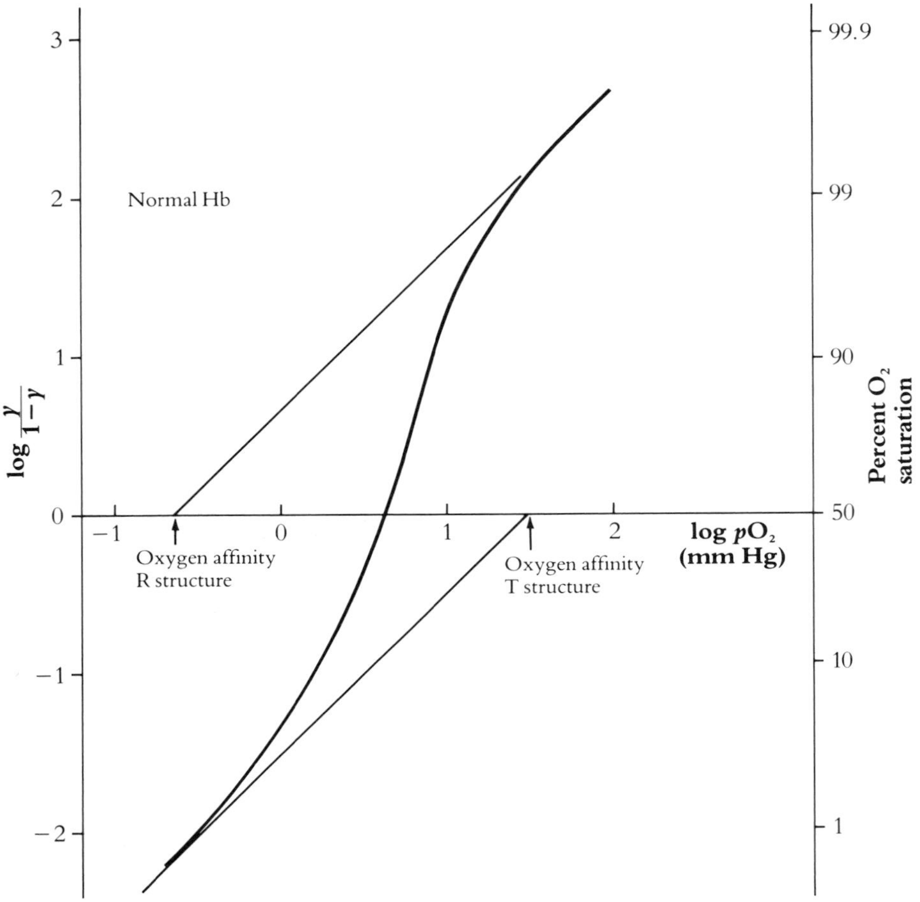

Figure 2.7 Hill plot of oxygen-hemoglobin equilibrium reaction of normal hemoglobin A at pH 7.4 and 25°C. See text for explanation.

the p_{50} and is an indicator of the oxygen affinity of a hemoglobin. The two straight lines indicate the type of plots one would have if all four hemes bound oxygen with equal affinities. The upper straight line represents the oxygen affinity of fully oxygenated hemoglobin that remains in the R or relaxed conformational state. This affinity is high as we can see by its intercept with the horizontal axis. The lower straight line represents the oxygen affinity of deoxygenated hemoglobin. Its intercept with the horizontal line is at a high p_{50} value. This latter line is typical of a hemoglobin that remains in the T or tense conformational state.

Figure 2.8 shows the Hill plot of normal hemoglobin A in the middle and the curves for two abnormal hemoglobins. On the top, shown as a heavy solid line, is the Hill plot of hemoglobin Vanderbilt (β89 Ser → Arg), which has virtually the affinity of oxyhemoglobin throughout its entire range of reaction with oxygen.[3]

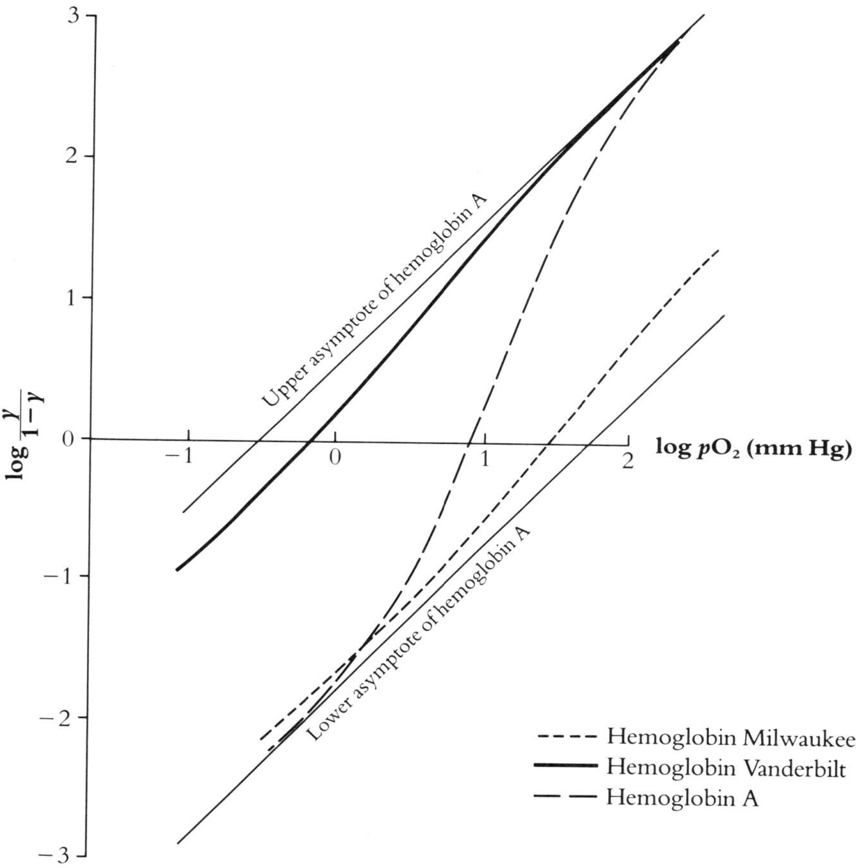

Figure 2.8 Hill plot of normal hemoglobin A (middle), hemoglobin Vanderbilt (β89 Ser ⟶ Arg) (top), hemoglobin Milwaukee (β67 Val ⟶ Glu) (bottom). (Measurements made in 0.05 *M* potassium phosphate buffer, pH 7.2 at 25°C.)

Shown below as the short dashed line is hemoglobin M Milwaukee (β67 Val ⟶ Glu), which has the oxygen affinity of deoxyhemoglobin throughout its range of reaction with oxygen. The structure of hemoglobin Vanderbilt is believed to remain in the compact or R form characteristic of normal oxyhemoglobin even in the absence of oxygen. Hemoglobin M Milwaukee is believed to remain in the expanded or T structure of normal deoxyhemoglobin even when oxygen is present.

FUNCTIONALLY ABNORMAL HUMAN HEMOGLOBINS

Let us shift to the question of how some of these abnormal hemoglobins with altered oxygen affinities are discovered. One of the first abnormal, high-affinity

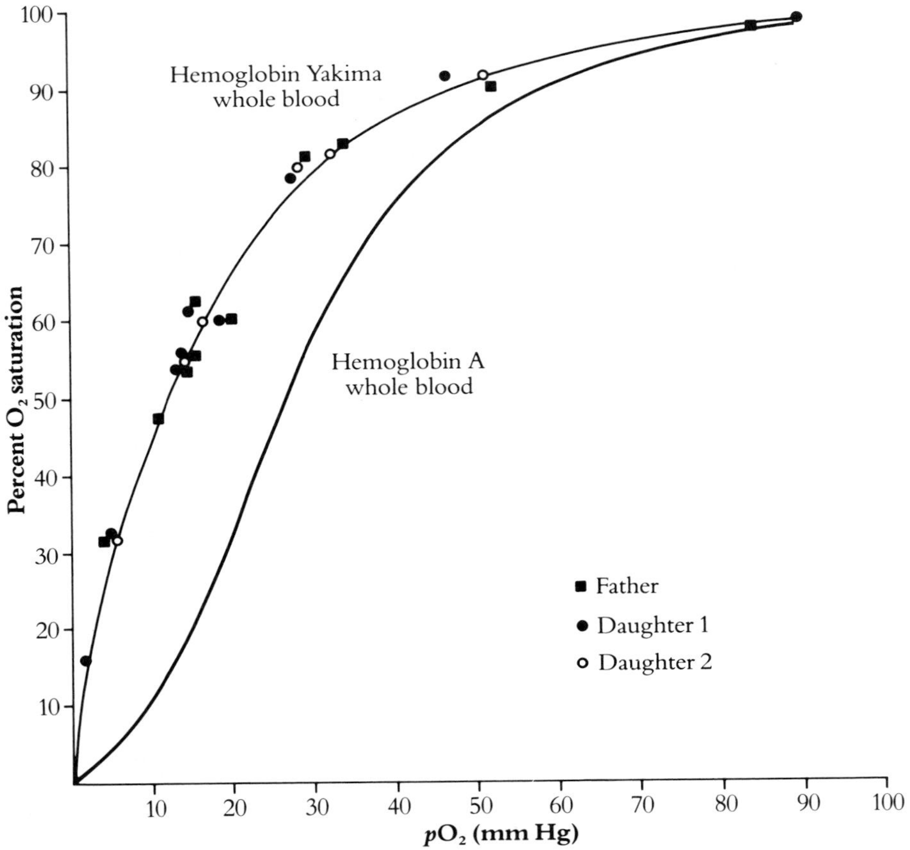

Figure 2.9 Oxygen-hemoglobin saturation curves of blood from individuals with hemoglobin Yakima (β99 Asp ⟶ His) compared with normal blood. (From Novy et al.[5])

hemoglobins was identified by the late Dr. Edwin Osgood, Dr. Robert Koler, and Dr. Jones in the mid-1960s.[4] Dr. Osgood had been following a patient for about 10 years who had unusual polycythemia or, more properly, erythrocytosis because only his red cells were elevated in total numbers. When the patient's two daughters were found also to have erythrocytosis, Dr. Osgood's associate, Dr. Koler, suggested the possibility that an abnormal hemoglobin might be present. This was demonstrated by electrophoresis, and hemoglobin Yakima (β99 Asp ⟶ His) was discovered. In pursuit of an explanation for the increased number of red cells, an oxygen saturation curve was determined. Figure 2.9 shows the normal curve and the abnormal curve from the patients.[5] Data points for individuals are shown in different symbols. The patients' blood has a higher-than-normal affinity for oxygen and has

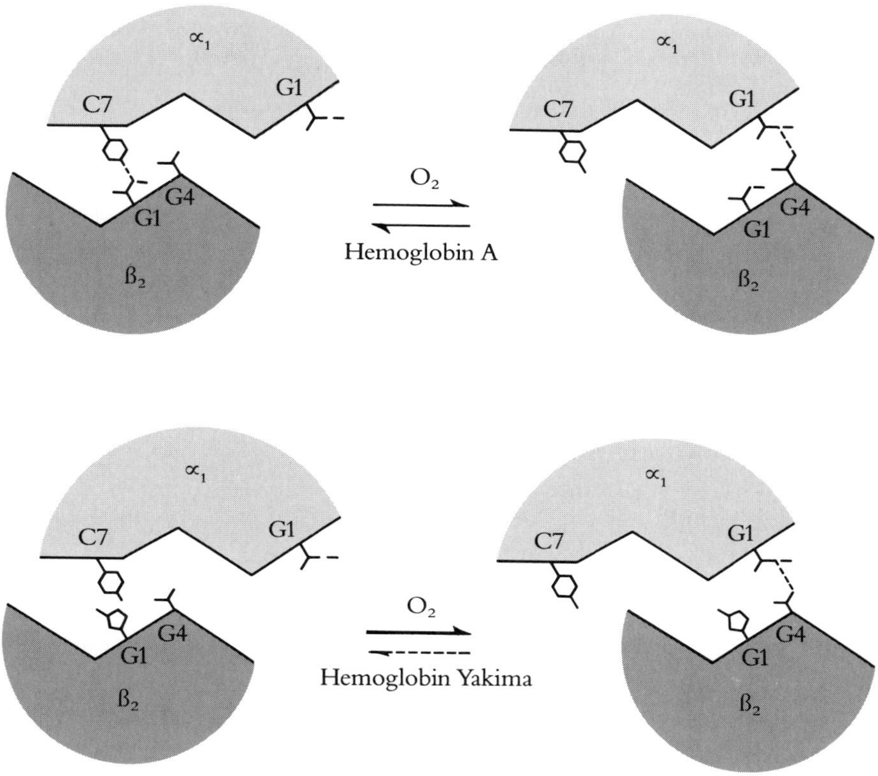

Figure 2.10 Change at the $\alpha_1\beta_2$ interface on oxygenation. The hydrogen bond between aspartyl β99 (G1) and tyrosyl α42 (C7) cannot be formed by hemoglobin Yakima with its substitution of histidyl β99.

lost most of its normal heme–heme interaction, as indicated by a curve that is more like that of myoglobin than of normal hemoglobin.

How does the structural change in hemoglobin Yakima explain the alteration in its oxygen-binding affinity? The α and β chains form a complementary interface in the interior part of the hemoglobin molecule; one of the important groups at this interface is the β99 aspartyl residue. Hemoglobin Yakima has a histidyl residue in place of the normal aspartyl residue. This histidyl residue lacks the negative charge of and is much larger than the carboxyl group of the aspartyl side chain.

Figure 2.10 shows part of the interface between an α chain and one of its complementary β chains at the so-called $\alpha_1\beta_2$ contact region. When the normal molecule changes from the oxy configuration (top right) to the deoxy structure (top left) there is a shift of about 8 Å between the groups along this interface. In

Hemoglobin Alberta Gly

Hemoglobin Potomac Asp

Hemoglobin British Columbia Lys

Hemoglobin Rush Gln

Hemoglobin A Glu

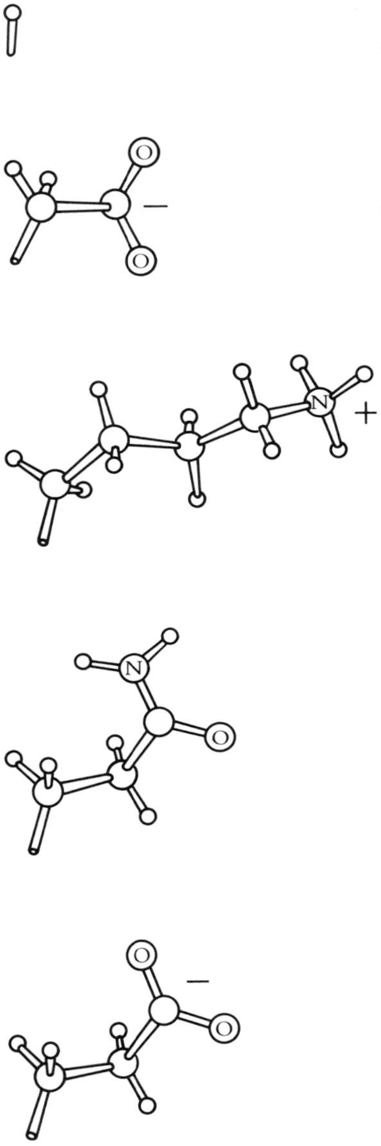

Figure 2.11 The side groups of the amino acid residues of the β101 mutants.

the deoxy structure, a hydrogen bond is formed between the aspartyl residue at G1 of normal hemoglobin A and the hydroxyl (—OH) of the tyrosyl at position C7 of the α chain. This hydrogen bond helps to stabilize the deoxy tense, or T, conformation. With the transition to the oxy structure, this hydrogen bond between βG1 and αC7 is broken but a new hydrogen bond is formed now between the threonyl residue of βG4 and an aspartyl residue at αG1. This bond later stabilizes the oxy relaxed, or R, structure. The equilibrium between these two normal structures is influenced in part by the energy of stabilization provided by these two different hydrogen bonds. Below in Figure 2.10 we see what Morimoto, Lehmann, and Perutz[6] proposed in 1971 to explain the abnormal oxygen binding of hemoglobin Yakima. At the lower right side is shown hemoglobin Yakima in the oxy or R configuration, with the normal hydrogen bond between βG4 and αG1 intact. However, as we can see at the left on the bottom, the hydrogen bond normally present between βG1 and αC7 is not present in deoxy hemoglobin Yakima because its abnormal histidyl residue cannot form this bond properly. With a loss of the stabilizing influence of this hydrogen bond in the deoxy or T conformation of hemoglobin Yakima, the equilibrium between the T and R conformation is shifted toward the oxy or R structure. As mentioned earlier, this oxy structure has a higher affinity for oxygen than the deoxy structure. Thus this shift in the equilibrium between the structures of deoxy and oxy hemoglobin Yakima results in its higher oxygen-binding affinity. We have studied three other mutants of this β99 residue and each has a high oxygen affinity compared to normal, apparently due to the inability to form this one important hydrogen bond.

A different set of hemoglobin mutants involves a nearby residue, β101 or βG3. This is also at the $\alpha_1\beta_2$ contact region of the molecule at a point at which a major shift occurs between the oxy and deoxy structures.

Figure 2.11 illustrates the amino acid side chains of the four mutants of this residue, which we have studied, as well as the normal hemoglobin A residue. In hemoglobin Alberta, a glycyl residue is present in place of the normal glutamyl residue. In hemoglobin Potomac the substitution is an aspartyl group. In hemoglobin British Columbia a lysyl is present, and in hemoglobin Rush, a glutaminyl residue.

Figure 2.12 shows the oxygen-hemoglobin saturation curves for red cells containing these abnormal hemoglobins; for comparison, the curve for normal subjects is shown by the light line. Under physiological conditions, hemoglobin Rush is similar to hemoglobin A but shifted slightly to the right. The other three mutants are quite abnormal and shifted to the left, indicating high affinities for oxygen. Each one is a little different from the others. The oxygen-binding properties of these β101 mutants have been studied under a variety of conditions after isolating each abnormal hemoglobin by column chromatography. The oxygen affinities of the variants differ from one another, and all are different from that of normal hemoglobin A. Even hemoglobin Rush is quite abnormal. The molecular explanation for the altered oxygen binding by these β101 mutants is less clear than that for hemoglobin Yakima. It is not due to loss of a negative charge or change to a positive charge alone. It seems to be more dependent on the size of the substituted residue. Presumably the normal glutamyl residue at position β101 is just the right size and charge to permit a balanced transition between the oxy and the deoxy

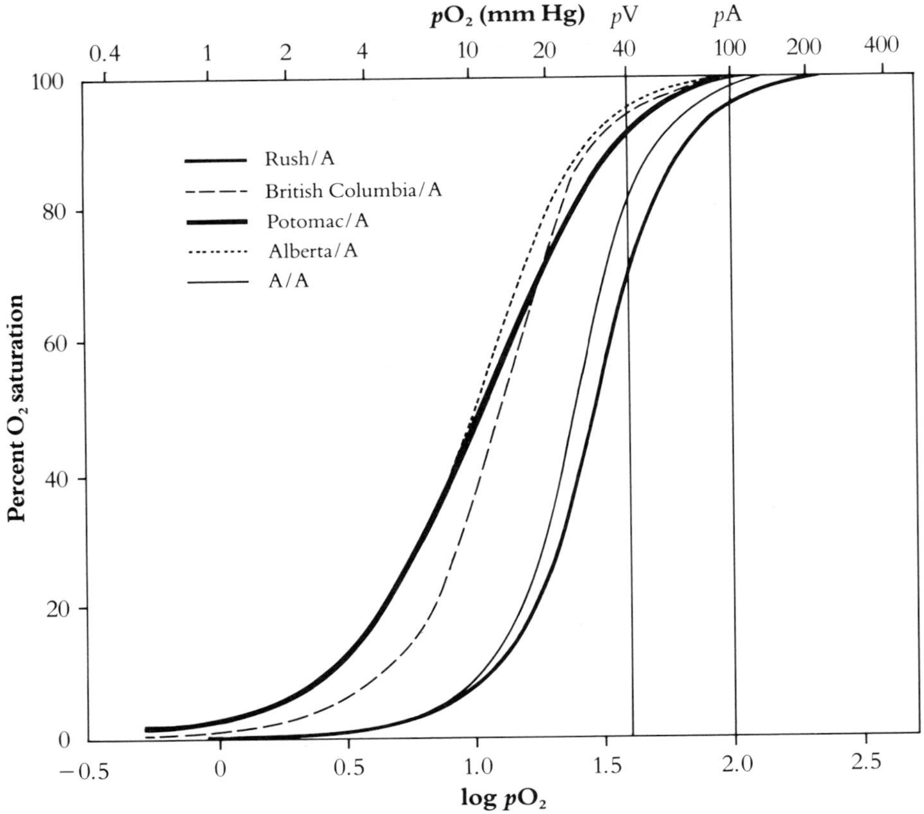

Figure 2.12 Oxygen-hemoglobin saturation curves of erythrocyte suspensions from a normal individual and individuals with the β101 abnormal hemoglobins. (Measurements made in isotonic phosphate buffer, pH 7.4 at 37°C.)

conformation. Its replacement by any other residue results in a shift in the conformational equilibrium towards the R or oxy structure. It is interesting to note that at this position of the β chain is a glutamic acid in most of the animal hemoglobins so far studied.[7]

Structural changes of the C-terminal residue of the β chain (see Figures 2.3 and 2.4) also can result in changes in oxygen-binding properties. An example of this can be found in studies of hemoglobin Cowtown.[8] This abnormal hemoglobin was found in the blood of a person from Texas who had an erythrocytosis. The saturation curve of blood containing hemoglobin Cowtown was found to be shifted to the left of normal, again indicating a higher-than-normal oxygen affinity. The reason for the increased oxygen affinity of hemoglobin Cowtown became clear

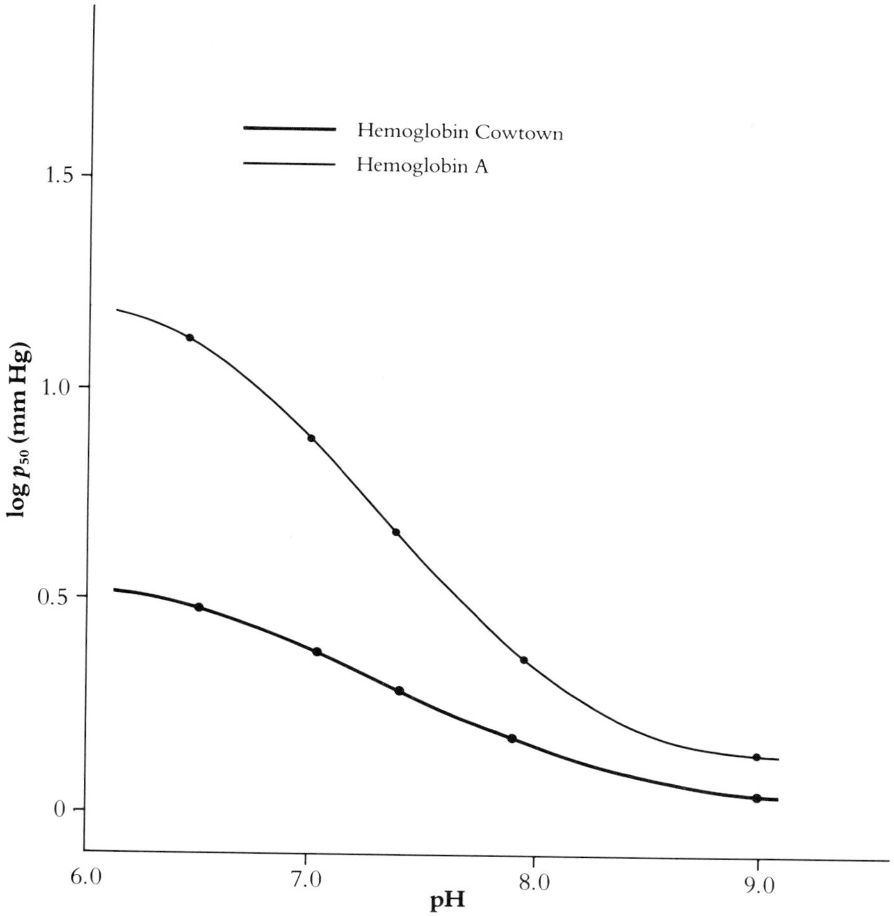

Figure 2.13 Bohr effects of hemoglobin A and hemoglobin Cowtown at different pHs. (From Shih et al.[8])

from comparisons of the oxygen equilibria of hemoglobin Cowtown and hemoglobin A measured at different pHs. We found that the Hill plots of hemoglobin Cowtown shifted only half as far as did the curves for hemoglobin A with the same change in pH. These data are reflected in Figure 2.13. The p_{50} values are plotted along the y axis and the pH along the x axis. The upper curve is for hemoglobin A, whereas the lower curve is for hemoglobin Cowtown. The slope of the lower curve around pH 7 is about half the slope of the normal hemoglobin A curve above. The slopes of these curves are a measure of the Bohr effect or the effect of hydrogen ion on oxygen binding. Hemoglobin Cowtown has half the normal Bohr effect. This is why its oxygen binding at physiological pHs is abnormal.

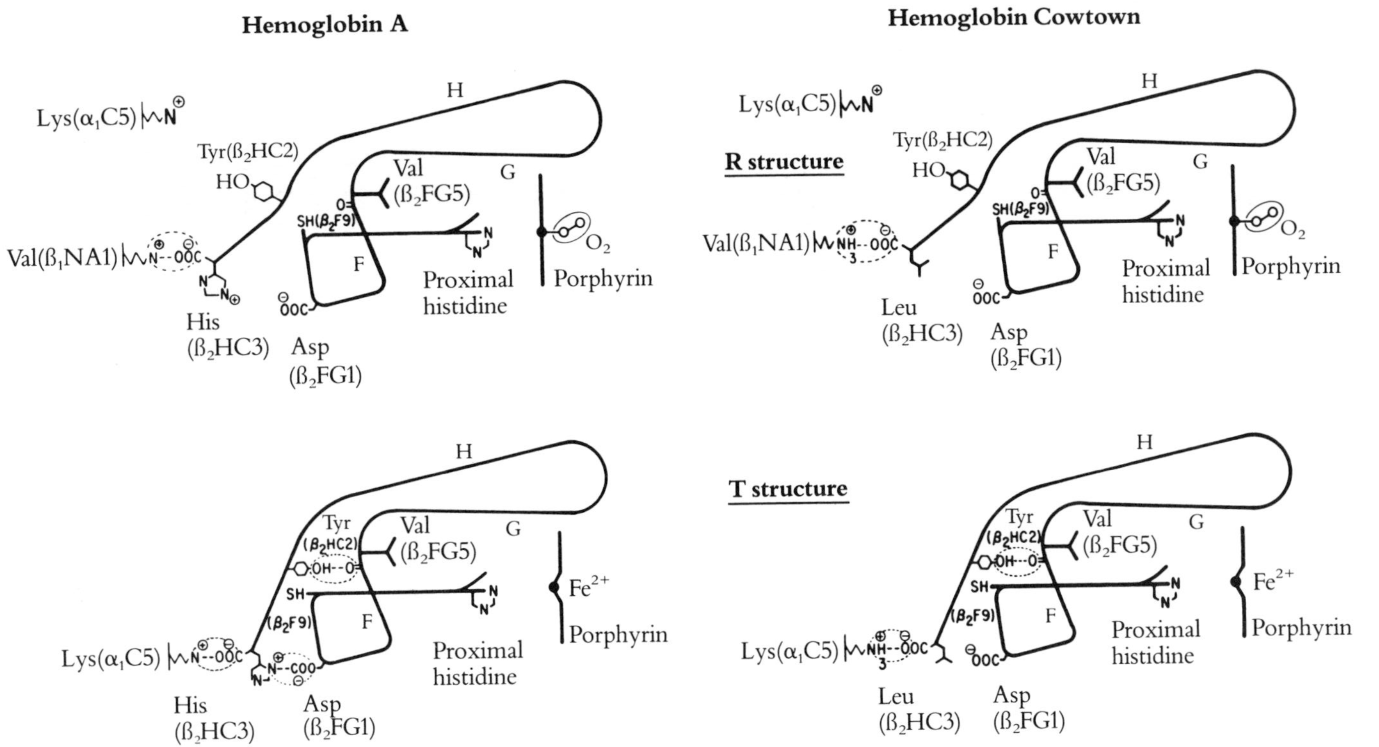

Figure 2.14 Differences in bonds involving the C-terminal residue of the β chain between oxyhemoglobin and deoxyhemoglobin of hemoglobin A and hemoglobin Cowtown. See text for explanation. (From Shih et al.[8])

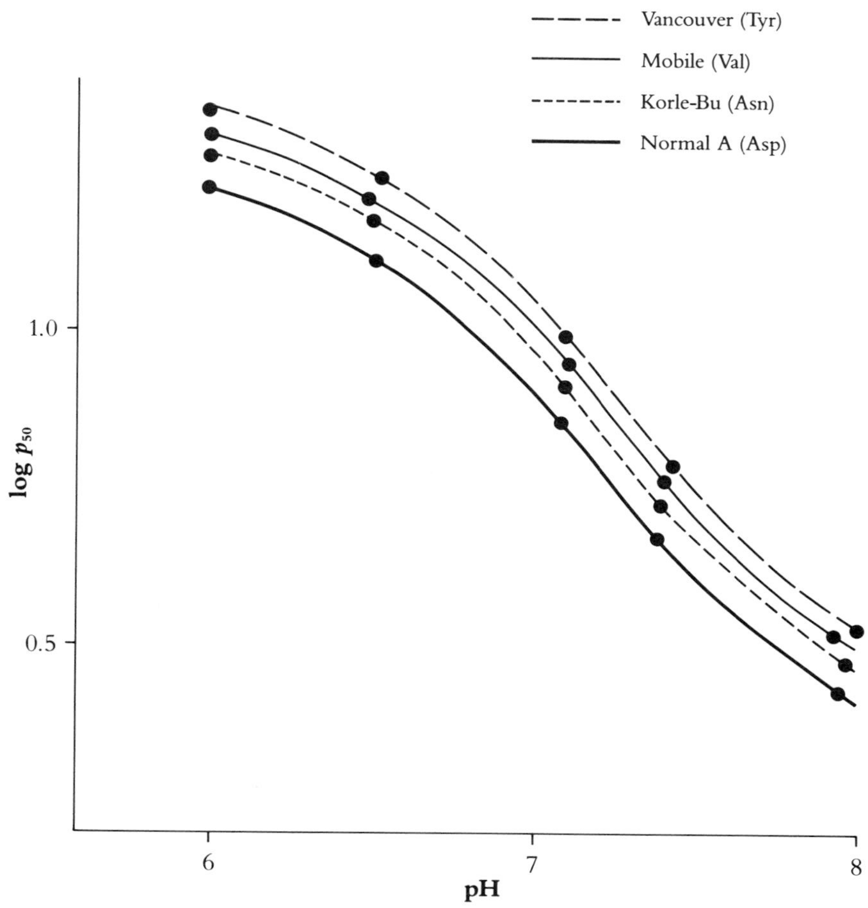

Figure 2.15 Bohr effects of β73 hemoglobin variants.

Figure 2.14 indicates the source of the functional alteration in hemoglobin Cowtown. On the left is the oxy or R structure of hemoglobin A above and the T or deoxy structure below. The important ionic bonds formed by the terminal histidyl group, here identified as β_2HC3, are indicated. On the right side of the figure is shown the same part of the structure of hemoglobin Cowtown. Its amino acid abnormality is a leucyl in place of the terminal histidyl residue. Although it can form the normal salt bridges with its carboxyl group in both the R and T conformations, it cannot form the important ionic bond with the aspartyl residue β_2FG1. Hemoglobin Cowtown does not have a side chain that can pick up a proton and form this ionic bridge. Thus, at neutral and acid pHs the T conformation is less stable than normal, and its equilibrium with the R or oxy configuration is shifted towards the oxy structure. This accounts for its higher-than-normal affinity and loss of part of the normal Bohr effect. The rest of the Bohr effect present in hemoglobin Cowtown and hemoglobin A is due to other residues that are not altered.

The last example is a set of mutants involving the 73rd residue of the β chain, which normally is an aspartyl group. This residue is near the surface of the molecule toward the end of the crevice that holds the heme group in the β chain. Figure 2.15 shows the Bohr effect curves for these and normal hemoglobin. The Bohr effects are normal, i.e., the slopes near pH 7 are all the same, but the curves for the abnormal hemoglobins are shifted up, each in relationship to the size of the substituted group. Hemoglobin Korle-Bu with an asparaginyl is shifted up slightly; hemoglobin Mobile with a valyl is shifted further; and hemoglobin Vancouver with its relatively large tyrosyl is shifted the furthest. Although the β73 residue is near the heme group, it is too far away to touch it or directly affect its binding of oxygen. We speculate that the substituted residues bridge across the gap between the E and F helices of the β chain and in some way help to stabilize slightly the structure of deoxyhemoglobin, which causes the shift in the oxygen curve.

CONCLUSION

A small fraction of the more than 300 abnormal hemoglobins that have been discovered to date were discussed here. We selected examples studied in our laboratory that were found to have abnormal oxygen-binding properties. The majority of mutant hemoglobins appear to have normal or nearly normal oxygen-binding properties. This indicates that a majority of the amino acid residues in the molecule can be changed without altering the molecule's functional properties. However, as the examples we have presented illustrate, there are sites in the molecule not in direct contact with the heme group that cannot be altered, even slightly, without changing the molecule's reactivity with oxygen, hydrogen ions, or various anions. Most of these mutations in some way alter the balance between the T or deoxy conformation of the molecule and the R or oxy conformation. By detailed studies of these mutant hemoglobins it is possible to map out the parts of the molecule that affect oxygen binding and those that do not. Insights into the mechanism of oxygen binding at the atomic level can be gained from such studies. Dr. Pauling's contributions to this field of study, his original and fundamental work on the structure of proteins, his contributions to the understanding of the functional properties of hemoglobin, his discovery with Drs. Itano, Singer, and Wells[9] of sickle cell hemoglobin, and his thinking about complex molecules like proteins at the level of atoms, all underlie the work described in this paper. The questions are ones he already asked years ago; we simply provided somewhat more detailed or precise answers.

ACKNOWLEDGMENT

This work was supported in part by NIH grants AM17850 and HL20142. The figures of the hemoglobin models were kindly provided by Dr. Richard J. Feldman of the National Institutes of Health. These figures represent only one view of the stereoscopic pictures prepared by Dr. Feldman.

REFERENCES

1. Imai K: *Allosteric Effects In Haemoglobin.* Cambridge, Cambridge Univ. Press, 1982, pp 57–89.

2. Pauling L: The oxygen equilibrium of hemoglobin and its structural interpretation. *Proc Natl Acad Sci USA* 1935; 21: 186–191.

3. Paniker NV, Kuang-Tzu DL, Krantz SB, et al.: Haemoglobin Vanderbilt ($\alpha_2\beta_2$ 89 Ser → Arg): a new haemoglobin with high oxygen affinity and compensatory erythrocytosis. *Br J Haematol* 1978; 39: 249–258.

4. Jones RT, Osgood EE, Brimhall B, et al.: Hemoglobin Yakima. I. Clinical and biochemical studies. *J Clin Invest* 1967; 46: 1840–1847.

5. Novy MJ, Edwards MJ, Metcalfe J: Hemoglobin Yakima. II. High blood oxygen affinity associated with compensatory erythrocytosis and normal hemodynamics. *J Clin Invest* 1967; 46: 1848–1854.

6. Morimoto H, Lehmann H, Perutz MF: Molecular pathology of human haemoglobin: stereochemical interpretation of abnormal oxygen affinities. *Nature* 1971; 232: 408–413.

7. Dickerson RE, Geis I: *Hemoglobin: Structure, Function, Evolution, and Pathology.* Menlo Park, Benjamin-Cummings, 1983, pp 68–69.

8. Shih T-b, Jones RT, Bonaventura J, et al.: Involvement of His HC 3 (146) β in the Bohr effect of human hemoglobin: studies of native and *N*-ethylmaleimide-treated hemoglobin A and hemoglobin Cowtown (β146 His → Leu). *J Biol Chem* 1984; 259: 967–974.

9. Pauling L, Itano HA, Singer SJ, et al.: Sickle cell anemia, a molecular disease. *Science* 1949; 110: 543–548.

CHAPTER THREE

SCURVY, THE COSMIC CONNECTION: AN ANCIENT SUPERNOVA AND THE PRACTICE OF MEDICINE IN THE TWENTIETH CENTURY

IRWIN STONE, DSc

One of the most important medical events of the twentieth century thus far has been the discovery (by Albert Szent-Györgyi), synthesis, and inexpensive commercial production of ascorbic acid. This compound has been identified as the human liver metabolite which, when missing, is responsible for scurvy. After about 1940 and certainly after 1967, for the first time in history and 65 million years of human prehistory,[1-4] it became possible to cure and eliminate scurvy by giving the required (many *grams*) daily doses of ascorbate.

Yet the pandemic of chronic subclinical scurvy (CSS syndrome)[5] continues to afflict humans in the twentieth century.[6] The efforts of nutritionists to stem it have been hindered by prescription of grossly inadequate daily intakes of ascorbate, based on the incorrect and outdated guidelines of the "vitamin C dietary deficiency disease" hypothesis.[7] Unless current human RDAs[8] for ascorbate (vitamin C) are drastically increased to correspond with the daily amounts found to be normally synthesized in the livers of nonprimate mammals under various degrees of stress, mankind risks extinction. A lifetime of CSS compounded by the stresses of living in the modern, overpopulated world (increasing deterioration and pollution of air, water, and foodstuffs) recreates a physiological insult that may place *Homo sapiens* among this planet's endangered species. This intelligent primate must control its evolutionary destiny and convert itself into the more robust human subspecies, *Homo sapiens ascorbicus*.[9-11] Otherwise, its continued survival in this hostile, polluted world is in question.

THE DAWN OF ASCORBIC ACID

Speculations and conclusions on the evolutionary natural history of ascorbic acid were published in 1972.[4] That treatise essentially took the reader on a speculative tour billions of years back in time, using as a spaceship the trained human mind. This is a safe and convenient way to travel because the vehicle is not subject to the usual physical limitations of the speed of light or the irreversibility of time; it is inexpensive, weightless, and requires no shielding against the hazards of outer space. The first landing was at a point when the primitive living process was beginning to evolve. There were no sharp distinctions then between plants and animals. Photosynthesis, the means for storing the sun's energy as carbohydrates, had been in operation successfully for a long time. The earth was a green haven where the land and the waters were covered with cells containing chlorophyll that converted atmospheric carbon dioxide and water into glucose, the main source of food and energy for the living process.

The atmosphere in those days was quite different from what it is today. The living process developed in an essentially oxygen-free atmosphere. Today the atmosphere contains about 20 percent oxygen, which is a by-product of the chemical reactions of photosynthesis. Early life forms produced so much oxygen that the atmosphere gradually changed from a reducing to an oxidizing one. This oxygen was toxic to living cells, creating the planet's first air-pollution crisis. The situation threatened to kill the living cells that had been so successful up to that point.

Nature developed ascorbic acid to save the living process from extinction. This same procedure occurred many times in subsequent evolutionary crises, so that ascorbic acid became, in a sense, the favorite evolutionary life saver. Nature developed four enzymes to convert the abundant glucose product of photosynthesis into ascorbic acid. These four enzymes were similar or identical to the four-enzyme system being used by present-day plants and animals.

Ascorbic acid was first used as a detoxicant to counteract the increasing toxic levels of oxygen in the atmosphere. It is a member of the labile oxidation–reduction system (ascorbic acid–dehydroascorbic acid), and it functions by buffering the oxidation-reduction potential of living cells at the proper, optimum, low pH values. The higher the concentration of ascorbate in the living cell, the better is the cell's buffering capacity. In this way, ascorbic acid protects all plants and animals against the high concentration (now stabilized at about 20 percent) of toxic oxygen in our atmosphere.

ASCENT OF THE VERTEBRATES

About 425 million years ago, Nature began a major experiment, which resulted in the evolution of the vertebrates. Comparing the biochemical physiologies of present and ancient vertebrates can lead to some educated guesses and interesting conclusions on how problems of survival were solved during the evolution of increasingly complex animals.

The fish were the earliest vertebrates. Amphibians, about 325 million years ago, started their lives in the waters and then adapted to dry-land living. Reptiles, mostly terrestrial forms although some returned to the waters, arose about 205 million years ago. These three groups were cold-blooded creatures: they had no internal mechanism for maintaining a uniform body temperature, and hence their metabolism tended to be sluggish at times. The next two groups, the warm-blooded birds and mammals, arrived about 165 million years ago.

The amount of ascorbate produced each day in modern vertebrates increases as we go up the evolutionary scale. The largest increase is found in the step between the cold-blooded, sluggish reptiles and the warm-blooded, highly active mammals.

Amphibians and reptiles synthesize ascorbate in their kidneys. The locus of ascorbate-producing enzymes in present-day mammals is the liver. This change in site appears to have an evolutionary importance. When the warm-blooded, highly active, and highly stressed mammals came into existence, the problem arose of how to provide them with enough ascorbic acid each day to act as an antistressor and to maintain biochemical homeostasis in their unusually high rate of metabolism. The problem was neatly solved in early mammals by the transference of the site of ascorbate synthesis from the small kidneys to the liver, the largest organ in the mammalian body. An additional safeguard was provided by the development of a biochemical feedback mechanism that increased the liver production of ascorbate in accordance with incident stresses.[12]

These changes assured not only the survival of the mammals for the next 165 million years, but also their world dominance. Modern nutritionists and physicians should note that those early mammals that did not make this kidney-to-liver transfer became extinct because they were unable to produce the daily dose of ascorbate required for survival.

The present-day birds provide living examples of this kidney-to-liver transfer of ascorbate synthesis.[13] The oldest evolutionary species of birds produce ascorbate in the kidneys; the intermediate species produce in both kidney and liver, and the most recent, the song birds, produce only in the liver. Some tropical birds, like the red-vested bul-bul, have the same genetic defect as humans and cannot make any ascorbate. They are among the few types of birds that can die of scurvy.

AGE OF THE PRIMATES

About 70 million years ago mammals were thriving as long as they kept out of the way of the dinosaurs, which flourished on land, in the waters, and even in the air. Nature was ready to launch another extended experiment that would culminate 60 or 70 million years later with the appearance of subhuman hominids and finally *Homo sapiens*. It was about this time that some evolving mammals developed advantageous primate characteristics. These early primates looked more like squirrels than monkeys, but they were the beginning of a major group of mammals that would form the two present-day primate suborders, the Prosimiae and the Anthropoidea. The next several million years would be times of great adversity and stress, not only for the evolving primates, but for all forms of life on Earth.

About 65 million years ago a catastrophe occurred that had mixed consequences for primitive primates. This is the "cosmic connection" that so greatly affects present-day health, longevity, and practice of medicine. There are at least two hypotheses about what happened. The supernova theory of Russell and Tucker[14] states that there was a supernova explosion in a nearby galaxy; the Earth was showered with large fluxes of high-energy radiation, which caused extensive damage. The second hypothesis, by Alvarez et al.,[15] blames the holocaust on the impact of a large asteroid. I support the supernova theory because it accounts for the high-energy mutagenic radiation needed to cause the conditional-lethal mutations that occurred in the evolving primates.

Whatever the cause of this cataclysm, the results were the sudden disappearance of the dinosaurs, great changes in the worldwide distribution of fossil invertebrates, and mutational destruction of the gene for the liver enzyme L-gulonolactone oxidase, as well as the possible similar loss of the enzyme uricase from the primate line.* The changes were good for the primates in that they could now evolve without competition from the dinosaurs. They were bad because the mutated mammals were handicapped by the loss of essential enzymes. They survived at great cost in lives, sickness, and misery, and the genetic defects still affect the lives of humans today.

EARLY RESEARCH ON SCURVY

Scorbutic prehistory and early history of *Homo sapiens* has been described elsewhere.[16] But let us now skip to a point in the eighteenth century to evaluate the work of the early outstanding figure in scurvy research, Dr. James Lind. During the winters or early springs of the eighteenth century, scurvy weakened and reduced the population. Every baby was born after a 9-month intrauterine bout with scurvy, and most infants died in their first year from the scurvy-induced sudden infant death syndrome (SIDS).[17] Many that survived the first year succumbed

*The enzyme uricase controls the last chemical step in mammalian purine metabolism—conversion of the rather insoluble uric acid into the more soluble allantoin. In *Homo sapiens* the absence of uricase causes gout, another disease peculiar to humans, because most other nonprimate mammals have active uricase in their bodies. In a few preliminary tests, Dr. Frank Levy and I found in vitro that uric acid is unstable in the presence of sodium ascorbate and gradually disappears. This could mean that ascorbate might, like uricase, catalyze the oxidation of uric acid.

before the fourth year because they lacked resistance to infections and other diseases, owing to scurvy-induced defects in the human immune system. It was a rare, hardy individual who managed to stay alive after his or her twentieth birthday.

Folk medicine vaguely related scurvy to the lack of fresh vegetation, but we know now that even the best of diets will not "cure" scurvy. It is likely that the early development of the human female's sexual trait of copulation at any time without estrus prevented the extinction of *Homo sapiens;* it provided a means of supplying new individuals at a slightly faster rate than scurvy killed them.

Dr. James Lind (1716–1794) of Britain's Royal Navy, the "Father of Nautical Medicine," became interested in scurvy on shipboard. He devised the protocol of and conducted the first scientific, controlled test for treatment of scorbutic sailors. Lind showed that an orange or a lemon, fed daily to scorbutic sailors, would delay the onset of terminal symptoms of scurvy so that sailors could stand their watches and man the ships. He published his results in 1753,[18] and they have been misinterpreted until today.

At the beginning of the twentieth century, Lind's results were distorted into the nutritionists' belief that something in a single orange or lemon had the power to prevent or cure scurvy. Additional work in the early years of the twentieth century[19] prompted the publication of Polish chemist Casimir Funk's seemingly logical explanation of the scurvy phenomenon, the "vitamin C dietary deficiency disease" hypothesis.[7] This hypothesis, published some 20 years before the discovery of ascorbic acid, dominated the thoughts and actions of nutritionists for the next seven decades, up to the present time. Nutritionists have become so attached to the hypothesis that they have been unable to realize, even after 1967,[1–3] that in 1912 they set for themselves the impossible task of treating a deadly, liver-enzyme, genetic disease by the ineffectual methods of home economists. The medical profession adopted this theory so long ago that it has become established dogma.[20] The low daily dosage of ascorbate inherent in any "vitamin" theory has made the seven decades of work by nutritionists into a major blunder of twentieth-century medicine.[21]

In 1959, the biochemist John J. Burns showed that scurvy resulted from the absence of the enzyme L-gulonolactone oxidase (GLO) in the human liver.[22] GLO is the last enzyme in the series of four used by the mammals to convert blood sugar (glucose) into ascorbic acid. In the absence of GLO, this important synthesis is halted, and the potential for scurvy plagues *Homo sapiens.*

A PERSONAL EXPERIENCE

A year after Burns's crucial discovery, my wife and I were involved in an accident that nearly cost us our lives. The accident was serendipitous in that it provided insights into human physiology in the scurvy-free condition.

The experiment began when a drunken driver crashed her car head-on into mine on a South Dakota highway. My wife and I were severely injured; no accident victim with injuries as severe as ours had survived at the hospital to which we were transported. The emergency room doctors and nurses did not expect me to survive the first night. They could not understand why my wife and I were conscious and lucid, and not in a state of deep shock from the trauma, severe bone injuries, and blood loss.

Since the 1930s we had been taking on a regular basis gradually increasing megadoses of ascorbate. By 1960 our dose was up to 5 to 10 g daily, or more if we were under heavy stress. One of the physiological effects of megadoses of ascorbate is the prevention of shock, the physiological response that kills the severely injured accident victims.

Our bodies were scurvy-free, and we tried to remain scurvy-free during our 2¾-month hospital stay by taking about 60 g of ascorbate daily. The hospital had never had patients like us before. From the start we began disproving all the medical prognostications based on scorbutic patients. Our physiology was more robust than that of the usual scorbutic hospital population. I healed so rapidly that I was able to walk out of the hospital on the broken legs that the doctors had said could not bear my weight for at least a year. I have no doubt that without ascorbate, our lives would have ended on the night of the accident.

I also made the observation that patients entering a hospital do not necessarily die of the disease for which they entered. Scurvy is so rife in hospitals that it is probably involved in every hospital death. Subclinical scurvy is rampant not only among patients, but among doctors, nurses, and other individuals who limit their ascorbate intake to 60 mg daily. Tests on the urinary spillover of ascorbate establish the correctness of this observation.*

Four and a half months after the accident, I returned to work, convinced of the necessity of immediate publication of my work on the genetics of scurvy. I found out, the hard way, that it was much easier to conduct the research and write the paper than it was to have it published in an orthodox medical journal. I went through the routine of submitting the manuscript and having it rejected by six medical journals before it was finally published in 1966.[1]

*Urinary ascorbate spillover has been shown by Kalokerinos and Dettman of Australia, in their successful studies of the sudden infant death syndrome, to be a reliable criterion for detecting CSS. C-Stix®, the plastic dip-sticks for conducting this simple and inexpensive test, are available from the Ames Division of Miles Laboratories. The method revealed low ascorbate excretion (0–10 mg/dl) among sick patients in an unpublished study of admissions to San Jose hospitals; among autopsy cases, the level of ascorbate in the residual urine in the bladder was always zero.

GAINING CREDIBILITY

Publication of the research data was not the only problem; convincing medical professionals to initiate clinical trials with megadoses of ascorbate was even more formidable. Because available information indicated that the viral diseases were likely to be successfully treated by megadoses of ascorbate, my first approach was to try to interest the National Institutes of Health in investigating ascorbic acid as a nontoxic, nonspecific virucidal agent. Literature of the 1930s indicated the inactivation of viruses by ascorbate;[24] the pioneering work of Dr. Frederick R. Klenner showed that megadoses of ascorbate were successful in treating viral disease,[25] and my anecdotal studies suggested that a two-phase, megadose ascorbate regimen prevented or aborted the common cold with over 95 percent success. However, in all my attempts I have never succeeded in inducing publicly or privately supported research foundations to test megadose ascorbate therapy clinically. Orthodox medicine has failed to recognize the importance of the "cosmic connection."

IN GRATITUDE TO DR. PAULING

Thus was the situation regarding megadose ascorbic acid therapy in the years before Linus Pauling. Through the efforts mainly of Dr. Klenner and myself, this new medical modality was struggling against the well-financed hostility and studied indifference of orthodox nutritionists and their medical colleagues. The entry of Dr. Pauling into the arena was the impetus that proponents of this field needed to bring these revolutionary concepts to the millions of people who are now benefiting from improved general health, greater resistance to disease, and a longer, healthy life span. No other person but Dr. Pauling could have accomplished this.

Orthodox medicine regarded the 1970 publication of *Vitamin C and the Common Cold*[26] and its favorable public reception as an unwarranted incursion by a nonmedical worker into their sacred, exclusive territory. The protocols of the large-scale tests they proceeded to set up were designed to show that the procedure would not work and that Dr. Pauling was wrong. They used daily doses too low to be effective and in most tests did not include the important abortive phase of this two-part procedure; they only carried out half a test. Those who did try to include an abortive phase lacked understanding of the size and proper timing of the ascorbic acid doses. The result, predictably, was a fiasco, and physicians wrongly deduced that the two-phase, common cold treatment was ineffective. However, millions of citizens who had read Dr. Pauling's books[26, 27] and were concerned about their health, conducted "anecdotal" tests of their own and found their well-being and resistance to the common cold greatly improved.

Cameron and Pauling's 1979 book[28] showed the usefulness of ascorbic acid in cancer therapy. This is to be expected because all cancer cases are complicated by the "cosmic connection"—CSS that oncologists fail to correct. I fully agree with

Dr. Pauling when he states that "in the not too distant future, supplemental ascorbate will have an established place in all cancer treatment regimes." In the meantime oncologists will be faced with hundreds of thousands of terminally ill cancer patients who must be told that they are beyond hope and near death. Orthodox medicine can offer little to these pathetic victims of the "cosmic connection," but I believe that orthomolecular medicine can rescue many of them from their misery and death.

In conclusion, I would like to acknowledge the great debt I owe to Linus Pauling. He gave me the first and only encouragement I needed in the 1960s for a chemical engineer and biochemist to continue working with a revolutionary concept in the unfamiliar and often hostile field of medical genetics. I am proud to call him my friend. In a larger sense, he is friend to all human beings. For his achievements in improving human health, we are all in his debt.

REFERENCES

1. Stone I: On the genetic etiology of scurvy. *Acta Geneticae Medicae et Gemellologiae* (Rome) 1966; 15: 345–350.

2. Stone I: Hypoascorbemia: the genetic disease causing the human requirement for exogenous ascorbic acid. *Perspect Biol Med* 1966; 10: 133–134.

3. Stone I: The genetic disease, hypoascorbemia: a fresh approach to an ancient disease and some of its medical implications. *Acta Geneticae Medicae et Gemellologiae* (Rome) 1967; 16: 52–62.

4. Stone I: The natural history of ascorbic acid in the evolution of the mammals and primates and its significance for present-day man. *J Orthomolec Psych* 1972; 1(2,3): 82–89.

5. Stone I: The CSS syndrome, a medical paradox. *J NW Acad Prev Med* 1977; 1: 24–28.

6. Stone I: Eight decades of scurvy: the case history of a misleading dietary hypothesis. *J Orthomolec Psych* 1979; 8(2): 58–62.

7. Funk C: The etiology of the deficiency diseases. *J State Med* 1912; 20: 341–368.

8. *Recommended Dietary Allowances,* 9th ed. Washington, DC, The National Research Council, National Academy of Sciences, 1980.

9. Stone I: Mankind's 65-million-year-old potentially fatal mutation and its reversal. Presented at the International Symposium on Vitamin C and Its Uses, organized by the Comision Nacional de Fruticultura, Mexico City, March 26–28, 1980.

10. Stone I: *Homo sapiens ascorbicus:* the profile for health in the 21st century. Presented at the International Symposium on the Conquest of Cancer, sponsored by the Livingston-Wheeler Foundation, San Diego, California, June 15, 1980.

11. Stone I: *Homo sapiens ascorbicus:* the "missing link" in clinical medicine and health. Presented at the Ascorbate Seminar, Sunnyvale, California, October 4, 1981.

12. Subramanian N, Nandi BK, Majumder AK, et al.: Role of L-ascorbic acid on detoxification of histamine. *Biochem Pharmacol* 1973; 22: 1671–1673.

13. Chaudhuri CR, Chatterjee IB: Ascorbic acid synthesis in the birds: phylogenetic trend. *Science* 1969; 164: 435–436.

14. Russell D, Tucker VV: Supernovae and the extinction of the dinosaurs. *Nature* 1971; 229: 553–554.

15. Alvarez W, Alvarez LW, Asaro F, et al.: Current status of the impact theory for the terminal cretaceous extinction. Geological Society of America, Special Paper 190, 1982.

16. Stone I: *The Healing Factor: "Vitamin C" Against Disease.* New York, Grosset & Dunlap, 1972.

17. Kalokerinos A: *Every Second Child.* New Canaan, Conn, Keats, 1981.

18. Lind J: *A Treatise of the Scurvy.* Edinburgh, A. Kincaid & A. Donaldson, 1753.

19. Stone I: *The Healing Factor: "Vitamin C" Against Disease.* New York, Grosset & Dunlap, 1972, ch. 6–8.

20. Stone I: Ascorbate dependency: a human mutation. *J Holistic Med* 1982; 4(2): 158–162.

21. Stone I: Scurvy, the most misunderstood epidemic disease in 20th century medicine. Presented at the Health Freedom Convention of the National Health Federation, June 26, 1982. (Transcript is available through the IS-FACT Foundation, Box 9283, Westgate Station, San Jose, Calif, 95157.)

22. Burns JJ: Biosynthesis of ascorbic acid: basic defect in scurvy. *Am J Med* 1959; 26: 740–748.

23. Stone I: Studies of a mammalian enzyme system for producing evolutionary evidence on man. *Am J Physical Anthropol* 1965; 15: 83–85.

24. Stone I: *The Healing Factor: "Vitamin C" Against Disease.* New York, Grosset & Dunlap, 1972, pp. 202–203.

25. Klenner FR: Significance of high daily intake of ascorbic acid in preventive medicine. *J Internat Acad Prev Med* 1974; 1(1): 45–69.

26. Pauling L: *Vitamin C and the Common Cold.* San Francisco, W. H. Freeman, 1970.

27. Pauling L: *Vitamin C, the Common Cold, and the Flu.* San Francisco, W. H. Freeman, 1976.

28. Cameron E, Pauling L: *Cancer and Vitamin C.* Menlo Park, California, The Linus Pauling Institute of Science and Medicine, 1979.

CHAPTER FOUR

LIPID PEROXIDATION–INDUCED DISEASES: A MODEL OF MOLECULAR DISEASE

JEFFREY BLAND, PhD

There is no known single cause of degenerative diseases such as coronary heart disease (CHD; coronary atherosclerosis) and cancer. Risk factors have been identified, which include physiological properties and lifestyle habits associated with increased incidence of these diseases, but there still exists no comprehensive unified theory to explain how these risk factors relate to the genesis of these diseases. The situation is reminiscent of that with sickle cell anemia, which was known to have a relationship to genetic background and exposure to malaria, but no proven cause. This was the case until Linus Pauling related the mechanism of this disorder to a genetic defect in hemoglobin synthesis, and thus defined the first molecular disease.[1]

A molecular disease is one produced by a fundamental alteration, originating genetically or environmentally, in the normal biochemical functioning of cells, tissues, or organs. Pauling's contribution to the understanding of molecular disease has led to the recognition of the vitamin-dependent, genetic-metabolism diseases such as homocystinuria and methylmalonic aciduria (considered to result from conditional lethal mutations), and a host of other metabolic disorders such as Wilson's, Fabry's, Tay Sachs, and Gaucher's diseases.[2] There is now increasing evidence to suggest that atherosclerosis, cancer, and possibly certain autoimmune disorders are also molecular diseases, the origin and pathogenesis of which are related to in vivo lipid peroxidation. This review will develop the hypothesis that by better understanding lipid peroxidation we may uncover a common factor in the origin of many of the degenerative diseases that may allow their prevention and treatment.

Dormandy alerted the medical community about the role that free-radical peroxidation may play in the degenerative diseases.[3] Free-radical compounds can produce degeneration of biological systems by one-electron oxidation processes and can initiate chain-carrying sequences. This results in a small number of initial radicals producing thousands of cellular damaging reactions.[4] These oxidation processes come from functional groups of membrane lipids, proteins, and nucleic acids undergoing reactions with oxygen-deriving electrophilic species.

OXYGEN: BOON OR BANE?

We live on a planet surrounded by an atmosphere that is 20 percent oxygen. This gas is important for supporting oxidative phosphorylation, which gives oxygen-utilizing organisms a selective metabolic advantage over anaerobes due to increased efficiency of food substrate conversion. The evolution of sophisticated oxygen-transport and tissue-delivery systems has allowed mammals to become the dominant class of organisms on the planet. This dependency on oxygen does not come without a cost, however. The biomolecules that make up all living systems react with various forms of oxygen and, therefore, are constantly being degraded by oxidation. Under usual circumstances this oxidation of host tissue is slow, but in many pathological states the process can be greatly accelerated by lipid peroxidation or highly reactive oxidants.[5]

The major oxidants that accelerate the rate of free-radical damage include superoxide anion radical, ozone, hydrogen peroxide, hydroxyl radical, lipid peroxides, and singlet oxygen (Table 4.1). These substances can be produced by high-energy radiation, sunlight, drugs and chemicals, enzyme action, or electron transport, as is the case with hydroxyl radical.[6] These oxidants act as electrophiles seeking out biomolecules of high electron density. One such class of substances is the unsaturated linkages found in lipids. Figure 4.1 illustrates how these oxidants, once generated, can initiate a free-radical propagation of cellular pathology.[7]

Table 4.1 Major lipid peroxidation agents

Species, name	Source
$O_2^{-}\cdot$ = superoxide anion	Enzymes, high-energy radiation
O_3 = ozone	Atmospheric pollution
H_2O_2 = hydrogen peroxide	From superoxide dismutase
$^1O_2$ = singlet oxygen	Photodynamic action, dismutation of O_2
$\cdot OH$ = hydroxyl radical	Electron transport, high-energy reduction
ROOH = lipid peroxides	Product of fat oxidation

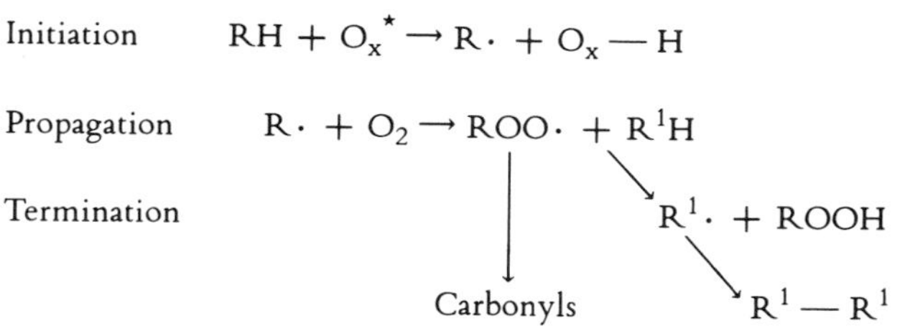

$O_x^{\star}$ = active peroxidation species

Figure 4.1 Free-radical propagation.

Dietary Relationships to Lipid Peroxidation

Horwitt et al. have reported that with increasing intake of dietary unsaturates there is increasing tendency toward oxidatively induced hemolysis. This is particularly aggravated by low vitamin E (tocopherol) intake in humans.[8] Harman has reported that increasing the unsaturate content in animals' diets results in increasing incidence of malignancy unless the intake of antioxidants is increased.[9] Pryor has found that animals exposed to oxidant stress in the absence of proper dietary antioxidants age more rapidly than animals administered antioxidants.[10] Dillard and Tappel have found that exposure of animals to oxidative stress leads to accumulation in cells of damaged membrane debris, termed lipofuscin or ceroid, and the rate of its accumulation is increased when the animals are deprived of tocopherol.[11]

This information has been summarized by Chow and Tappel in the scheme shown in Figure 4.2.[12] Increased lipid peroxidation in vivo, which results either from accelerated generation of oxidants or from a reduced antioxidant or reductant potential, produces damage at the subcellular level that destroys lipid membranes, changes permeability, and alters cellular regulation processes.[13]

Relationship of Lipid Peroxidation to Atherosclerosis

Shamberger has reported that people in areas of the United States with low soil selenium levels had increased incidence of heart disease and cancer.[14] Selenium is the cofactor for the enzyme glutathione peroxidase. Glutathione peroxidase is important in regenerating tissue levels of reduced glutathione, which serves as a reducing agent for lipid peroxides, converting them to innocuous alcohols (Figure 4.2). Alfthan and Salonen have found that in Finland those individuals who are at high risk of myocardial infarction or have had a previous coronary event have low glutathione peroxidase and low selenium blood levels.[15] Wilson et al. have reported that vitamin E–deficient rabbits have increased lipid peroxidation rates and increased atherosclerosis when fed a high-fat diet.[16] Ceroid pigment, which results

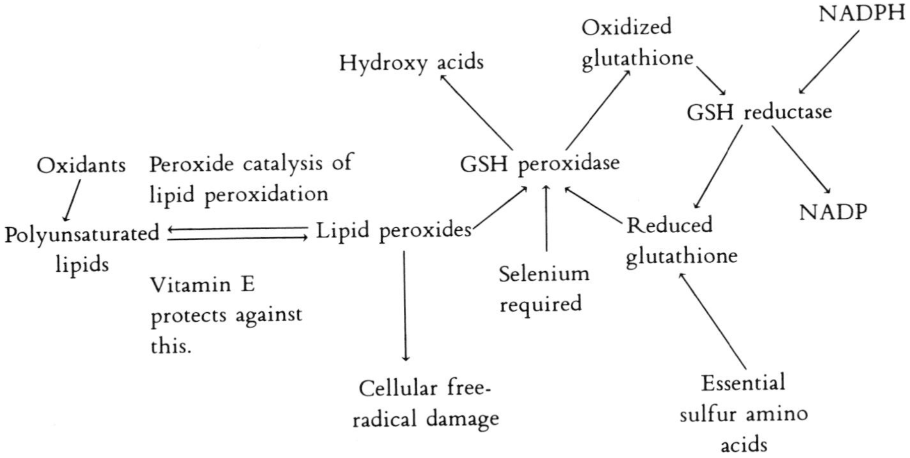

Figure 4.2 Effects of antioxidants in the inhibition of lipid peroxidation.

from lipid peroxidation, has been found to accumulate in coronary arteries of atherosclerosis patients.[17] These observations can be consolidated with the Benditt model for the origin of atherosclerosis, known as the "monoclonal theory."[18]

Benditt has found that the plaque cell of atherosclerosis is of monoclonal origin, suggesting that its initiation was a mutagenic change in a single intimal cell that started proliferating as a benign tumor. Arterial thrombi in fact show increasingly monoclonal characteristics as they become increasingly organized,[19] suggesting clonal selection. The initial event could be triggered by a mutagen delivered from some component of the blood to the artery wall. Plausible mutagens are electrophilic peroxidizing species.[20] Ludwig and Hoidal have found that polymorphonuclear leukocytes (PMNL) from subjects with hyperlipoproteinemia release more superoxide anion than do those of age-matched nonlipidemic controls.[21] Low-density lipoprotein (LDL) cholesterol and serum cholesterol are directly correlated with superoxide anion production by PMNLs.[21] This suggests that in patients with elevated LDL cholesterol, known to be at increased risk for atherosclerosis, there may be increased mutagenic assault on the artery wall due to superoxide anion.

Table 4.2, which lists the risk factors for atherosclerosis, indicates how lipid peroxidation may account for the origin of atherosclerosis, given this mutagenic monoclonal model. Elevated serum LDL cholesterol is a well-known CHD risk factor; however, there is some question as to whether the average daily dietary cholesterol intake constitutes a major determinant of risk. Recently, Taylor et al. have found that when animals are fed diets enriched in zone-refined cholesterol (ultrapure) there is no increase in atherosclerosis, whereas feeding the same level of reagent-grade (lower purity) cholesterol results in marked increases of CHD.[22]

Table 4.2 Risk factors for atherosclerosis

Elevated serum cholesterol
Reduced high-density lipoprotein (elevated LDL)
Decreased copper status
Increased platelet adhesion
Decreased selenium status
Smoking
Stress
Elevated blood pressure

The impurities in reagent-grade cholesterol are predominantly cholesterol hydroperoxides, and it was subsequently found that when these were added to cultured human fibroblastic aorta cells there were growth changes consistent with monoclonal fibroplasia.[23] Peters has reported that when cholesterol is exposed to air at 20°C for 48 hours, enough cholesterol hydroperoxide, a lipid peroxide initiator, is formed to diminish membrane integrity by 48 percent and constitute a potential cardiac hazard.[24] This may indicate that the relationship between serum cholesterol and atherosclerosis is explained by the delivery of mutagenic cholesterol hydroperoxide or other lipid free-radical initiators to the artery wall, which triggers a monoclonal hyperplasia. Reducing agents such as vitamin E, selenium, and others, which would trap these oxidants, would then help prevent this transformation. Why atherosclerosis attacks arteries and not veins may be related to the higher oxygen tension and mutagen load as well as the unique three-layered tissue morphology of arteries, versus the two layers found in veins. Also, a higher level of adhesion of lipoproteins and platelets to arterial rather than venous walls may allow for more pro-oxidant delivery to arteries.[25]

Given this model, the other risk factors can all be understood at the molecular level. Smoking introduces potential lipid oxidants directly into the bloodstream. Pryor et al. have found that cigarette tar introduces considerable numbers of free-radical initiating species, some of which may be involved directly or indirectly as mutagens.[26] Increased platelet adhesion to the arterial wall is also known to be a risk factor for atherosclerosis and is associated with dietary saturated fat. Platelets elaborate lipid peroxides, which might be directly transferred to the artery wall if activated.[27] Certain drugs that activate lipid peroxidation, namely doxorubicin or clofibrate, can produce vascular changes.[28, 29] Cardiac toxicity induced by doxorubicin appears to result from increased lipid peroxidation of the heart. Vitamin E has been found in animal studies to prevent this adverse side effect without altering the antineoplastic activity of the drug.[28] Drugs like clofibrate are known to decrease serum lipids by oxidative metabolism of lipoproteins, but their use is associated with increased cancer incidence.[30] This increase may be due to the increased production of carcinogenic substances associated with oxidative free-radical pathology. This same pattern is seen with other drugs that increase oxidative enzyme activities, such as alcohol, phenobarbitone, and phenytoin, all known, free-radical initiators in vivo.[31]

Klevay has proposed that copper deficiency leads to increased risk of atherosclerosis.[32] Copper is required by liver enzymes to convert cholesterol to bile salts, which is the major route of elimination of serum cholesterol. Therefore, reduced copper status increases the risk of persistence of cholesterol in the body with increased potential for mutagenic conversion. The high-density lipoprotein (HDL) cholesterol is the immediate cholesterol pool from which bile salts are manufactured; therefore, it would be expected that elevated HDL and reduced LDL cholesterol would be associated with a decreased risk of coronary atherosclerosis.[33]

Finally, psychosocial stress is associated with increased serum catecholamines, which are known to be oxidative stimulators.[34] This may explain why Type A behavior in individuals is associated with high serum catecholamines and increased risk of heart disease.[35]

THE CANCER CONNECTION

The risk factors for cancer appear remarkably similar to those of cardiovascular disease and include the examples listed in Table 4.3. Low fiber in the diet increases bowel transit time and thus increases the potential for oxidation of lipids, such as cholesterol-related carcinogens, in the colon.[36] Smoking, high-fat diet, low selenium status, and exposure to pro-oxidant drugs and chemicals, all encourage the conversion of unsaturated compounds to carcinogens.[37] Excessive exposure to carbon tetrachloride, for example, has been shown to induce free-radical pathology in the liver, which may explain why exposure to this chemical is associated with increased cancer risk.[38] Hyperestronism in women is known to stimulate estrogen-positive receptor sites on the breast and result in increased lipid peroxidation of mammary lipid stores.[39] Recently, the cancer chemotherapeutic agent bleomycin has been found to induce strand breaks in DNA by increasing superoxide, hydrogen peroxide, and hydroxyl radical concentrations.[40] This observation may account not only for the mechanism of bleomycin's antineoplastic activity, but also for the secondary, tumor-producing properties of many chemotherapeutic agents that encourage lipid peroxide–induced carcinogenesis. Kahn and Kasha have demonstrated that active oxidants are capable of initiating intracellular carcinogen formation.[41]

Table 4.3 Risk factors for cancer

Low dietary fiber
Smoking
High-fat diet
Low beta-carotene
Low selenium status
Pro-oxidant drugs
Hyperestronism
Low vitamin C
Low vitamin E
Psychological stress

Reduced serum levels of beta-carotene (derived from orange-red vegetables and fruits) are associated with an increased incidence of cancer in humans.[42] Beta-carotene is a powerful photochemical quenching agent of the oxidant species, singlet oxygen.[43] If not quenched, singlet oxygen ($^1O_2$), which is 22 kcal/mole above the ground-state energy of normal molecular oxygen, can react with unsaturated lipids to yield hydroperoxides.[44] These hydroperoxides can then initiate free-radical damage to DNA, resulting in mutagenesis or possibly carcinogenesis.[45] Singlet oxygen is produced in cellular systems by dismutation of superoxide anion, either enzymatically or chemically as shown below[46]:

$$2O_2^{-}\cdot + 2H^+ \xrightarrow{\text{superoxide dismutase or chemically}} H_2O_2 + O_2$$

Singlet oxygen also can be produced directly by photodynamic action, which is the transfer of sun energy through a photosensitizer such as hemoglobin to the oxygen molecule. Much of the sun-induced damage to skin, with associated potential for skin cancer, may be due to the secondary effects of photodynamically produced singlet oxygen which induces DNA alteration.[47] By quenching singlet oxygen, beta-carotene has the same protective role against this peroxidizing agent as the enzyme superoxide dismutase does for superoxide anion. Bland et al. have demonstrated that singlet oxygen is one of the major oxidant species responsible for oxidation of the erythrocyte membrane when the red cell is exposed to light and oxygen.[48]

The currently accepted view of chemical carcinogenesis is that powerful electrophiles such as ^{+}NO, R_3C^+, or ROO^- add to the electron-rich purines or pyrimidines of DNA, thereby resulting in substitution or mutations.[49] Agents that can inhibit the production of these nucleic acid hydroperoxide–inducing processes would then be expected to reduce potential carcinogenicity. Because there is a similar set of risk factors for cardiovascular disease and cancer, and because of the common relationship of both diseases to mutagenic processes, one unified explanation for their etiology could be through lipid peroxidation. The site of generation, type of peroxide, and sensitivity of the exposed tissue would then determine the susceptibility to atherogenesis or carcinogenesis.

Natural Lipid Peroxide Defensive Agents

The human physiology is not without protection against lipid peroxide assault. As is shown in Table 4.4, we possess a number of systems to defend against peroxidation. This may explain in part why different individuals have differing susceptibilities to the lipid peroxide–induced diseases. The genetic uniqueness of an individual may encode for differing structures and, therefore, quantitatively different activities of superoxide dismutase, catalase, peroxidase, glutathione peroxidase and reductase, and coenzyme Q. The nutritional status of the individual with regard to

Table 4.4 Natural antioxidant defense systems

Tocopherols
Glutathione peroxidase
Glutathione reductase
Peroxidase
Catalase
Beta-carotene
Superoxide dismutase
Glutathione
Coenzyme Q
Ascorbic acid
Sulfur amino acids
Riboflavin

vitamin E, selenium, zinc, copper, manganese, riboflavin, and beta-carotene also influences the integrity of the antioxidant system. It has been shown that marginal deficiencies of manganese and copper decrease superoxide dismutase activity in red blood cells.[50] This may help to explain in part why low copper status is associated with an increased risk of atherosclerosis and radiation-induced tissue damage, as well as rheumatoid arthritis.[51] The tissues most likely to be affected by peroxidation would be expected to be the oxygen-rich tissues such as lung, blood cells, brain, heart, liver, and kidneys. These are also the tissues found to have the highest concentrations of the antioxidant substances. The determination of optimal individual requirements for the antioxidant nutrients is of primary importance in establishing a defense against the effects of peroxides.

Establishing Optimal Intake of Antioxidants

Bland et al. have examined the effect of orally administered vitamin E on the oxidative hemolysis of red blood cells in humans.[52] In this study they demonstrated that 600 IU of vitamin E administered orally increased the resistance of red cells to oxidative stress some 20-fold over the unsupplemented level, as shown in Figure 4.3. They also demonstrated that the optimal serum tocopherol level for oxidative protection was 1.2 mg of tocopherol per 100 mg of triglyceride per 100 ml of serum, which is around twice the average serum tocopherol level in the population at large. Because doubling the serum tocopherol level requires nearly 10 times the dietary intake, it was suggested from this work that optimal peroxidative protection would be achieved at vitamin E intakes between 100 and 400 IU/day rather than the average 15 to 50 IU consumed in the standard Western diet.[53]

Studies on dietary selenium intakes versus activities of glutathione peroxidase indicated that many individuals consuming the standard American diet were well below maximal activity, as shown in Figure 4.4. The data indicate that selenium intakes in the range of 200 to 300 μg/day would be desirable for maximal protection against lipid peroxidation-induced damage in the average individual. More profound, naturally occurring selenium deficiencies are accompanied by liver and muscle necrosis due to increased lipid peroxidation, resulting in elevated serum GOT, GPT, and CPK.[54] Changes in fingernail-bed integrity, with imperfect nail growth, are also a manifestation of chronic selenium deficiency.[55] Selenium deficiency is found in neonates with respiratory distress syndrome on delivery, and may predispose them to higher risk of lipid peroxidation-induced damage if they are not repleted with selenium.[56] Vitamin E and selenium have been used to treat bronchopulmonary dysplasia in infants.[57] Incubator babies exposed to high oxygen environments have been treated with vitamin E to prevent peroxidation of the eye's lens, which results in retrolental fibroplasia.[58] Finer and Peters, in looking at 126 low-birth-weight infants who received intramuscular vitamin E along with oxygen ventilation, found much less eye damage associated with retrolental fibro-

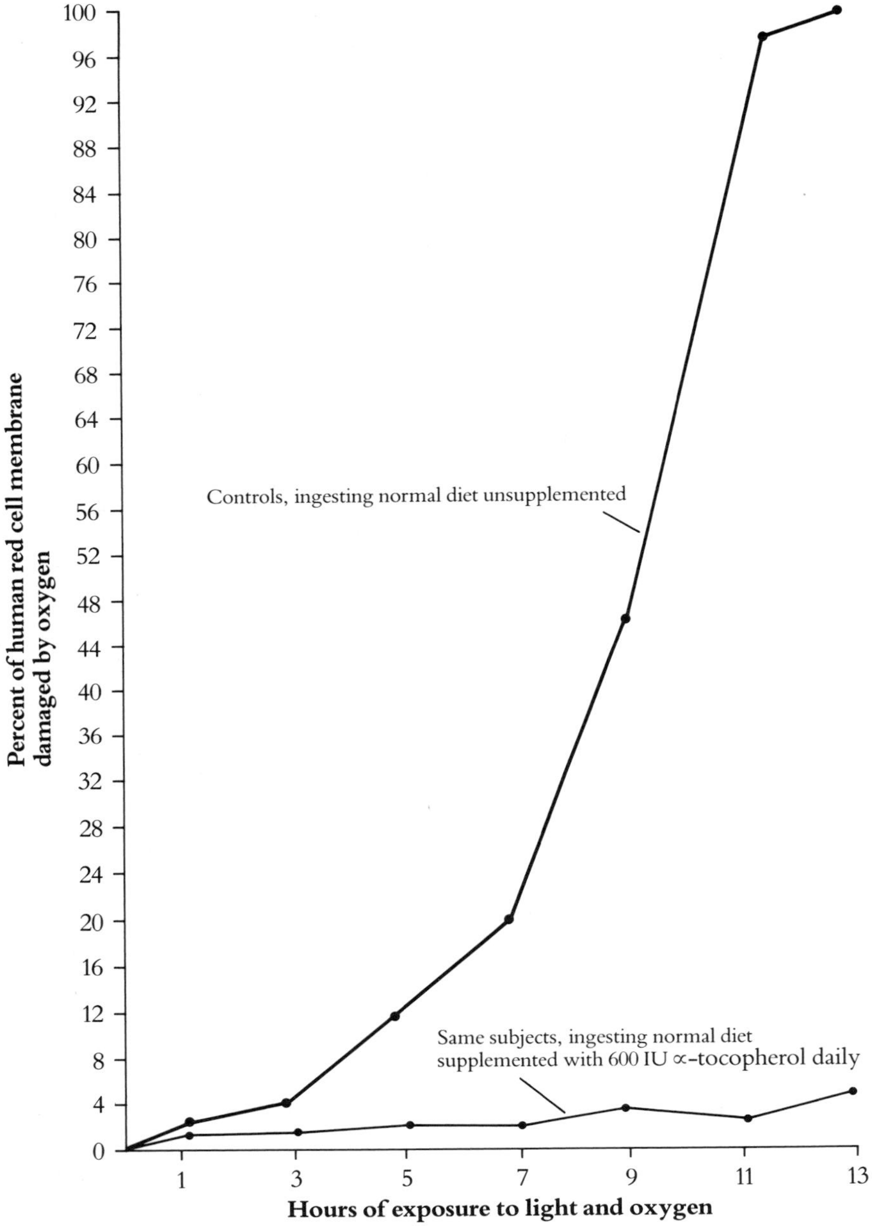

Figure 4.3 Effect of supplemental vitamin E on red cell survival under oxidant stress. (From Bland et al.[52])

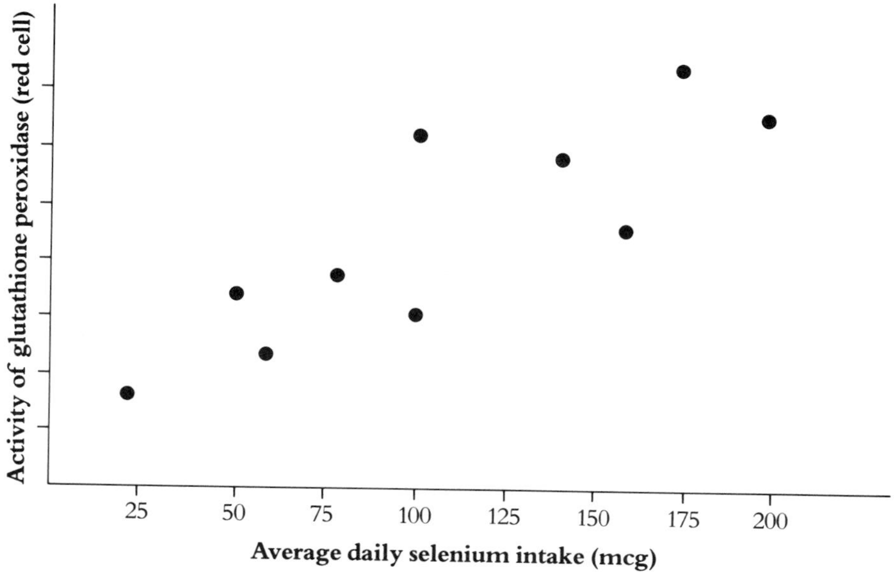

Figure 4.4 Activity of glutathione peroxidase in relation to dietary selenium intake.

plasia and recommend vitamin E therapy for all infants under 1250 g who require supplementary oxygen.[59] It has also been found that supplementary vitamin E was helpful in reducing oxidant damage to PMNs in an infant born with congenital glutathione synthetase deficiency, a defect that prevents proper quenching of free-radical oxidants.[60]

All of these examples indicate the sensitivity of oxygen-rich tissues to peroxidative damage if they are not adequately protected by antioxidants. Recently, Down's syndrome children have been suggested to carry on their trisomy-21 chromosome the genotype to synthesize high levels of superoxide dismutase (SOD) but not catalase or peroxidase. This results in considerable production of hydrogen peroxide from the dismutation of superoxide in the brain. The hydrogen peroxide is not enzymatically converted to water and oxygen by catalase or peroxidase, but rather remains available to react with unsaturated-lipid-rich brain tissue, and thus might be responsible for the defects of the dendritic spines observed in Down's children.[61] Lipid peroxidation is noted to be consistently elevated in Down's syndrome,[62] and the suggestion from this work is that increased vitamin E levels may be desirable in Down's fetuses to protect against this oxidative process.[62] Cerebrospinal fluid from infants with neuronal ceroid lipofuscinoses, such as Batten's disease or Santavuori-Halti, associated with greatly accelerated aging and central nervous system degeneration, has been shown to have lower antioxidant protection.[63]

Effect of a Purine-rich Diet on Lipid Peroxidation

The role of dietary purines in gout is well established.[64] These nucleic acids, found especially in rich foods such as organ meats, sardines, and yeast, encourage the production of uric acid, resulting in gout in sensitive individuals. These purines are metabolized by the action of xanthine oxidase, an enzymatic reaction known to produce superoxide anion.[65] If this oxidant is not trapped by SOD, then tissue damage can result. This may explain why injectable SOD has been reported to be useful in the treatment of hyperuricemia (gout) in humans.[66] This may also explain why zinc and copper have both been found useful in the treatment of some forms of arthritis; these trace elements are important in activating superoxide dismutase and protecting against superoxide anion–induced damage.[67]

Inflammatory Diseases and Lipid Peroxidation

Damage to connective tissue due to peroxidation may be involved in various inflammatory processes.[68] Trauma, bacteria, viral insult, or allergy can all result in inflammation due to activation of the arachidonic acid cascade.[69] This process, identified in Figure 4.5, produces the proinflammatory substance leukotriene C from arachidonic acid.[70] This hormonal substance induces fluid retention, mucus secretion, peripheral pain, and lymphocyte activation. The lymphocytes, once activated, are known to secrete superoxide anion into adjacent tissues, thereby initiating oxidative tissue damage. Agents that prevent the release of arachidonic acid, such as ω-3-eicosapentaenoic acid (EPA), or prevent the conversion of arachidonic acid to leukotriene, such as vitamin E, are known to ameliorate the inflammatory process.[71] Displacement of arachidonic acid from mast cell phospholipids has been accomplished by administering 5 to 10 g of ω-3-EPA orally daily.[72] This may reduce the hypersensitivity reaction mediated through leukotriene C and the resultant increase in superoxide anion radical associated with inflammatory diseases. This may also explain why vitamin E was found to be helpful at high supplemental doses in reducing the symptoms of the autoimmune diseases scleroderma, myasthenia gravis, and systemic lupus erythematosus.[73]

FUTURE APPLICATION OF THE LIPID PEROXIDATION MODEL

As outlined, the lipid peroxidation model consolidates a wealth of biochemical, physiological, and clinical data into a comprehensive working model for the molecular explanation of many of the degenerative diseases that are presently without mechanistic understanding. This model also provides new hypotheses on prevention and treatment; these require testing. It has been demonstrated that Erlich ascites tumors in mice are successfully treated by administering oral selenium at levels that would ordinarily be considered toxic.[74] The lack of toxic effect may be

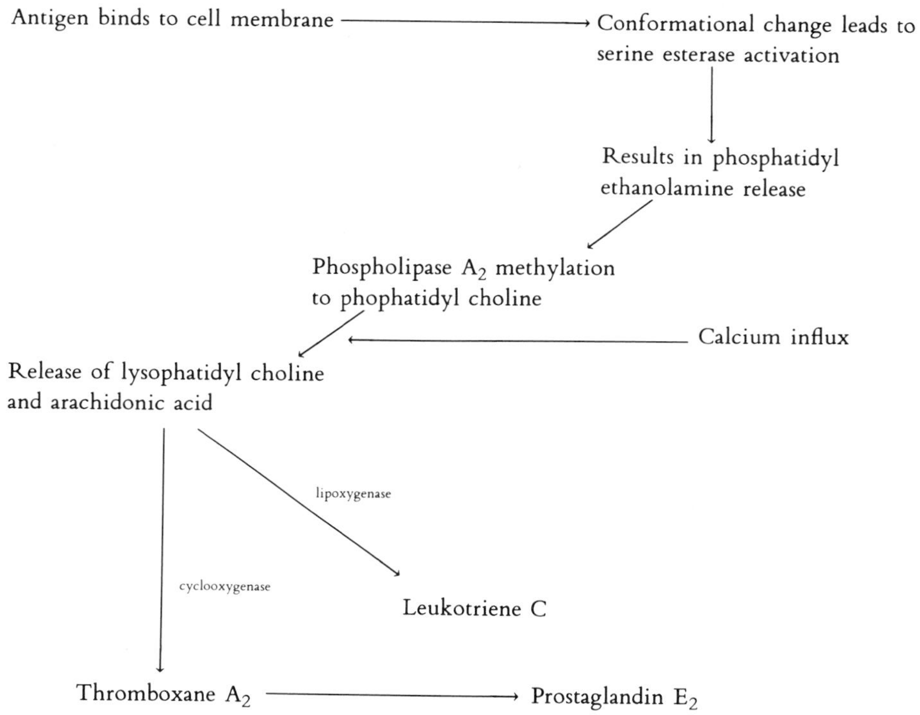

Figure 4.5 The arachidonic acid cascade in most cells.

explained by the fact that selenium is lost in the urine much more rapidly during times of oxidative stress, such as during malignancy, infection, or trauma.[75] Studies are under way to determine whether selenium does play a role in therapeutic doses in the management of human cancer.

New methods of determining genetic susceptibilities to lipid peroxidation-induced diseases are being explored. Recently it has been found that the enzyme aromatic hydrocarbon hydroxylase (AHH) is found in higher quantities among genetically related individuals who smoke and have increased incidence of lung cancer than in those families who smoke and have lower lung cancer incidences.[76] This enzyme converts aromatic hydrocarbons to epoxides that can undergo electrophilic addition to DNA. This may mean that in the future certain enzyme tests could be used to evaluate an individual's risk of oxidative damage, permitting the adjustment of an individual's antioxidant intake to meet his own specific genetic requirements.

Work is also proceeding to isolate and characterize new biological or dietary reducing agents to serve as lipid peroxide quenchers. It is known that cabbage, garlic, asparagus, and brussels sprouts all contain reducing substances that may be helpful in preventing lipid peroxidation when administered orally.

The use of injectable or intravenous antioxidant compounds may become important in the management of specific oxidation-related diseases. Orgotein, which is the buffered injectable form of SOD, has been used for some time in the treatment of hip dysplasia in dogs and arthritis in race horses.[77] Pauling and Cameron have suggested that intravenous ascorbic acid is of value in the treatment of cancer.[78] This may be due to its powerful free-radical quenching ability, allowing it to serve as an antioxidant.

New oral delivery systems will be developed for promoting better absorption of fat-soluble antioxidants like vitamin E. Such systems could prove especially helpful in such conditions as cystic fibrosis and muscular dystrophy in which malabsorption of fat-soluble nutrients results in low tissue levels of these nutrients and increased degeneration of unsaturated-lipid-rich nervous system tissue.[79]

The supplementary use of antioxidant therapy may even prove useful in conditions such as fatty liver, alcoholic hepatitis, and cirrhosis associated with alcohol abuse. It has been suggested that peroxidation of liver lipids by alcohol-induced oxygen free radicals, such as superoxide anion, is the mediating factor in these conditions.[80]

Lastly, greater effort toward reducing environmental exposure to lipid peroxide initiators from the air, water, food, and lifestyle will help reduce the load of oxidants that human defensive systems have to deal with. Better identification of the lipid peroxide initiators in the environment, and more public awareness of the problem, should be a major focus of our future efforts for public health improvement.

The etiology of the major degenerative diseases is still largely unknown, but the model of lipid peroxide-induced pathogenesis provides a common thread that may tie many of them together and offer a working hypothesis for future studies. Since Pauling first uncovered the explanation of sickle cell anemia, and defined a molecular disease, there has been the stimulus to understand disease at the subcellular level. The lipid peroxide-induced model of certain diseases adds another chapter to the unfolding narrative of Dr. Pauling's contributions to the evolution of the health sciences.

REFERENCES

1. Pauling L, Itano HA, Singer SJ, et al.: Sickle cell anemia, a molecular disease. *Science* 1949; 110: 543–548.

2. Sanbury JB, Fredrickson DO: *The Metabolic Basis of Inherited Disease,* 4th ed. New York, McGraw-Hill, 1978.

3. Dormandy TL: Free radical oxidation and antioxidants. *Lancet* 1978; March 25: 647.

4. Bland J: Biochemical consequences of lipid peroxidation. *J Chem Education* 1978; 55: 151.

5. Chow CK: Nutritional influence on cellular antioxidant defense systems. *Am J Clin Nutr* 1979; 32: 1066.

6. Cohen G, Cederbaum A: Chemical evidence for the production of hydroxyl radicals during microsomal electron transport. *Science* 1979; 204: 66.

7. Pryor WA (ed): *Free Radicals in Biology,* vols I and II. New York, Academic, 1976.

8. Horwitt MK, Duncan GD, Wilson DC: Effects of limited tocopherol intake in man with relationship to erythrocyte hemolysis. *Am J Clin Nutr* 1956; 4: 408.

9. Harman D: Effect of the amount and degree of unsaturation on mortality rate. *J Am Geriatr Soc* 1971; 26: 451.

10. Pryor WA: Antioxidant effects on free radical pathology. *Federation Proc* 1973; 32: 1870.

11. Dillard CJ, Tappel AL: Lipofuscin accumulation after oxidant exposure. *Lipids* 1973; 8: 183.

12. Chow CK, Tappel AL: The natural defense to biological oxidants. *Lipids* 1972; 7: 518.

13. Tonna EA: The age-related changes associated with accelerated lipid peroxidation. *J Gerontol* 1975; 30: 3.

14. Shamberger RS: Possible inhibitory effect of selenium on human cancer. *Can Med Assoc J* 1969; 100: 682.

15. Alfthan G, Salonen JT: Association between cardiovascular death and myocardial infarction and serum selenium. *Lancet* 1982; July 24: 175.

16. Wilson RB, Middleton CC, Sun GY: Vitamin E, antioxidants, and lipid peroxidation in experimental atherosclerosis. *J Nutr* 1978; 108: 1858.

17. Schornagel HE: Occurrence of iron and ceroid in coronary arteries. *J Pathol Bacteriol* 1956; 72: 267.

18. Benditt E: Origin of atherosclerosis. *Scientific American* 1977; February: 74–85.

19. Pearson TA, Dillman J, Solez K, et al.: Monoclonal characteristics of organising arterial thrombi: significance in the origin and growth of human atherosclerotic plaques. *Lancet* 1979; January 6: 7–11.

20. Freese E: Antioxidants and mutagens, in Hollander A (ed): *Chemical Mutagens.* New York, Plenum, 1971.

21. Ludwig PW, Hoidal J: Increased leucocyte oxidative metabolism in hyperlipoproteinemia. *Lancet* 1982; August 14: 348.

22. Taylor CB, Peng S-k, Lee K-t: Spontaneously occurring angiotoxic derivatives of cholesterol. *Am J Clin Nutr* 1979; 29: 40.

23. Peng S, Taylor CB: Cytotoxicity of oxidation derivatives of cholesterol on cultured aortic smooth muscle cells and their effects on cholesterol biosynthesis. *Am J Clin Nutr* 1979; 29: 1033.

24. Peters RA: Cholesterol hydroperoxide—a potential cardiac hazard. *J Roy Soc Med* 1978; 71: 459.

25. Wilcken DEL, Wilcken B: The pathogenesis of coronary artery disease. *J Clin Invest* 1976; 72: 1079.

26. Pryor WA, Hales BJ, Church DF: Radicals in cigarette tar: their nature and suggested physiological implications. *Science* 1983; 220: 425.

27. Steiner M, Anastasi J: Vitamin E as an inhibitor of platelet release reaction. *J Clin Invest* 1976; 57: 732.

28. Myers CE, Young RC: Adriamycin: the role of peroxidation in cardiac toxicity and tumor response. *Science* 1977; 197: 165.

29. Vessby B, Boberg J: Supplementation with vitamin E in hyperlipidemic patients treated with diet and clofibrate. *Am J Clin Nutr* 1977; 30: 517.

30. Heller RF: Coronary heart disease, cancer and lipoproteins and the effects of clofibrate. *Lancet* 1961; December 5: 1258.

31. Victor A, Lundberg PO: Induction of binding globulin by phenytoin. *Br Med J* 1977; ii: 934.

32. Klevay L: Copper and atherosclerosis. *Atherosclerosis* 1978; 29: 81.

33. Loomis H: Preferential utilization of free cholesterol from high-density lipoproteins for biliary secretion in man. *Science* 1978; 190: 62.

34. Jenkins D: Psychologic and social precursors of coronary disease. *N Engl J Med* 1971; 290: 117.

35. Friedman M: The modification of type A behavior in postinfarction patients. *Am Heart J* 1979; 97: 97.

36. DeLeon MP, Carulli N: Influence of small bowel transit time on dietary cholesterol absorption. *N Engl J Med* 1982; 307: 102.

37. VanEys J: Nutrition and neoplasia. *Nutrition Rev* 1983; 41: 47.

38. DiLuzio NR: Carbon tetrachloride and liver peroxidation. *Federation Proc* 1975; 32: 1875.

39. Hankin J, Rawlins V: Diet and breast cancer: a review. *Am J Clin Nutr* 1978; 29: 2005.

40. Lin PS, Goodchild NT: Copper, superoxide radical and bleomycin cytotoxicity. *Lancet* 1979; April 7: 277.

41. Kahn AJ, Kasha M: Oxidation of polynuclear hydrocarbons to carcinogens. *Ann NY Acad Sci* 1970; 171: 24.

42. Wolf G: Is dietary beta-carotene an anticancer agent? *Nutrition Rev* 1982; 40: 257.

43. Foote CS, Wexler S: Quenching of singlet oxygen with beta-carotene. *J Am Chem Soc* 1964; 86: 3879.

44. Gollnick L: Singlet oxygen and the ene-reaction. *Advances in Photochemistry* 1968; 6: 1.

45. Kerenyi T, Haranghy L, Huttner I: Mutations due to lipid peroxidation. *Experimental Gerontology* 1968; 3: 155.

46. Bielski BHJ, Saito E: Dismutation of superoxide to excited state oxygen. *J Phys Chem* 1971; 75: 2263.

47. Chan JT, Black HS: Oxidation of cholesterol and its relationship to epidermal cancer. *Science* 1974; 186: 1216.

48. Bland J, Canfield W, Wells R: Effect of tocopherol on photooxidation rate of human erythrocyte membrane in vitro. *Physiol Chem and Physics* 1978; 10: 145.

49. Schweibert M, Daniels M: Hydroperoxide induced substitution mutations. *Int J Radiation Phys Chem* 1971; 3: 353.

50. Hall J: Superoxide dismutase as an index of copper, zinc, and manganese status. *Nutrition Rev* 1980; 38: 326.

51. Scudder P, Dormandy TL: The relationship between superoxide dismutase, erythrocyte copper and rheumatoid arthritis. *Clin Chem Acta* 1976; 69: 397.

52. Bland J, Madden P, Herbert EJ: Effect of alpha tocopherol on the rate of photohemolysis of human erythrocytes. *Physiol Chem and Physics* 1975; 7: 69.

53. Gallo-Torres HE, Weber F, Wiss O: The effect of different dietary lipids on lymphatic appearance of vitamin E. *Int J Vit Nutr Res* 1971; 41: 504.

54. Kien CL, Ganther HE: Manifestations of chronic selenium deficiency in a child receiving total parenteral nutrition. *Am J Clin Nutr* 1983; 37: 319.

55. Levander O, Moser PB: Platelet glutathione peroxidase activity as an index of selenium status in patients. *J Nutr* 1983; 113: 55.

56. Amin S, Maddaih VT, Klein SW: Selenium in premature infants. *Nutr Metab* 1980; 24: 331.

57. Ehrenkranz RA: Vitamin E and the Neonate. *Am J Dis Child* 1980; 134: 1157.

58. Johnson L, Boggs TR Jr: The premature infant, vitamin E, and retrolental fibroplasia. *Am J Clin Nutr* 1974; 27: 1158.

59. Finer NN, Peters KL: Effect of intramuscularly administered vitamin E on retrolental fibroplasia. *Lancet* 1982; May 15: 1087.

60. Boxer LA, Schulman JD: Reduction of granulocytes by vitamin E in glutathione synthetase deficiency. *N Engl J Med* 1979; 301: 901.

61. Brooksbank BWL, Balazs R: Superoxide dismutase and lipoperoxidation in Down's syndrome fetal brain. *Lancet* 1983; April 16: 881.

62. Boehme DH, Marks N: Lipoperoxidation in human and rat brain tissue—developmental and regional studies. *Brain Res* 1977; 130: 11.

63. Gutteridge JM, Westermarck T: Increased iron and decreased protection against superoxide anion damage in CSF of patients with neuronal ceroid lipofuscinoses. *Lancet* 1982; August 28: 459.

64. Seegmiller JE, Liddle L: Uric acid production in gout. *J Clin Invest* 1961; 40: 1304.

65. Pedersen TC, Aust SD: Xanthine oxidase and superoxide anion. *Biochem Biophys Res Comm* 1973; 52: 1071.

66. Proctor PH, McGinness JE: Superoxide-dismutase therapy in hyperuricemic subjects. *Lancet* 1979; July 8: 95.

67. Simpkin P: Zinc therapy in the treatment of rheumatoid arthritis. *Lancet* 1978; June 16: 1102.

68. McCord JM: Hyaluronic acid depolymerization by superoxide anion. *Science* 1974; 185: 529.

69. Marx J: The leukotrienes in allergy and inflammation. *Science* 1982; 215: 1380.

70. Fox J: Elusive asthma-related molecule synthesized. *Chem Eng News* 1980; Feb. 18: 28.

71. Harvath L, Anderson BR: Defective initiation of oxidative metabolism in polymorphonuclear leukocytes. *N Engl J Med* 1979; 300: 1130.

72. Chan AC, Choy PC: Differential effects of dietary vitamin E and antioxidants on eicosanoid synthesis in young rabbits. *J Nutrition* 1983; 113: 813.

73. Ayres S, Mihan R: Is vitamin E involved in the autoimmune mechanism? *Cutis* 1978; 21: 321.

74. Greeder G, Milner JA: Factors influencing the inhibitory effect of selenium on mice inoculated with Ehrlich ascites tumor cells. *Science* 1980; 209: 825.

75. Schrauzer GN: Selenium and cancer. *Bioinorganic Chemistry* 1976; 5: 275.

76. Lieberman J: Aryl hydrocarbon hydroxylase in bronchogenic carcinoma. *N Engl J Med* 1978; 298: 686.

77. Rister M, Gladtke E: Superoxide-dismutase deficiency in rheumatoid arthritis. *Lancet* 1978; May 20: 1094.

78. Cameron E, Pauling L: Clinical trial of high dose ascorbic acid supplements in advanced human cancer. *Chemico Biological Interactions* 1974; 9: 285.

79. Ovesen L, Chu R: Reversible neurological symptoms caused by vitamin E deficiency in a patient with short bowel syndrome. *Am J Clin Nutr* 1982; 36: 1243.

80. Lewis KO, Paton A: Could superoxide cause cirrhosis? *Lancet* 1982; July 24: 188.

CHAPTER FIVE

THE AGING PROCESS

DENHAM HARMAN, MD, PhD

Aging is the progressive accumulation of changes associated with or responsible for increasing susceptibility to disease and death.[1] The free-radical theory of aging assumes that there is a single basic cause of aging, modified by genetic and environmental factors, and postulates that free-radical reactions are involved in aging and age-related disorders. Supports for this theory include (1) studies on the origin of life and evolution, (2) life-span studies with diets formulated to lower free-radical reaction levels, (3) studies of disorders associated with age, and (4) the plausible explanations the theory provides for aging phenomena.

EVOLUTIONARY HISTORY OF LIFE

Life apparently arose spontaneously (Table 5.1)[2–5] about 3.5 billion years ago from amino acids, nucleotides, and other basic chemicals of living things. These basic elements of life were produced from simple, reduced components of the primitive, oxygen-free atmosphere by free-radical reactions, initiated mainly by ionizing radiation from the sun.

It seems likely that evolution was made possible initially by the constant presence of ionizing radiation. Radiation served, on the one hand, to create compounds in the environment necessary for the survival and growth of the first cells and, on the other, to produce more-or-less random free-radical-reaction-mediated changes throughout the cells. Some cellular changes were inheritable; of these, some were useful for cell function, whereas others were deleterious and led to cell death, thereby removing the cell from competition with its cohorts for food stores. Time for more complex cells to evolve and function was gained through the gradual selection and development of defenses against deleterious free-radical reactions.

The earliest cells gradually developed biochemical machinery to free them of the need for environmental sources of "building blocks" and to help provide protection from damaging radiation. Energy for these purposes was first derived from reactions involving organic compounds. Later, ferredoxin first appeared, per-

Table 5.1 Overview of the origin and evolution of life

No. years ago	Event
3.5 billion	Basic chemicals of life formed by free-radical reactions, largely by ionizing radiation from the sun
	Life begins
	Excision repair
	Recombinational repair
	Ferredoxin $RH \text{ or } H_2S + CO_2 \xrightarrow{h\nu} CH$
2.6 billion	Blue-green algae $H_2O \xrightarrow{h\nu} 2H + O_2$
1.3 billion	Atmospheric O_2 reaches 1 percent of present value
	Anaerobic prokaryotes disappear
	Eukaryotes become dominant cells Eukaryotes + blue-green algae ⟶ the green-leaf plants Eukaryotes + a prokaryote able to reduce O_2 to H_2O ⟶ animal kingdom Emergence of multicellular organisms and plants
	Meiosis
500 million	Atmospheric O_2 reaches 10 percent of present value
	Ozone screen allows emergence of life from sea
65 million	Primates appear
5 million	Human beings

mitting photosynthetic reduction of carbon dioxide with organic compounds or with hydrogen sulfide as a source of hydrogen. Then about 2.6 billion years ago followed the blue-green algae, which utilized water as a hydrogen source. Still later, as oxygen liberated by the blue-green algae began to build up in the atmosphere, some cells developed the ability to obtain energy from the reduction of oxygen to water.

Approximately 1.3 billion years ago the atmospheric concentration of oxygen reached about 1 percent of the present value, which was the toxic level for anaerobes. The anaerobic prokaryotes disappeared, except for a few in oxygen-deficient niches, and the more complex eukaryotes, better equipped to minimize damaging oxygen reactions, appeared and became the dominant cells. The progenitor of the green-leaf plants apparently acquired a blue-green alga to assist with its energy needs, whereas that of the animal kingdom took in a prokaryote able to reduce oxygen to water. Subsequently, colonies of cells appeared that evolved into multicellular organisms and plants.

Until about 500 million years ago, all plant and animal life was confined to the sea in order to escape destructive uv radiation from the sun. About that time, the increasing amounts of atmospheric oxygen absorbed uv radiation, reducing the amount of radiation reaching the earth to a level compatible with existence on land. Evolution then accelerated. Primates appeared about 65 million years ago, and man some 4 to 5 million years ago.

The original basic pattern of evolution does not appear to have changed, except that now the sun-initiated free-radical reactions have largely been replaced by those derived from enzymatic and nonenzymatic reactions. In mammalian systems, enzymatic reactions that serve as sources of free radicals include those involved in the respiratory chain,[6-8] phagocytosis,[9] prostaglandin synthesis,[10] and the cytochrome P-450 system.[11] Free radicals also arise in the nonenzymatic reactions of oxygen with organic compounds,[12, 13] as well as in those initiated by ionizing radiation.[14]

Changes attributed to free radicals include (1) accumulative oxidative alterations in the long-lived molecules collagen,[15] elastin,[16] and chromosomal material,[17, 18] (2) breakdown of mucopolysaccharides through oxidative degradation,[19] (3) accumulation of metabolically inert material such as ceroid and age pigment through oxidative polymerization reactions involving lipids (particularly polyunsaturated lipids) and proteins,[20, 21] (4) changes in membrane characteristics[22-24] of such cell components as mitochondria and lysosomes because of lipid peroxidation, and (5) arteriolocapillary fibrosis secondary to vessel injury by products resulting from peroxidation of serum and vessel-wall components.[25, 26]

Natural defenses that limit the rate of production of free-radical damage have evolved. These protectants include antioxidants, such as tocopherols[27] and carotenes,[9] heme-containing peroxidases,[28] selenium-containing glutathione peroxidase,[28] superoxide dismutases,[29, 30] elevated serum uric acid levels,[31] and DNA repair mechanisms.[32, 33] The evolution of such defenses has permitted longer life spans to evolve by enabling critical, fixed, postmitotic cells—for example, those of the respiratory center or myocardium—to function longer.

Thus, studies on the origin and evolution of life are compatible with the possibility that more-or-less random damage produced by free-radical reactions constitute the basic aging process.

LIFE SPAN STUDIES

Dietary manipulations expected to lower the rate of production of free-radical-reaction damage are also in accord with the foregoing possibility.[34] For instance, minimizing dietary components such as copper and polyunsaturates tends to decrease free-radical reaction levels. On the other hand, dietary inhibitors of free-radical-reaction-induced damage exist; 2-mercaptoethylamine (2-MEA), α-tocopherol, butylated hydroxytoluene (BHT), and 1,2-dihydro-6-ethoxy-2,2,4-trimethylquinoline (ethoxyquin) are some of these.

Dietary antioxidants have been shown to increase the life span of mice,[35–40] rats,[41] fruit flies,[39, 40] nematodes,[42] and rotifers,[43] and lengthen the "life span" of neurospora.[44] In mice, addition of 1.0 wt % (percent by weight) 2-MEA to the diet of male LAF_1 mice,[35] starting shortly after weaning, increased the *average* life span by 30 percent. This benefit is equivalent to increasing the average expected human life span from 73 to 95 years. Corresponding increases produced by 0.5 percent ethoxyquin in the diet of male and female C3H mice were 18.1 percent and 20.0 percent, respectively.[36]

Although antioxidants increase the average and maximum life spans of fruit flies and nematodes, they have not produced any certain extension of the *maximum* life span of mice. This failure is probably largely a result of the depression of respiration and oxidative phosphorylation by antioxidants.[45–49] This effect may largely account for the approximately 10 percent decrease in body weight of mice given effective antiaging antioxidants[14–15] such as 2-MEA or ethoxyquin. The depression of respiration and oxidative phosphorylation could arise in part by the reaction of the antioxidants with $O_2^-\cdot$ and/or $HO\cdot$, followed by combination of the antioxidant free radical with ubisemiquinone or other free radicals involved in the respiratory chain.

Apparently as the dietary level of an antioxidant is increased, average life span lengthens. This is attributed to inhibition of free-radical reactions involved in disease processes and nonspecific damage. The effect continues until the trend is halted and then reversed, primarily by accompanying decreases in oxidative phosphorylation.

The level or type of antioxidant in the diet associated with maximum *average* life expectancy of mice is probably not sufficient to depress significantly mitochondrial aging. The mitochondria may serve as the "biological clock," determining the maximum life span.[45] This could explain why none of the antioxidants evaluated increase the *maximum* life expectancy, with the possible exception of two pyridine derivatives, 2-ethyl-6-methyl-3-hydroxypyridine[37] and 2,6-dimethyl-3,5-diethoxycarbonyl-1,4-dihydropyridine.[50]

In contrast to mice, both the average and maximum life spans of *Drosophila*[39, 40] and nematodes[42] are increased by antioxidants. These effects, at least in *Drosophila,* are associated with decreased respiration[47] and presumably oxidative phosphorylation. Antioxidants that have a beneficial effect on maximum life span of these two poikilotherms may operate in the same manner as in mice, coupled with the greater capacity of fruit flies and nematodes to live at reduced levels of ATP production.

DISEASES IN WHICH FREE-RADICAL REACTIONS PLAY A ROLE

Increases in average life span by antioxidants may be due in part to decreases in the incidence of specific diseases in which free-radical reactions play an etiologic role.[51] The growing number of diseases in which free-radical reactions are implicated include the two major causes of death, atherosclerosis[52-55] and cancer.[34, 56-60] They also may play a role in other common degenerative diseases, including hypertension,[34, 57] senile dementia of the Alzheimer type,[61-63] amyloidosis,[64, 65] osteoarthritis,[66] senile macular degeneration,[67] immune deficiency of age,[68, 69] and Parkinson's disease.[70, 71] Other disorders in which free-radical reactions are implicated include Fanconi's anemia,[72] Bloom's syndrome,[73] Batten's disease,[74] insulin-dependent diabetes mellitus,[75] systemic lupus erythematosus (SLE),[76] and Huntington's chorea.[77, 78]

Some of the data implicating free-radical reactions in cancer, atherosclerosis, senile dementia of the Alzheimer's type, and disorders of the immune system are briefly presented below.

Cancer

Results of a number of studies have indicated that antioxidants inhibit cancer development in some model systems.[58-60] The incidence of mammary carcinoma in C3H female mice increases as the amount and/or degree of unsaturation of the dietary fat is increased.[79] In geographic areas where the selenium intake is relatively high, the incidence of some forms of human cancer tends to be low.[80, 81]

Atherosclerosis

Lipid peroxides inhibit prostacyclin synthetase.[82] Prostacyclin is a potent inhibitor of platelet aggregation,[83] which is believed to be one of the events contributing to the development of atherosclerosis.[85] The incidence of cardiovascular disease is low in areas in which the dietary intake of selenium is high, and vice versa.[80, 85, 86]

Senile Dementia of the Alzheimer Type

Lipofuscin (age pigment) accumulates with age in the various areas of the central nervous system (CNS)[87] in parallel with the activities of oxidative enzymes.[88, 89] Age pigment is formed by oxidative polymerization of lipids (probably largely mitochondrial) and proteins.[90] The accumulation of lipofuscin can be slowed by antioxidants.[91]

Relatively large amounts of lipofuscin may be associated with adverse effects in the CNS, including loss of neurons.[88, 92] Large deposits of neuromelanin, essentially a melanized lipofuscin, also appear to be associated with detrimental changes.[71] Vitamin E-deficient diets increase CNS lipofuscin and depress function.[93] It is a reasonable possibility that the excessive loss of neurons[94] in the nucleus basalis of Meynert and other areas of the brain associated with senile dementia of the Alzheimer type is due to free-radical reactions associated with the accumulation of pigment.

Immune System

Humoral and cell-mediated immune responses in mice are enhanced by adding antioxidants to the diet.[69] Ethoxyquin and 2-MEA are particularly effective; addition of 0.25 wt % ethoxyquin or 0.5 wt % 2-MEA increases the humoral response of female C3HB/FeJ mouse spleen cells by 94 percent and 79 percent, respectively. This suggests that the decline of the immune system with age may be ameliorated to some extent by antioxidants.

Development of amyloidosis[64, 65] and the autoimmune disorders of NZB and NZB/NZW mice are slowed by antioxidants.[76] Thus, addition of 0.25 wt % ethoxyquin to the diet markedly inhibited amyloid formation in LAF_1 male mice. Ethoxyquin (0.25 wt %) also increased the average life span of male NZB mice by 32 percent, whereas the water-soluble antioxidant, disodium-*N*-(carboxyphenyl)-4-chloroanthranilate, had similar beneficial effect on the life span and kidney disease of NZB/NZW mice.

Systemic Lupus Erythematosus

The reported beneficial effect of ethoxyquin on the life span of NZB mice[76] prompted a review of the literature on systemic lupus erythematosus (SLE). In light of the ethoxyquin study, the basic defect in SLE appears to be an increased susceptibility of the nuclear material of one or more cell types to free-radical reaction damage. This leads to the formation of immune complexes and activation of complement, with the C5A fraction causing clumping of leukocytes with the subsequent release of oxyradicals, which give rise to the symptoms associated with SLE. Diets formulated to minimize the endogenous level of free-radical reactions should be helpful in SLE.

EXPLANATIONS FOR AGING PHENOMENA

The free-radical theory of aging also provides reasonable explanations for more general aging phenomena,[45] including the relation of the average life spans of mammalian species to their basal metabolic rates, the clustering of degenerative diseases in the terminal part of the life span, the beneficial effect of food restriction on life span, the increase in autoimmunity with age, and the greater longevity of females. For example, a study in mice of the effect of maternal dietary antioxidants on the life span of the offspring[95] led to a possible explanation for the greater longevity of females. Addition of 2-MEA, the most effective of the compounds evaluated, at a level of 0.5 percent in the maternal diet, increased the average life span of the male offspring by 15 percent and that of the females by 8 percent; the offspring were fed a pellet control diet throughout life. Also, the degree to which the females' longevity exceeded the males' was decreased from 11.5 percent in the control offspring to 6 percent in the 2-MEA–fed offspring. Consideration of these results in light of early embryogenesis led to the suggestion that the greater longevity of females is due, at least in part, to the greater protection of female embryos from free-radical damage during a period of about 48 hours of both high mitotic and metabolic activity just prior to the random inactivation of one of the two functional X chromosomes in the late blastocyst stage. The X chromosome codes for glucose-6-phosphate dehydrogenase, a key enzyme in the production of NADPH. NADPH acts to maintain glutathione in the reduced form. Glutathione serves as a free-radical reaction inhibitor and as a substrate for glutathione peroxidase, keeping the cellular concentrations of H_2O_2 and hydroperoxides low.

SUMMARY

The aging process, beyond reasonable doubt, is the sum of deleterious free-radical reactions continuously occurring in cells and tissues. The process has never changed: in the beginning free-radical reactions were initiated by ultraviolet radiation from the sun whereas now free radicals arise mainly endogenously from enzymatic and nonenzymatic free-radical reactions.

To judge from the animal studies, reduction of adverse free-radical reactions in man by dietary manipulations may increase average life span by 5 to 10 or more years, along with a possible slight increase in maximum life span. These increases in life span should lengthen the period of functional life, decrease the period of senescence, and lessen the social and economic problems associated with aging.

REFERENCES

1. Harman D: The aging process. *Proc Natl Acad Sci USA* 1981; 78: 7124–7128.

2. Calvin M: *Chemical Evolution.* New York, Oxford Univ. Press, 1969.

3. Rutten MG: *The Origin of Life by Natural Causes.* New York, Elsevier/North-Holland, 1971.

4. Cairns-Smith AG: *The Life Puzzle.* Toronto, Univ. of Toronto Press, 1971.

5. Day W: *Genesis on Planet Earth.* East Lansing, House of Talos, 1979.

6. Harman D: Free radical theory of aging: consequences of mitochondrial aging. *Age* 1983; 6: 86–94.

7. Nohl H, Hegner D: Do mitochondria produce oxygen radicals in vivo? *Eur J Biochem* 1978; 82: 863–867.

8. Chance B, Sies H, Boveris A: Hydroperoxide metabolism in mammalian organs. *Physiol Rev* 1979; 59: 527–605.

9. Klebanoff SJ: Oxygen metabolism and the toxic properties of phagocytes. *Ann Intern Med* 1980; 93: 480–489.

10. Porter NH: Prostaglandin endoperoxides, in Pryor WA (ed): *Free Radicals in Biology* (vol 4). New York, Academic, 1980, pp 261–294.

11. Sato R, Omura T (eds): *Cytochrome P-450.* New York, Academic, 1978.

12. Scott G: *Atmospheric Oxidation and Antioxidants.* New York, Elsevier, 1965.

13. Mead JF: Free radical mechanisms of lipid damage and consequences for cellular membranes, in Pryor WA (ed): *Free Radicals in Biology* (vol 1). New York, Academic, 1976, pp 51–68.

14. Altman KI, Gerbes GB, Okada S: *Radiation Biochemistry* (vols 1 and 2). New York, Academic, 1970.

15. LaBella FS, Paul G: Structure of collagen from human tendon as influenced by age and sex. *J Gerontol* 1965; 20: 54–59.

16. LaBella FS, Vivian S, Thornhill DP: Amino acid composition of human aortic elastin as influenced by age. *J Gerontol* 1966; 21: 550–555.

17. Harman D: Chromatin template capacity: effect of oxygen (abstr). *Gerontologist* 1967; 7(II): 29.

18. Tas S, Tam CF, Walford RL: Disulfide bonds and the structure of the chromatin complex in relation to aging. *Mech Ageing Dev* 1980; 12: 65–80.

19. Matsumura G, Herp A, Pigmon W: Depolymerization of hyaluronic acid by autoxidants and radiations. *Radiation Res* 1966; 28: 735–752.

20. Hartroft WS, Porta ES: Ceroid. *Am J Med Sci* 1965; 258: 324–344.

21. Norkin SA: Lipid nature of ceroid in experimental nutritional cirrhosis. *Arch Pathol* 1966; 82: 259–266.

22. Robinson JD: Structural changes in microsomal suspension. III. Formation of lipid peroxides. *Arch Biochem Biophys* 1965; 112: 170–179.

23. Witting L: Vitamin E and lipid antioxidants in free-radical-initiated reactions, in Pryor WA (ed): *Free Radicals in Biology* (vol 4). New York, Academic, 1980, pp 295–317.

24. Hegner D: Age-dependence of molecular and functional changes in biological membrane properties. *Mech Ageing Dev* 1980; 14: 101–118.

25. Casarett GW: Similarities and contrasts between radiation and time pathology, in Strehler BL (ed): *Advances in Gerontological Research* (vol 1). New York, Academic, 1964, pp 109–163.

26. Harman D, Piette LH: Free radical theory of aging: free radical reactions in serum. *J Gerontol* 1966; 21: 560–565.

27. deDuve C, Hayaishi O (eds): *Tocopherol, Oxygen and Biomembranes.* New York, Elsevier/North-Holland, 1978.

28. Flohé L, Günzies WA, Ladenstein R: Glutathione peroxidase, in Arias IM, Jakoby WB (eds): *Glutathione: Metabolism and Function.* New York, Raven, 1976, pp 115–138.

29. Fridovich I: Oxygen radicals, hydrogen peroxide, and oxygen toxicity, in Pryor WA (ed): *Free Radicals in Biology* (vol 2). New York, Academic, 1977, pp 239–277.

30. Michelson AM, McCord JM, Fridovich I (eds): *Superoxide and Superoxide Dismutases.* New York, Academic, 1977.

31. Ames BN, Cathcart R, Schiviers E, et al.: Uric acid provides an antioxidant defense in humans against oxidant- and radical-caused aging and cancer: A hypothesis. *Proc Natl Acad Sci USA,* 1981; 78: 6852–6858.

32. Hart RW, D'Ambrosio SM, Ng KJ, et al.: Longevity, stability and DNA repair. *Mech Ageing Dev* 1979; 9: 203–223.

33. Nichols WW, Murphy DG (eds): *DNA Repair Processes.* Miami, Miami Symposium Specialists, 1977.

34. Harman D: Free radical theory of aging: nutritional implications. *Age* 1978; 1: 145–152.

35. Harman D: Free radical theory of aging: effect of free radical inhibitors on the mortality rate of male LAF_1 mice. *J Gerontol* 1968; 23: 476–482.

36. Comfort A: Effect of ethoxyquin on the longevity of C3H mice. *Nature* 1971; 229: 254–255.

37. Emanuel NM: Free radicals and the action of inhibitors of radical processes under pathological states and aging in living organisms and in man. *Quart Rev Biophysics* 1976; 9: 283–308.

38. Clopp NK, Satterfield LC, Bowles ND: Effects of the antioxidant butylated hydroxytoluene (BHT) on mortality in BALC/C mice. *J Gerontol* 1979; 34: 497–501.

39. Miquel J, Economos AC: Favorable effects of the antioxidants sodium and magnesium thiazolidine carboxylate on the vitality and life span of Drosophila and mice. *Exper Gerontol* 1979; 14: 279–285.

40. Miquel J, Johnson Jr JE: Effects of various antioxidants and radiation protectants on the life span and lipofuscin of Drosophila and C57BL/6J mice (abstr). *Gerontologist* 1975; 15(II): 25.

41. Bun-Hoi NP, Ratsunamanga AR: Age retardation in the rat by nordihydroguaiaretic acid. *Comptes Rendues Seânces Soc Biol* 1959; 153: 1180–1182.

42. Epstein J, Gershon D: Studies on aging in nematodes. IV. The effect of antioxidants on cellular damage and life span. *Mech Ageing Dev* 1972; 1: 257–264.

43. Enesco HE, Verdone-Smith C: α-Tocopherol increases lifespan in the rotifer Philodina. *Exper Gerontol* 1980; 15: 335–338.

44. Munkres KD, Minssen M: Aging of Neurospora Crassa. 1. Evidence for the free radical theory of aging from studies of a natural death mutant. *Mech Ageing Dev* 1976; 5: 79–98.

45. Harman D: Free radical theory of aging: consequences of mitochondrial aging. *Age* 1983; 6: 86–94.

46. Pardini RS, Cotlin JC, Heidker JC, et al.: Specificity of inhibition of coenzyme Q-enzyme systems by lipoidal benzoquinone derivatives. *J Med Chem* 1972; 15: 195–197.

47. Miquel J, Fleming J, Economos AC: Antioxidants, metabolic rate and aging in Drosophila. *Arch Gerontol Geriatrics* 1982; 1: 159–165.

48. Cadenas E, Boveris A, Ragan CI, et al.: Production of superoxide radicals and hydrogen peroxide by NADH-ubiquinone reductase and ubiquinol-cytochrome c reductase from beef-heart mitochondria. *Arch Biochem Biophys* 1977; 180: 248–257.

49. Boveris A, Cadenas E, Stoppani AOM: Role of ubiquinone in the mitochondrial generation of hydrogen peroxide. *Biochem J* 1976; 156: 435–444.

50. Emanuel NM, Duburs G, Obukhov LK, et al.: Drugs for prophylaxis of aging and prolongation of lifetime. *Chem Abst* 1981; 94: 96326a.

51. Harman D: Role of free radicals in aging and disease, in Johnson H (ed): *Aging: Relations Between Normal Aging and Disease.* New York, Raven, 1985, pp 45–84.

52. Harman D: Atherosclerosis: hypothesis concerning the initiating steps in pathogenesis. *J Gerontol* 1957; 12: 199–202.

53. Harman D: Atherogenesis in minipigs: effect of dietary fat unsaturation and of copper, in Jones RJ (ed): *Atherosclerosis: Proceedings of the Second International Symposium.* New York, Springer-Verlag, 1970, pp 472–475.

54. Moncada S: Prostacyclin and arterial wall biology. *Atherosclerosis* 1982; 2: 193–207.

55. Ludwig PW, Hunninghake DB, Hoidal JR: Increased leucocyte oxidative metabolism in hyperlipoproteinaemia. *Lancet* 1982; 2: 348–350.

56. Harman D: Aging: a theory based on free radical and radiation chemistry. *J Gerontol* 1956; 11: 298–300.

57. Harman D: Prolongation of life; role of free radical reactions in aging. *J Am Geriatr Soc* 1969; 17: 721–735.

58. Harman D: Prolongation of the normal lifespan and inhibition of spontaneous cancer by antioxidants. *J Gerontol* 1961; 16: 247–254.

59. Harman D: Free radical theory of aging: effect of vitamin E on tumor incidence (abstr). *Gerontologist* 1972; 12(3): 33.

60. Wattenberg LL: Inhibition of chemical carcinogenesis by antioxidants, in Slaga TJ (ed): *Carcinogenesis,* vol 5: *Modifers of Chemical Carcinogenesis.* New York, Raven, 1980, pp 85–98.

61. Harman D, Eddy DE, Seibold J: Free radical theory of aging; effect of dietary fat on central nervous system function. *J Am Geriatr Soc* 1976; 24: 301–307.

62. Eddy DE, Harman D: Free radical theory of aging: effect of age, sex and dietary precursors on rat brain docosahexanoic acid. *J Am Geriatr Soc* 1977; 25: 220–229.

63. Brizzee KR, Ordy JM: Age pigments, cell loss and hippocampal function. *Mech Ageing Dev* 1979; 9: 143–162.

64. Harman D, Eddy DE, Noffsinger J: Free radical theory of aging: inhibition of amyloidosis in mice by antioxidants; possible mechanism. *J Am Geriatr Soc* 1976; 24: 203–210.

65. Harman D: Secondary amyloidosis and antioxidants. *Lancet* 1980; 2: 593.

66. Menandes-Huber KB, Huber W: Orgotein, the drug version of bovine Cu-Z superoxide dismutase. II. A summary account of clinical trials in man and animals, in Michelson AM, McCord J, Fridovich (eds): *Superoxide and Superoxide Dismutases.* New York, Academic, 1977, pp 537–549.

67. Feeney-Burns L: Lipofuscin of human retinal pigment epithelium. *Am J Ophthal* 1980; 90: 783–791.

68. Kay MMB: Aging and the decline of immune responsiveness, in Fudenberg HH, Stites, DP, Caldwell JL, et al. (eds): *Basic and Clinical Immunology.* Los Altos, Calif, Lange Medical Publ, 1976, pp 267–278.

69. Harman D, Heidrick ML, Eddy DE: Free radical theory of aging: effect of free radical reaction inhibitors on the immune response. *J Am Geriatr Soc* 1977; 25: 400–407.

70. Pearce JMS: Etiology and natural history of Parkinson's disease. *Br Med J* 1978; 2: 1664–1666.

71. Mann DMA, Yates PO: Lipoprotein pigments—their relationship to aging in the human nervous system. II. The melanin content of pigmented nerve cells. *Brain* 1974; 97: 489–498.

72. Joenje H, Arwert F, Eriksson AW, et al.: Oxygen-dependence of chromosomal aberrations in Fanconi's anemia. *Nature* 1981; 290: 142–143.

73. Emerit I, Cerutti P: Clastogenic activity from Bloom syndrome fibroblast cultures. *Proc Natl Acad Sci USA* 1981; 78: 1868–1872.

74. Armstrong D, Koppang N, Rider JA (eds): *Ceroid-lipofuscinosis (Batten's disease).* New York, Elsevier Biomedical Press, 1982.

75. Gandy SF, Buse MG, Crouch RK: Protective role of superoxide dismutase against diabetogenic drugs. *J Clin Invest* 1982; 70: 650–658.

76. Harman D: Free radical theory of aging: beneficial effect of antioxidants on the life span of male NZB mice: role of free radical reactions in the deterioration of the immune system with age and in the pathogenesis of systemic lupus erythematosus. *Age* 1980; 3: 64–73.

77. Tellez-Nagel I, Johnson AB, Terry RD: Ultrastructural and histochemical study of cerebral biopsies in Huntington's chorea, in Barbeau A, Chase TN, Paulson GW (eds): *Advances in Neurology,* vol 1: *Huntington's Chorea, 1872–1972.* New York, Raven, 1973, pp 387–398.

78. Moshell AN, Barrett SF, Tarone RE, et al.: Radiosensitivity in Huntington's disease: implications for pathogenesis and presymptomatic diagnosis. *Lancet* 1980; I: 9–11.

79. Harman D: Free radical theory of aging: effect of the amount and degree of unsaturation of dietary fat on mortality rate. *J Gerontol* 1971; 26: 451–457.

80. Shamberger RJ, Tytko SA, Willis CE: Antioxidants and cancer. VI. Selenium and age-adjusted human cancer mortality. *Arch Environ Health* 1976; 31: 231–235.

81. Schrauzer GN, White DA: Selenium in human nutrition: dietary intake and effects of supplementation. *Bioinorgan Chem* 1978; 8: 303–318.

82. Ham EA, Egan RW, Soderman DD, et al.: Peroxidase-dependent deactivation of prostacyclin synthetase. *J Biol Chem* 1979; 254: 2191–2194.

83. Moncada S, Vane JR: Unstable metabolites of arachidonic acid and their role in haemostasis and thrombosis. *Br Med Bull* 1978; 34: 129–135.

84. Ross R, Harker L: Hyperlipidemia and atherosclerosis. *Science* 1976; 193: 1094–1100.

85. Shamberger RJ, Willis CE: Epidemiological studies on selenium and heart disease (abstr). *Fed Proc* 1976; 35: 578.

86. Frost DV: The two faces of selenium: can selenophobia be cured?, in Goldberg L (ed): *Chemical Rubber Company Critical Review on Toxicology.* Cleveland, Chemical Rubber Co, 1972, pp 467–514.

87. Brizzee KR, Ordy JM, Kaack B: Early appearance and regional differences in intraneuronal and extraneuronal lipofuscin accumulation with age in the brain of a nonhuman primate (Macaca mulatta). *J Gerontol* 1974; 29: 366–381.

88. Friede RL: The relation of the formation of lipofuscin to the distribution of oxidative enzymes in the human brain. *Acta Neuropathol* 1962; 2: 113–125.

89. Ferrendelli JA, Sedgwick WG, Suntzeff V: Regional energy metabolism and lipofuscin accumulation in mouse brain during aging. *J Neuropathol Exper Neurol* 1971; 30: 638–649.

90. Miquel J, Oro J, Bensch KG, et al.: Lipofuscin: fine-structural and biochemical studies, in *Free Radicals in Biology* (vol. 3). New York, Academic, 1977, pp 133–182.

91. Tappel A, Fletcher D, Deamer D: Effect of antioxidants and nutrients on lipid peroxidation fluorescent products and aging parameters in the mouse. *J Gerontol* 1973; 28: 415–424.

92. Mann DMA, Yates PO: Lipoprotein pigments—their relationship to aging in the human nervous system. I. The lipofuscin content of nerve cells. *Brain* 1974; 97: 481–488.

93. Lal H, Pogacar S, Daly PR, et al.: Behavioral and neuropathological manifestations of nutritionally induced central nervous system "aging" in the rat, in Ford DH (ed): *Progress in Brain Research,* vol 40: *Neurobiological Aspects of Maturation and Aging.* New York, Elsevier, 1973, pp 129–140.

94. Harman D: Free radical theory of aging: the "free radical" diseases. *Age* 1984; 7: 111–131.

95. Harman D, Eddy DE: Free radical theory of aging: beneficial effect of adding antioxidants to the maternal mouse diet on life span of offspring; possible explanation of the sex difference in longevity. *Age* 1979; 2: 109–122.

CHAPTER SIX

ANTIOXIDANT BIOCHEMICAL ADAPTATION: A UNIFIED DISEASE THEORY

STEPHEN A. LEVINE, PhD

PARRIS M. KIDD, PhD

Aerobic metabolism is a paradox of evolution. Aerobic (air-breathing) organisms have advanced beyond their anaerobic ancestors in the efficiency with which they can convert foods to chemical energy. They achieved this heightened metabolic efficiency by using molecular oxygen as an electron acceptor in the process of oxidative phosphorylation. With efficiency, however, came a liability: the potential toxicity of oxygen because of its reactivity and other unique properties. To counter this threat, air-breathing organisms have evolved an antioxidant defense system. This system protects cells, tissues, and organs against endogenous oxidative stress mediated by free-radical and other activated derivatives of oxygen.

Living organisms are, however, also subject to the potentially toxic effects of a vast array of exogenous stressors, also through oxidant attack by free-radical and other activated molecules derived from the parent compound. In this paper we outline the role of oxidant/antioxidant balance in maintaining the optimal healthy state and in generating inflammatory-degenerative symptomatologies.

An intact antioxidant defense system is crucial for the maintenance of a normal oxidant/antioxidant (redox) balance. The system in mammals appears to be highly integrated and capable of reacting adaptively to oxidant challenge. Antioxidant adaptation does have limits, however. After presenting our hypothesis, we outline a hypothetical multistage progression to degenerative disease. We believe this is the likely progression as the individual's antioxidant defenses become severely compromised and eventually exhausted.

ANTIOXIDANT DEFENSES, TOLERANCE, AND ADAPTATION

Oxygen radicals and other reactive, free-radical intermediates are continuously produced by all living cells in aerobic environments.[1, 2] The processes of cellular respiration (oxidative phosphorylation to produce ATP), intermediary metabolism (oxidase and dehydrogenase enzymes), phagocytosis by macrophages and neutrophils (the "respiratory burst"), and the production of inflammatory mediators (prostaglandins, thromboxanes, and leukotrienes) are all examples of cellular aerobic mechanisms that generate free radicals in both health and disease.[2, 3]

In healthy cells and tissues, free radicals produced by oxidative phosphorylation, biological oxidations, and chemical and drug detoxification reactions are normally insulated from susceptible molecules and enzymes by cell membrane barriers that contain numerous antioxidant molecular species derived from nutrients. Such antioxidant molecules function in concert with protective antioxidant enzyme systems to maintain optimal cellular redox balance—a healthy balance between oxidative stress and the antioxidant defense capacity of the cell.[4] It is our thesis that any substantial shift in the local oxidation-reduction balance in response to chemical oxidant exposure, intensified endogenous generation of oxidant molecular species, physical trauma, or infection can directly affect the viability and functioning of the cell, tissue, or organ system. A patient's health is, therefore, related to the additive oxidative stress imposed on the individual's antioxidant defense system by exogenous and endogenous oxidant stressors.

The molecules and enzymes necessary for maintaining optimal integrity of the antioxidant defense system are derived from essential nutrients, which must be either obtained from the diet or provided as nutritional supplements. These nutrients and enzymes function to prevent local free-radical damage and the generation of fatty acid peroxides in biological membranes by propagation of free radicals. The major nutrients and enzymes essential for the antioxidant defense system are listed in Table 6.1.

Tolerance and Adaptation

The antioxidant defense system can adapt to severe, localized oxidative stress, whether acute or chronic, as evidenced by the augmentation of antioxidant factors in the tissue or organ subject to oxidant attack. Acquisition of tolerance to oxidant attack was first demonstrated biochemically for the lung tissue of rodents undergoing adaptation to ozone, cigarette smoke, and other airborne oxidant stressors.[5]

Stokinger, a pioneer investigator of ozone toxicology, was the first to show that laboratory animals exposed to a single, sublethal dose of ozone can become *tolerant* to this oxidant.[5] Test animals rendered tolerant to ozone can survive re-exposure to

Table 6.1 Major enzymatic and nonenzymatic components of the antioxidant defense system

Enzymes	Cofactors/ cosubstrates	Nonenzymatic compounds	Distribution
Superoxide dismutase	Cu, Zn (cytosol); Mn (mitochondria)	Ascorbate (vitamin C)	Water phase; intra- and extracellular
Glutathione peroxidase	Se; reduced glutathione	Reduced glutathione	Water phase; intracellular
Catalase	Fe	Tocopherols (vitamin E)	Cell membrane, hydrophobic phase
Glutathione reductase	Oxidized glutathione	Beta-carotene	Cell membrane, hydrophobic phase
Glucose-6-phosphate dehydrogenase	NADP	Uric acid Ceruloplasmin	Blood (plasma) Blood (serum)
Glutathione-S-transferases	Reduced glutathione	L-Cysteine, L-Methionine (—SH amino acids)	Glutathione precursors

concentrations of the gas that would be lethal to nontolerant animals. Animals rendered tolerant to ozone simultaneously develop a *cross-tolerance* to other oxidant gases, i.e., those that attack lung tissue by free-radical–mediated oxidative mechanisms. These include ketene, nitrogen dioxide, nitrosyl chloride, and phosgene.[6]

Stokinger found that the development of tolerance to ozone in his test animals required only a single, brief exposure (one hour or less) to concentrations of from 0.3 to 3.0 ppm.[5] Tolerance can develop rapidly (beginning within 30 minutes) and is a *local* phenomenon; it develops preferentially in the lung that has been exposed to ozone but not in the accompanying lung that has not been exposed.[7] The tolerant state can remain in effect for several weeks. Stokinger found that tolerance can be repeatedly reinstated by intermittent oxidant exposures, and can become reduced by continual, repetitive oxidant stress.

Tolerance to oxidant gases is manifested biochemically in lung tissue as increased activities of protective antioxidant enzymes. Chow and his collaborators[8] and Mustafa et al.[9] showed that the pulmonary activities of glutathione peroxidase

(GP) and its "support" enzymes glutathione reductase (GR) and glucose-6-phosphate dehydrogenase (G6PD) became elevated as the exposed rat became tolerant to ozone.* This linked triad of enzyme activities also becomes increased after exposure of rats to cigarette smoke.[10]

The enzymatic adjustments that are manifested as increased tolerance to oxidant attack are subject to nutritional modulation, i.e., by the dietary availability of antioxidant cofactors and cosubstrates. Dietary sufficiency of the trace element selenium (Se, the metal cofactor of GP) and the sulfur amino acids cysteine and methionine (precursors of the GP cosubstrate-reduced glutathione) is essential for GP to function. Thus dietary restriction of Se lowers the "baseline" activity of GP in the unstressed mouse lung, and on subsequent exposure to ozone the usual adaptive increase in lung GP activity does not occur.[11] Dietary supplementation with cysteine and methionine protects against the toxicity of hyperbaric oxygen, which is also an oxidant stressor. Lung glutathione levels normally increase during the development of tolerance to hyperbaric oxygen; dietary deficiency in cysteine prevents this adaptive increase and results in higher mortality on re-exposure of the test group to this oxidant.[12]

Human Tolerance to Airborne Oxidants

Humans continually exposed to oxidants may well be in an adapted state. Southern California residents suffer chronic exposure to ozone and the other oxidants present in the polluted air of the Los Angeles basin, whereas Canadians are not generally exposed to such high levels of photochemical oxidant pollutants. When experimentally exposed to ozone, a group of Canadian subjects exhibited greater clinical and physiological reactivity than a group of "healthy" Southern Californians, who were only minimally reactive.[13] These findings suggest that the Californians may have been somewhat adapted to photochemical smog (i.e., "used to it"). In the light of these preliminary findings and the more extensive animal studies that we have just reviewed, more such comparative studies should help establish the extent to which selected human populations are adapted to oxidant stressors.

Potential High Cost of Adaptation

Adaptation to ozone or other oxidant stressors (by the development of tolerance in the target tissue) has an obvious short-term advantage: survival. In Stokinger's

*These "support" enzymes regenerate supplies of antioxidant cosubstrates. GR reconverts oxidized glutathione to reduced glutathione, one substrate required for GP; G6PD is the first enzyme in the hexosemonophosphate shunt, the pathway through which "reducing equivalents" (electrons) are made available for GP in the form of NADPH.

experiments, many animals not preadapted to ozone, i.e., those which had not been previously exposed to sublethal levels, died on their initial exposure to high ozone levels. Adapted animals were able to survive re-exposure to comparably high levels of ozone or other oxidant gases. However, such adapted animals are likely to pay a subsequent price. According to Stokinger, ongoing (repeated) exposure to oxidants led to the premature development of chronic degenerative diseases.[5]

Whereas the development of tolerance appears to be essential for the survival of experimental animals exposed to high doses of oxidant chemicals, Stokinger[5] has cautioned against any "misimpression" that tolerance is all-encompassing. Stokinger recognized three categories of long-term degenerative effects from repeated exposure in mice rendered tolerant to ozone: chronic pulmonary effects, premature aging, and lung-tumor acceleration in a cancer-susceptible strain. Chronic bronchitis, bronchiolitis, and emphysematous and fibrotic changes developed in the pulmonary parenchyma of rats and mice exposed daily to 1 ppm ozone. Also, in rabbits exposed to ozone just once per week for one hour, the walls of the alveolar air sacs progressively collapsed, leading eventually to emphysematous changes.

Adaptation and Glutathione Peroxidase

Adaptation to oxidant attack apparently occurs by way of selective utilization of antioxidant factors by those tissues and organs currently subject to greater degrees of oxidative stress, at the expense of others less vulnerable. According to Tappel, tissue distributions of antioxidant factors are heterogenous even in the "unstressed" state,[14] possibly reflecting greater vulnerability of certain tissues to oxidative stress, and therefore greater need for protective antioxidant factors in these tissues. In the face of sustained oxidant attack, unless the body's systemic complement of antioxidant factors can increase rapidly, we might expect to see a concomitant *decrease* in antioxidant defenses in certain less vulnerable (or less essential) tissues and organs accompanying the observed *increases* in antioxidant defenses in certain tissues.

Glutathione peroxidase (GP) is a critical enzyme of the antioxidant defense system.[4, 15] Increased GP activity in the target tissue(s) appears to be a characteristic feature of adaptation to oxidative stress.[16] The enzymes that "support" GP activity, i.e., GR and G6PD, often undergo a parallel increase in activity,[8, 9] apparently feedback-regulated by the increased demand for reduced glutathione and NADPH as the activity of GP increases. Hence some tissues appear to have priority over others in synthesizing and deploying GP and other critical antioxidant defenses.

The patterns of distribution of Se in the tissues and organs of the body may regulate local ability to adapt to oxidant attack. Se atoms are located at the active site of the GP tetramer and are essential for its activity.[15, 17] Under conditions of dietary Se deficiency, this essential trace metal is selectively retained by certain tissues, particularly those of the immune system.[18] Tissues of the spleen, lymph nodes, thymus, and adrenal glands selectively retain Se during dietary deprivation;

Se falls to very low levels in red blood cells, liver, kidney, muscle, heart, pancreas, and thyroid. Since the increase in GP activity that occurs in lung tissue in response to oxidant attack appears to be modulated by Se availability,[11] those tissues least able to retain Se (and by implication GP activity) are likely to be those that become most easily compromised by sustained oxidative stress.

Lipid Peroxidative Stress and Glutathione Peroxidase Activity

Because the primary function of GP is to detoxify peroxides, the ability of tissues to respond adaptively to oxidative stress with increases in GP activity can be tested directly by feeding lipid peroxides to test animals. Normally the GP of the intestinal mucosa can detoxify small amounts of lipid peroxides ingested as part of the normal diet by reducing them to their corresponding nontoxic alcohols. In contrast, dietary administration of high levels of lipid peroxides can apparently overwhelm the capacities of intestinal GP to detoxify oxidants. Significant quantities of peroxides enter the circulation and gain access to other tissues, subjecting them to free-radical stress.[1]

Reddy and Tappel[19] studied the effects of dietary Se on the ability of rats to detoxify dietary lipid peroxides (peroxidized corn oil). Interestingly, in the test group not fed peroxides, the specific activity of GP in the gastrointestinal tract, liver, blood, and adipose tissue was higher with Se supplementation than without Se supplementation. Thus, limited Se availability appears to modulate tissue GP activity in rats, even in the absence of oxidative stress.

Among the two groups of rats fed lipid peroxides in Reddy and Tappel's study,[19] those *supplemented* with Se *showed no increase* in GP activity above the basal levels while those *not supplemented* showed *selectively increased* GP activity in their red blood cells, plasma, liver, and adipose tissue. This finding suggests that Se-supplemented rats were capable of detoxifying the dietary levels of peroxides to which they were subjected, without a need for adaptive augmentation of GP in selected tissues. The animals not supplemented with Se apparently were not similarly capable: peroxides accumulated in their adipose tissue in spite of an increase in GP activity therein. It seems that these nonsupplemented rats attempted to react adaptively by way of marked augmentation of GP activity in selected tissues, but nevertheless suffered toxic effects from their continual exposure to peroxidized lipids in the diet, as evidenced by their markedly lower weight gain over the course of the experiment.

In related studies, Tappel and his collaborators[14] showed that the levels of GP and its support enzymes can become increased in response to oxidative stress arising from deficiencies in other critical antioxidant factors. One of these was alpha tocopherol—vitamin E. In rats fed a tocopherol-deficient corn oil diet, the activities of GP, GR, and G6PD increased in several adipose tissues and in muscle, concomitant with abnormal increases in lipid peroxide content in these tissues. In contrast, the activities of these enzymes did not increase in the liver, lung, or kidney, those organs in which lipid peroxides did not accumulate. In reviewing these results, Tappel concluded:[14]

> The ability of animals to respond to oxidative stress by increasing the activity of glutathione peroxidase is the main feature of the protective system. . . . The presence in various tissues of the glutathione peroxidase system supports the view that the protective mechanism is operative throughout the body. (p. 44)

RED CELL OXIDATIVE STRESS AND DISEASE STATES

The interrelated functioning of GP and the various other components of the antioxidant defense system has been particularly well studied in mammalian red blood cells, which are highly susceptible to free-radical-mediated peroxidative damage.

The circulating red cell is normally subject to a high level of oxidative stress. It is bathed alternately in high oxygen concentrations in arterial blood and low oxygen concentrations in venous blood. The red cell has a high content of iron, a redox-active metal which facilitates oxidative electron transfer even under non-stressed conditions, and its ability to repair damaged macromolecular constituents is limited, due to its lack of a nucleus. Nevertheless, the red cell demonstrates marked ability to respond adaptively to abnormal elevations in oxidative stress to which it is subject. In an experiment by Wilkins,[20] sheep red cell GP activity increased in *direct proportion* to hydrogen peroxide added to the experimental medium. This finding was a direct demonstration that red cells can become tolerant to oxidative stress by enhancement of their enzymatic antioxidant protective mechanisms.[21]

Reactions that occur between hemoglobin and oxygen in the red cell (catalyzed by iron at the active site of hemoglobin) normally produce significant amounts of superoxide anion as a byproduct.[21] The accumulation of superoxide anion and other "activated" oxygen species presents a potential threat to the integrity of the red cell. The antioxidant enzyme superoxide dismutase (SOD), which converts the superoxide anion to hydrogen peroxide, is thought to present "the first line of defense" against free-radical damage in the red cell.[2,21] Hydrogen peroxide is also potentially toxic, and must in its turn be detoxified by GP, which converts peroxides to alcohols. The following examples serve to establish that GP increases adaptively in response to hereditary defects that increase oxidative stress on the red cell, subject to modulation by the availability of its metal cofactor selenium and its cosubstrate reduced glutathione.

Glutathione Peroxidase, NADPH, and G6PD Deficiencies

GP has an indirect requirement for NADPH as a source of reducing equivalents (electrons). NADPH is required to reconvert oxidized glutathione, an end product of the GP reaction, to reduced glutathione for reuse by GP as necessary. Under conditions that limit NADPH availability the red cell becomes more susceptible to oxidative hemolytic destruction, resulting in acute or chronic hemolytic disease.[22]

The extra NADPH required for GP to function optimally is generated from glucose oxidation by way of the hexose monophosphate (HM) shunt. Four enzymes make up this metabolic pathway, and abnormalities or deficiencies in any of these could compromise the pathway and limit NADPH availability. Hereditary abnormalities in G6PD, the first enzyme in the HM shunt, are by far the most common group of conditions that limit NADPH production in human red cells. Their usual clinical manifestation is chronic hemolytic anemia.[22] This disease state is characterized by spontaneous red blood cell hemolysis, liberation of Heinz bodies (products of hemoglobin autoxidation) into the plasma, and a rapid fall in hematocrit.

Most G6PD-deficient individuals are hematologically normal in the absence of exacerbated high oxidative stress. On oxidative challenge, however, the G6PD-deficient red cell can undergo structural transformations which culminate in cell lysis (hemolysis). Spectrin, a "peripheral" membrane protein which lies against the cytoplasmic face of the plasma membrane of the red cell, is linked with proteins deeply embedded in the membrane and is thought to regulate red cell deformability through these linkages.[23] It appears that in G6PD-deficient cells, spectrin is particularly sensitive to oxidative stress, tending to aggregate and render the cell membrane abnormally rigid.[21] These changes eventually result in the premature hemolytic destruction of the cell.

The degree of clinical expression of the G6PD-deficiency phenotype can vary markedly from patient to patient, but elevated GP activity is a consistent finding. Beutler surveyed red cell GP activity in 69 subjects with various hematologic disorders, including several with G6PD deficiencies.[24] The subjects as a group exhibited significantly higher GP activity than normal, but the G6PD subjects exhibited a more marked elevation in red cell GP activity.

Sickle Cell Anemia and the Thalassemias

Inherited hemoglobin abnormalities also can exacerbate oxidative stress on the red cell. Sickle cell anemia arises from a hereditary defect that leads to altered structure of the β-globin chain of hemoglobin.[25] Sickled hemoglobin has a tendency to aggregate on deoxygenation of the red cell, thereby deforming the cell into a sickle shape. On reoxygenation, most cells resume their biconcave shape but some do not. Such "irreversibly sickled cells" (ISC) can become stuck in capillaries, thereby occluding them and often precipitating painful ischemic episodes for the afflicted individual. Peroxidative damage to the red cell plasma membrane may be important in episodes of sickling, because the lipid-phase antioxidant vitamin E can prevent sickling.[21] Approximately 3 percent of the hemoglobin in the red cell is normally converted daily to methemoglobin, generating superoxide anion and peroxidizing polyunsaturated fatty acids in the red cell membrane. Deficiency in vitamin E exacerbates the tendency of "sickle" hemoglobin towards irreversible, peroxidative crosslinking accompanying structural deformation of the affected cell.

The thalassemias are another family of inherited hemoglobin diseases, also characterized by defects in the globin chains, which render them more susceptible to oxidation.[26] As in sickle cell anemia, superoxide anion is produced in greater quantities in the thalassemic red blood cell. Malondialdehyde (MDA) production is increased; this causes peroxidative crosslinking of polyunsaturated fatty acids in the membrane, and eventually hemolysis of the affected red cell. Thalassemic patients are often overloaded with iron from frequent blood transfusions; the presence of elevated quantities of free iron in the vicinity of the red cell may enhance the peroxidative hemolysis process. Due to its redox-active character,[27] the iron atom will catalyze the formation of peroxidative oxygen radical derivatives from superoxide anion radical and hydrogen peroxide.[1]

Red blood cell GP levels are elevated in both sickle cell anemia and the thalassemias.[21] In the G6PD deficiencies measurable GP activity goes up even though the availability of reducing equivalents (NADPH) as GP cosubstrates is limited. This observation can be explained from in vivo and in vitro experiments by Perona and coworkers,[28] which demonstrated that GP can become allosterically activated by oxygen radicals generated via the superoxide anion. According to this model, GP could "turn on" concurrent with increased oxidative stress on the red cell, subject to the availability of Se, its trace metal cofactor. The measured GP activity in the circulating red cell would be the net result of Se availability, enzyme activation from oxidative stress, and enzyme decay during cellular aging.

The foregoing examples make it clear that red cell GP activity can increase adaptively in certain hereditary disease states, i.e., sickle cell anemia, G6PD deficiencies, and the thalassemias.[22] These inborn errors of metabolism damage the organism largely by enhancing the susceptibility of the circulating red blood cell to oxidative stress. The red cell attempts to increase its production of NADPH with which to fuel the reduction of glutathione (the reduced form of which is an essential substrate for GP); in G6PD deficiency this attempt can be futile. Most individuals who have these genetic defects are generally asymptomatic except under conditions of elevated oxidative stress, conditions which act selectively to exacerbate the inherent metabolic defect.

Red Cell GP Activity and Human Chemical Exposures

Results of studies with humans indicate that GP activity can be altered significantly as a result of environmental chemical exposure. Reliable data on tissue GP activities and Se status is generally lacking for humans, but the limited information available is nevertheless consistent with our thesis of antioxidant biochemical adaptation.

Griffin and Lane studied 229 normal subjects (with "unremarkable" medical histories) for red cell and plasma Se concentrations, and red cell GP activities.[29] They compared subjects who were considered to have been occupationally exposed to chemicals (these individuals worked in an oil refinery) with others considered to have been less chemically exposed (employed at schools and a hospital). The mean values for all three measures of Se status were lower in the occupationally exposed population. Griffin and Lane also compared smokers with nonsmokers from the same sample population. The group that smoked had lower mean erythrocyte Se and GP activity. There were relatively high standard deviations in the data from both of these comparison studies. These high standard deviations reflect the possibility that the sampled subjects were experiencing varying degrees of adaptation to oxidant stress, as we discuss later in this paper.

Abnormal GP Activity in Systemic Disease

Data from other studies on human subjects indicate that GP activity is lowered in certain systemic disease states. These findings cannot be taken as direct proof that the patients studied were in an adapted state; rather they suggest a trend and justify the need for further studies to directly test the antioxidant biochemical adaptation hypothesis.

Goodwin and collaborators studied GP-Se levels in patients with cancer. They found that red cell GP activity and Se levels were significantly decreased in patients with untreated head and neck cancers (squamous cell carcinoma), and plasma Se levels were increased.[30] Plasma Se levels were further increased in those patients with advanced disease and significant weight loss. Goodwin et al. suggested these patients might have impaired ability to transport Se from the plasma into the red cell for incorporation into the GP enzyme. Such impairment of Se transport could result from damage to red cell membrane transport proteins, which are known to be highly sensitive to oxidants.[31] A possible alternative explanation is that Se is liberated into the plasma from damaged subunits of the GP enzyme, which is itself susceptible to oxidative damage.[17]

GP activity has also been found to be lower in common skin diseases. A Swedish study of more than 500 patients with a broad range of skin disorders found that (whole blood) GP activity was markedly reduced in the vast majority.[32] Disorders that manifested decreased GP activity included atopic dermatitis, eczema, psoriasis, vasculitis, mycosis fungoides, and dermatitis herpetiformis. Treatment with Se and vitamin E for 6 to 8 weeks raised red cell GP levels markedly and had an overall beneficial effect, particularly on those patients with severe protracted seborrheic dermatitis.

Although there have been relatively few studies that attempt to correlate red cell GP with human diseases, the data currently available suggest that a broad spectrum of oxidative stressors, both endogenous and exogenous, consistently affect red cell

GP activity. Red cell GP levels probably fluctuate with local and systemic fluctuations in oxidative stress to the organism.

ADAPTATION TO OXIDATIVE MENTAL IMBALANCES

Alterations in GP and in other antioxidant factors, particularly the enzyme SOD, are also evident in several common mental diseases. Certain mental diseases display abnormal oxidative metabolism, accompanied by indications of antioxidant enzyme adaptation to the resulting oxidative stress.[33] Down's syndrome (DS), which results from a congenital trisomy in chromosome 21, is probably the single most common mental disorder in the United States.[34] Down's syndrome is consistently associated with premature aging: Down's syndrome patients develop a progressive dementia that resembles that of Alzheimer's disease. Down's syndrome is also associated with increased frequencies of cataracts, diabetes, pulmonary infections, leukemia, endocrine dysfunction, and neurotransmitter abnormalities.[35]

Down's Syndrome: Genetic Model of Antioxidant Adaptation

Increased activity of the antioxidant enzyme copper, zinc-dependent superoxide dismutase (Cu, Zn-SOD) in both non-nucleated and nucleated cell types is a consistent characteristic of Down's syndrome subjects.[36] This finding is presently accepted as a gene dosage effect: the SOD gene is carried on chromosome 21 and is therefore inherited as a third copy. However, GP and HM shunt enzymes also are elevated in both the red and the white blood cells of Down's syndrome subjects.[36] This finding cannot be readily explained as a gene dosage effect; rather it seems that the GP enzyme complex is increased adaptively, possibly as a result of allosteric activation according to the model of Perona et al.[28] Such adaptive increase in GP could be the result of increased availability of its peroxide substrate (H_2O_2) due to increased SOD activity in trisomy-21 cells, hydrogen peroxide being the final product of the "dismutation" of superoxide by SOD.

Down's syndrome subjects, like individuals with Alzheimer's disease, show a tendency toward premature mental aging, which is attributable to accelerated peroxidative damage to their brain tissue. Brain neurons exhibit what may be premature degenerative changes, including lipofuscin pigment accumulation, a generally accepted indicator of peroxidative crosslinking of biomolecules.[36] Observations of accelerated senescence in fibroblasts cultured from Down's syndrome patients, and of premature immune system deterioration in these individuals, also support the conclusion that Down's syndrome subjects age faster.

The degenerative mental progression observed in Down's syndrome subjects appears consistent with oxidative damage from the generation of abnormally high quantities of hydrogen peroxide in their brain neurons. Red cell GP activity and IQ are positively correlated in Down's syndrome subjects—the higher the GP activity, the higher the subject's IQ.[36] It might be interesting to determine whether elevated GP activity in circulating red cells reflects elevated GP activity in brain tissue, since this would suggest that adaptive increases in GP activity help protect against the premature loss of IQ in Down's syndrome.

Since neural tissue is known to be preferentially susceptible to oxidative stress,[27] the most attractive interpretation of the Down's syndrome findings is that increased oxidative stress occurs in these subjects, mediated by abnormally high endogenous production of hydrogen peroxide. Degenerative neuronal damage then results in deterioration of brain function (manifested as lowered IQ), derangement of neuronal organization (manifested as the dementia that resembles premature senility), and deterioration of neurons (manifested as lipofuscin accumulation).

The elevated levels of GP and HM shunt activity in red blood cells of Down's syndrome subjects suggests systemic antioxidant adaptation to oxidative stress engendered by their systemic genetic affliction.

Certain inherited mental disease states closely resemble the oxidative damage characteristic of Down's syndrome. The biochemical phenotype for Down's syndrome appears to be elevated SOD activity, which results in elevated intracellular levels of hydrogen peroxide. This in turn results in an adaptive increase in GP-HM shunt activity as the body attempts to compensate. The consistent elevation of GP activity in this genetic model of endogenous elevated oxidative stress strongly supports our contention that *red blood cell GP levels can be used as an indicator of systemic oxidative stress.*

Oxidative Stress in Schizophrenia

Some 30 years ago Dr. Abram Hoffer and his collaborators suggested that oxidative stress was a causative factor in schizophrenia.[37] They proposed that adrenaline and related catecholamine neurotransmitters could become irreversibly oxidized in vivo to adrenochromes (highly reactive compounds with free-radical properties), which subsequently initiated peroxidative damage to the brain tissue in schizophrenia. Adrenochromes are hallucinogenic synaptic poisons, and are known to be generated in the course of damage to the brain from hyperbaric oxygen. Normally, oxidized catecholamines would be reconverted to their reduced forms in the presence of adequate levels of "reducing equivalents" carried in reduced pyridine nucleotides (NADH or NADPH). Deficiencies in reducing equivalents in the brain (e.g., from HM shunt impairment) could impair this re-reduction process or prevent it from occurring. Conversely, adequate levels of protective antioxidant factors in the brain would be expected to inhibit catecholamine oxidation to adrenochromes.[1]

Newer evidence lends support to Hoffer's hypothesis that brain tissue damage from oxidized neurotransmitter derivatives contributes to schizophrenia. At the Academy of Orthomolecular Psychiatry meeting in 1983, Pecora and Shriftman reported that chronic undifferentiated schizophrenics were often hypoglycemic, with a high fasting insulin level.[39] The vast majority of these patients (79 percent) also had *significantly elevated serum lipid peroxide levels.* The investigators attributed this to stimulation of fatty acid ligases via membrane-bound oxidases (perhaps as a consequence of hyperinsulinemia), with the production of hydrogen peroxide and subsequent peroxidation of serum lipids. An even higher proportion of these patients (86 percent) had *significantly lowered red cell GP levels.* Of the 14 percent who did not exhibit significantly lowered red cell GP, half (7 percent) had *significantly elevated red cell GP levels.* Only 7 percent had GP levels within the range considered normal.

We interpret these data to mean that chronic undifferentiated schizophrenics are subject to abnormally elevated oxidative stress, as indicated by the high percentage who displayed elevated serum lipid peroxide levels. We suggest that the comparative few (7 percent) who displayed *elevated* red cell GP have been *in the process of adapting* to elevated levels of circulating peroxides. The great majority, who had *decreased red cell GP* accompanying *elevated serum lipid peroxide* levels, may have passed the point of successful antioxidant adaptation. These schizophrenics may have already exhausted their ability to maintain increased levels of GP in their red cells to detoxify the abnormally high levels of lipid peroxides in their serum.* The vast majority of these chronic undifferentiated schizophrenics may have overstressed their systemic antioxidant capacities.

SOD and GP in Autism

Many *infant development psychoses* are characterized by absence of verbal communication, stereotyped behavior, and autism.[40] Michelson[41] has suggested that the biochemical mechanism underlying autism may involve alterations in the synthesis of certain neurotransmitters. Autistic children have *abnormally elevated* red cell and platelet Cu, Zn-SOD activity, as compared with healthy children.[41] In contrast, their red cell GP activity is *abnormally lowered,* to the extent that the ratio of their red cell SOD activity ([SOD]) to GP activity ([GP]) is approximately twofold higher than normal. The elevated [SOD]/[GP] ratio in autism is analogous with Down's syndrome, in which elevated SOD activity is thought to lead to greater production of hydrogen peroxide, a substrate for GP. Higher H_2O_2 then results in a compensatory (adaptive) increase in GP activity.

Autistic children appear to differ from schizophrenics in one important respect: in the face of abnormally increased SOD activity, they have *decreased* red cell GP levels rather than *increased* levels as measured in the majority of the schizophrenics. We might speculate that autistic children as a group have progressed further than

*Recall that the GP enzyme is itself susceptible to oxidant attack.

schizophrenics towards loss of their ability to adapt to endogenous oxidative stress.

The major substrates for GP in vivo are peroxides. This raises the question whether other disease states might be characterized by elevated serum lipid peroxide levels, thereby indicating a possible role for GP in successfully adapting to them.

ELEVATED LIPID PEROXIDATION IN HUMAN DISEASE STATES

There is little doubt that lipid peroxides mediate tissue injury in a variety of human disease states.[42] In 1952, Glavind et al. had detected and measured lipid peroxides in human atherosclerotic plaques, and reported that the degree of plaque development in each vessel correlated closely with its content of lipid peroxides.[43] More recently Yagi[44] showed that lipid peroxides injected into test animals can initiate vascular endothelial degeneration. Earlier lipid peroxide assays involved fluorometric quantitation of thiobarbituric acid-reactive products (usually malondialdehyde (MDA), a crosslinking breakdown product of lipid peroxides). A noninvasive method has been developed, one which involves measuring the levels of ethane or pentane (gaseous hydrocarbon products of ongoing lipid peroxidation in vivo) in air exhaled from the test animal or human subject.[45] Tappel's group has utilized this method in several studies to estimate ongoing lipid peroxidation in vivo under different experimental conditions. Thus Dillard et al. found that hydrocarbon exhalation from healthy human subjects is increased significantly during exercise, is further exacerbated by exposure to ozone, and can be minimized by vitamin E supplementation.[46]

Elevated lipid peroxidation, as assessed noninvasively in experimental animals by the hydrocarbon exhalation test, can be verified by later analysis of selected tissues and correlated with other indicators of oxidative tissue damage. Thus Hafeman and Hoekstra showed that carbon tetrachloride (CCl_4) increased ethane exhalation in rats, caused preferential lipid peroxide accumulation in the liver, and produced extensive liver lesions.[45, 47] Dietary supplementation with Se and the sulfur amino acid methionine protected against CCl_4-induced lipid peroxidative damage, and maintained GP activity and reduced glutathione at normal levels in the liver.

Recently, Yagi has refined the older thiobarbituric acid (TBA) method for detecting and measuring lipid peroxides as MDA into a "micro-fluorometric" method suitable for small samples.[44] Despite some age-dependent variation in healthy subjects, patients with various degenerative diseases consistently exhibited abnormally high tissue MDA levels. The availability of this simplified and accurate method for measuring lipid peroxides led to a proliferation of studies, which culminated in a symposium held in Japan in 1980. Some of the results presented at this symposium are summarized below.

Lipid Peroxides Injure Arterial Endothelia

Peroxidized ("rancid") lipids are known to decompose to free-radical and aldehydic crosslinking molecules that are potentially toxic.[1] Yagi used his improved methodology to investigate in rabbits the effects of intravenous administration of a lipid peroxide (linoleic acid hydroperoxide, with linoleic acid as control).[44] After injection of the peroxidized lipids, serum lipid peroxides immediately began an increase which peaked by 24 hours. The rabbit was then killed and several tissues were analyzed for their lipid peroxide content, namely the liver, lung, spleen, retina, aorta, pulmonary artery, and a major vein. The aorta was found to be the only tissue with significantly elevated lipid peroxide levels. Scanning and transmission electron microscopy revealed widespread endothelial disruption in the aortas of the peroxide-exposed rabbits, as well as adherence of platelets to zones of exposed subendothelium. Similar but less marked changes were observed in the pulmonary artery. Yagi attributed derangement of the aortic endothelium to the experimentally elevated serum lipid peroxide content, stating,[44] "it is plausible that the damage to the intima of the aorta provoked with lipid peroxides is the initial event in the pathogenesis of atherosclerosis." (p. 241)

Lipid Peroxides and Skin Burn Injury

Yagi also studied the *time course* of lipid peroxide production following experimental skin burn injury to rats.[44] At 1 hour after the controlled skin burn injury, the lipid peroxide content of the burned skin was significantly elevated. By 3 hours after the injury, the skin peroxide content was six times higher than control levels. After 1 day the skin peroxide levels had begun to fall, returning to the control range by the seventh day. Serum lipid peroxides increased in parallel with their decrease in skin lipid peroxides, suggesting release of peroxides from the skin into the circulation. On the seventh day the rats were killed and the lipid peroxide content was determined for several organs, along with the serum activities of several organ-specific enzymes as independent indicators of organ damage. Those enzymes characteristic of spleen, kidney, and liver were indeed significantly elevated in the serum, indicating they had leaked out of their parent organs due to peroxide-induced tissue damage. Lipid peroxides were significantly elevated in the spleen but not in the other organs sampled. Yagi concluded from his findings that lipid peroxides entered the circulation following burn injury, mediated damage to the spleen, kidney, and liver, and accumulated preferentially in the spleen.

Lipid Peroxides in Diabetes and Stroke

Also at the 1980 symposium, Goto reviewed several other studies that attempted to correlate degenerative disease states with elevations in serum lipid peroxide levels.[48] Diabetic patients with angiopathy (blood vessel degeneration) averaged 7.15 nanomoles (nmole) of MDA per milliliter of plasma, vs 3.74 for healthy subjects ($p <$ 0.001). Diabetics free of detectable blood vessel damage averaged 3.82 nmole/ml, not significantly different from healthy subjects.

Goto also reported a close correlation between events of cerebral ischemia or hemorrhage (stroke) and subsequent alterations in serum lipid peroxide levels, an observation likely to have great prognostic value. Those individuals destined to die soon after their stroke had levels of lipid peroxides trending upward (away from the control range), and those who subsequently survived had levels trending downward (towards the control range).

From the initial studies sparked by Yagi's refinement of the classical thiobarbituric acid–malondialdehyde assay, it appears that circulating lipid peroxide breakdown products are indeed elevated in several degenerative disease states. Following injection of peroxidized lipids into the test animal or the induction of lipid peroxidation in a tissue by a specific insult (as in skin burn injury), lipid peroxide levels become elevated in the blood, and subsequently in other organs.[42] Abnormally elevated levels of circulating lipid peroxides appear to correlate particularly well with damage to vascular endothelia, as in diabetic blood vessel disease and stroke in human subjects, and experimental atherosclerosis in rabbits. Further studies are in order, to better correlate findings on the degenerative effects of lipid peroxides with data on the activity of GP and other protective antioxidant factors in the tissues subjected to oxidant attack. The antioxidant defense status (pro-oxidant/antioxidant balance) locally and/or systemically is likely to determine whether the damage is halted at an early stage, is subsequently reversed, or becomes progressively more severe.

HYPOTHETICAL PROGRESSION TO DEGENERATIVE DISEASE

One of us (Stephen Levine) had suggested earlier that the development of adaptive tolerance to oxidative stress locally (i.e., in one organ) can deplete or reduce antioxidant reserves elsewhere in the body.[52] A clinical corollary of this hypothesis is that continued exposure to oxidative stress would result in a progression from the adapted state through an unstable state of health to clinical ill health, which would manifest inflammatory/degenerative symptomatology.

We have discussed elsewhere the mechanisms by which a wide variety of stressful stimuli manifest in vivo as oxidative stress.[1] These include polluted air and water, dietary and occupational chemical exposure, physical trauma, infection, and personal and job-related emotional stress. Many drugs are powerful pharmaceutical agents that contribute to oxidative stress following on their metabolic transformation to reactive radical derivatives. Individual genetic predispositions very likely dictate individual resiliency and determine which tissues and organ systems are particularly susceptible to oxidative stress.

Glucose-6-phosphate dehydrogenase deficiency is at present the most common disease-producing enzyme deficiency of human beings. G6PD provides a valuable genetic disease model wherein a hereditary aberration in the antioxidant defense system directly affects the ability of the organism to adapt to oxidant stress. G6PD-deficient red blood cells show a tissue-selective response to oxidative stress conditioned by inherent genetic predisposition and triggered by exogenous oxidant stressors.

Many exogenous oxidant stressors can stress the G6PD-deficient individual. According to Calabrese,[49] G6PD-deficient individuals could be preferentially susceptible to levels of ozone in the polluted air of major urban centers. Calabrese lists other common substances that may precipitate hemolytic episodes in G6PD-deficient individuals, and suggests that the use of oxidant chloramines or chlorine dioxide as biocides in our drinking water may be dangerous for G6PD-deficient individuals. In the "clinically significant" G6PD phenotypes, clinical symptomatology can be expressed on provocation by oxidative stress coming from exposure to oxidant environmental pollutant chemicals or from infection.

Human beings are also increasingly subject to exogenous oxidant attack resulting from the presence of reactive chemicals in our air, food, soil, and water supplies. As environmental chemical pollution becomes increasingly more widespread, we can expect more individuals to develop symptoms of oxidant damage: inflammation, immune dysregulation, cardiovascular pathologies, cancers, and other degenerative diseases. As Stokinger first showed,[5, 6] these are predictable consequences of chronic, excessive oxidative stress. Witschi[16] has suggested that the toxicity of oxidants to the lung is, in large part, a function of the individual's ability to adapt:

> We may also speculate that it is not necessarily the nature of the initial lesion that distinguishes a toxic agent from one harmless to the lung, but the subsequent failure of the tissue to maintain an adaptive response. (p. 1632)

We suggest that the effectiveness of the individual's antioxidant defense capabilities will determine initial response to oxidant stressors and long-term resiliency, and that adaptive antioxidant capacities are critical in determining the individual's health status. The antioxidant defense system is of course limited in its capacity to resist oxidative stress—when the body is overwhelmed by sustained oxidative stress, disease must result.

Chronic, excessive oxidative stress resulting from sustained oxidant insults may only be one side of the coin. The other may be acute, catastrophic oxidant stress precipitating an immediate biological "state of siege." To muster an adaptive defense, the individual may be forced to "borrow" reinforcements in the form of reducing equivalents (GSH, NADPH, and others), and protective antioxidant nutrients (Se, sulfur amino acids, and vitamins A, C, and E), from whatever systemic reserves are available. These antioxidant reserves would be essential for protecting those organs either inherently most susceptible or exposed to the most severe oxidant attack, i.e., the lung, liver, nervous system, and vascular system.

As seen from Stokinger's early work on ozone toxicology,[5] the development of localized antioxidant tolerance by systemic adaptation to oxidative stress may be a life-or-death issue. In the face of oxidant attack, the organism must adapt to survive, even at the expense of compromising constitutional antioxidant reserves. If the oxidative stress is maintained, the individual's capacity to adapt will become progressively more compromised and eventually clinical illness will merge. The timing and precise pattern of the emergence of disease will no doubt depend on the sum total and possible synergism of the oxidant stressors involved, and the genetic predispositions of the individual. It is possible to categorize, somewhat arbitrarily, the clinical progression to disease as a four-stage process.

Four-Stage Progression to Disease

At stage one of our hypothetical progression, an individual is in good health, comfortably protected against oxidant stressors, fully vibrant, and resilient to oxidative stress. But with the rapidly accelerating growth of modern technology has come a proliferation of synthetic chemicals totally unprecedented in human evolution. Thousands of pollutant chemicals are now dispersed in the ecosphere. Although these chemicals will differ in their physiochemical characteristics and in their mode of entry to the body, and although their biological effects will inevitably require thousands of toxicologists millions of hours to unravel, rest assured that the overriding theme of their toxicity is oxidative stress to our bodies.

The disease-producing chemical stressors of our environment may be rivaled only by the emotional stress of our twentieth-century life style. The intact nuclear family is disappearing; sexual roles are being redefined. With the rapid changing of social and economic structures and the massive environmental load of chemical stressors, the inevitable toll is stress, manifested biochemically as oxidative stress.

Stage Two: Adaptation to Oxidative Stress

At stage two, the individual has to compensate for various of life's stressors: oxidative stress from such everyday situations as breathing polluted Los Angeles air, living with a leaky gas stove or heating system, being exposed to chemicals at the workplace (perhaps merely fumes from the copying machine), or working in the garden with pesticides.

At stage two our overall level of health has been reduced. We become more susceptible to pathogens, and more and more we use pharmaceutical aids to offset our stressful life styles. "Our mode of life is emerging as today's principal cause of illness," according to Joel Elkes, director of the Behavioral Medicine program at the University of Louisville. Emotional stress translates into oxidative stress through the oxidative breakdown of circulating catecholamines.[50, 51] Most active individuals are likely to experience ongoing physiological and emotional stress as a normal part of their lives, and most are able to adapt without any encumbering signs of acute or chronic illness. Nonetheless, the "energy" (antioxidant capacities) required to handle life's stressors will eventually, to some degree, compromise our overall resistance to disease and our consequent sense of well-being.

Stage Three: Losing the Struggle

Stage three represents emerging clinical disease symptomatology. As our load of emotional and physical stressors accumulates, our waning ability to adapt impinges on our overall reserves and so greatly impairs our antioxidant defenses that normal metabolic functions begin to be compromised. At this stage, signs of chronic or acute illness appear in the more genetically susceptible organs. The characteristics of the particular stressors that topple the load will only in part affect the specific symptomatology that results. At this stage individuals may notice that they have developed acute intolerances to various foods and environmental chemicals.

The food and chemical hypersensitivities typical of ecological illness represent underlying pathologies that are the likely results of sustained (or, in some cases, high dose-acute) oxidative stress.[52] Reactive, oxidant molecular species generated from numerous exogenous and endogenous sources attack cell membranes, leading to the liberation of arachidonic acid metabolites, kinins, histamine, and serotonin. These mediators of inflammation are liberated as a consequence of uncontrolled, oxidant-induced, membrane peroxidative damage. Atopic reactions to foods and autoimmune phenomena may ensue as a secondary consequence of oxidative damage to proteins and glycoproteins, resulting in generation of nonself-antigenic species.[1, 52]

Masking and Inflammatory Symptoms

Many individuals may not immediately become aware of their acute food and chemical reactivities. Though they are under considerable oxidative stress, their bodies make a grand attempt to bolster antioxidant defenses at target organs at the cost of their reserve antioxidant capacities. At this stage, that of "masking," the individual will begin to display inflammatory symptoms of a more chronic nature. This is a very unstable state: nutrient absorption becomes diminished, and antioxidant nutrients quickly become limiting.* The nutrients lacking in ecologically ill patients are those most critical for the immune system, suggesting that individ-

*Reduced nutrient absorption may result from damage to the Na^+/K^+-ATPase enzyme, the activity of which is linked with glucose and amino acid uptake into the cell. Extracts from many common foods inhibit ATP-splitting activity by this enzyme in vitro.[53]

uals at this stage are prone to immune dysregulation. A list of such nutrients would include vitamin C, vitamin E, vitamin A, beta-carotene, selenium, zinc, and pantothenate. At this stage, continuing demand on antioxidant reserves (unaided with antioxidant supplements) would threaten exhaustion of the antioxidant defense system.

When antioxidant defenses are damaged enough by oxidative stress and/or nutritional deficiency, a vicious cycle becomes established. There comes a point beyond which the system degenerates further, rather than recuperating. This situation marks the progression to stage four. Impairment of GP function is one example of the compounding effect of severe oxidant damage at this stage of antioxidant deficiency.

Vulnerability of Glutathione Peroxidase to Oxidative Stress

GP activity is essential for the protection of cell membranes from oxidant damage, yet like many other critical redox enzymes GP is itself highly sensitive to oxidant attack. Under conditions of excessive oxidative stress, adaptive augmentation of reducing equivalents (based upon increased NADPH production from the HM shunt) normally compensates for these alterations. However, reduced functioning of the antioxidant defense system becomes compounded as antioxidant enzymes, themselves preferentially sensitive to oxidants, are damaged by sustained oxidative stress. Vulnerability to oxidative stress is an intrinsic feature of the GP enzyme.[15, 17] Its peroxidase function depends on the adequate availability of reduced glutathione (GSH) derived from nutrients, but GSH itself functions as a primary antioxidant and can become depleted from oxidant attack. For example, GSH is oxidized to its disulfide form (GSSG) in the lung during exposure to nitrogen dioxide, ozone, hyperbaric oxygen, or a variety of other radical/electrophile species, including solvents and chlorinated hydrocarbons.[54] As GSH becomes limiting, GP function can become impaired since the GP enzyme when not bound to GSH is more vulnerable to destruction from exposure to oxidants, i.e., to autoxidative degradation.[15]

The inducibility of GP activity is subject to the availability of nutrient-derived factors. Under conditions of Se deficiency,[12] the adaptability of the antioxidant system is severely compromised since increased GP activity is the cornerstone of the adaptive response and requires Se. Similarly, as glutathione precursors become limiting (as in cases of dietary insufficiency of sulfur-containing amino acids),[12] supplies of GSH become insufficient for the conjugation reactions that normally serve to neutralize the many toxic free-radical metabolites produced by enzymes of the mixed-function oxidase (MFO) system. Hundreds of potentially toxic chemicals are metabolized to radical/electrophile derivatives by the MFO systems in the liver, lung, kidney, skin, testes, and bone marrow. The toxicities of many of these metabolites can be greatly amplified as a result of glutathione depletion. The reduction in liver glutathione stores that results from the fasting of experimental animals has been correlated with greatly diminished tolerance to halogenated hydrocarbons.[55] We suggest that the increased food and chemical sensitivities of fasted patients is attributable (at least in part) to depletion of their hepatic glutathione reserves.[56]

Beyond Stage Four: Progression to Degenerative Disease

Once the vicious cycle of oxidant attack and antioxidant weakening has been set into motion under continued oxidative stress, the affected individual may eventually progress to a degenerative breakdown. At this stage antioxidant defenses have become severely compromised, and significant adaptation is no longer possible. Further oxidant exposures may precipitate acute inflammatory-degenerative symptomatology, with the widespread derangement of arachidonate catabolism to produce a chaotic array of locally acting autacoid tissue regulators (prostaglandins, leukotrienes, and thromboxanes), many of which are inflammatory and some of which are immunosuppressive.[57, 58] Unrestrained by a functioning antioxidant defense system, reactive oxidizing species are likely to react covalently with serum amino acids and oxidize serum lipids such as cholesterol. Oxidants may conjugate with the available sulfhydryl and aromatic groups of the amino acids of cytosolic proteins as well as membrane proteins. Peroxidation of membrane lipids and crosslinking of membrane proteins can impair membrane functioning and eventually disrupt the membrane. Proteins and glycoproteins conformationally modified from oxidation of cellular macromolecules can become immunogenic, with subsequent autoimmune effects.[59] Any of numerous other degenerative symptomatologies may develop.

CONCLUSION

The antioxidant adaptation hypothesis is well supported by findings from some of the best-studied human congenital metabolic diseases. It offers a rational biochemical interpretation for certain clinical phenomena in food- and chemical-hypersensitive patients. The antioxidant biochemical adaptation theory is based on the most recently elaborated principles of electronic biochemistry which underlie chemical toxicology and carcinogenesis. Inherent in this theory is the assumption that the myriad factors that precipitate oxidative stress operate through avenues involving direct tissue damage by free radicals and other activated oxygen species.[1] This theory, and its further implications, are also strongly supported by the extraordinarily broad therapeutic potential attributed to key antioxidant nutrient factors such as beta-carotene, vitamins A, C, and E, selenium, and zinc.[1, 52, 60]

ACKNOWLEDGEMENT

We gratefully acknowledge the typing and editorial assistance of David Brownell.

REFERENCES

1. Levine SA, Kidd PM: *Antioxidant Adaptation—Its Role in Free Radical Pathology.* San Leandro, CA, Allergy Research Group, 1985.

2. Di Guiseppi J, Fridovich I: The toxicology of molecular oxygen. *CRC Crit Rev Toxicol* 1984; 12: 315–342.

3. Freeman BA, Crapo JD: Biology of disease: free radicals and tissue injury. *Lab Invest* 1982; 47: 412–426.

4. Chow CK: Nutritional influences on cellular antioxidant defense systems. *Am J Clin Nutr* 1979; 32: 1066–1081.

5. Stokinger HE: Ozone toxicology. *Arch Environ Health* 1965; 10: 719–731.

6. Stokinger HF, Scheel LD: Ozone toxicity: immunochemical and tolerance-producing aspects. *Arch Environ Health* 1962; 4: 327–334.

7. Gardner DE, Lewis TR, Alpert SM, et al.: The role of tolerance in pulmonary defense mechanisms. *Arch Environ Health* 1972; 25: 432–438.

8. Chow CK, Dillard CJ, Tappel AL: Glutathione peroxidase system and lysozyme in rats exposed to ozone or nitrogen dioxide. *Environ Res* 1974; 7: 311–319.

9. Mustafa MG, Elsayed NM, Graham JA, et al.: Effects of ozone exposure on lung metabolism: influence of animal age, species, and exposure conditions, in Lee SD, Mustafa MG, Mehlman MA (eds): *The Biomedical Effects of Ozone and Related Photochemical Oxidants* (Proceedings of an International Symposium). Princeton, NJ, Princeton Scientific, 1982, pp 57–73.

10. York GK, Peirce TH, Schwartz LW, et al.: Stimulation by cigarette smoke of glutathione peroxidase system enzyme activities in rat lung. *Arch Environ Health* 1976; 31: 286–290.

11. Elsayed N, Hacker A, Mustafa M, et al.: Effects of decreased glutathione peroxidase activity on the pentose phosphate cycle in mouse lung. *Biochem Biophys Res Comm* 1982; 104: 564–569.

12. Forman HJ, Rotman EI, Fisher AB: Role of selenium and sulfur-containing amino acids in protection against oxygen toxicity. *Lab Invest* 1983; 49: 148–153.

13. Hackney JD, Linn WS, Mohler JG, et al.: Experimental studies on human health effects of air pollutants: II. Ozone. *Arch Environ Health* 1975; 30: 379–384.

14. Tappel AL: Measurement of and protection from in vivo lipid peroxidation, in Pryor WA (ed): *Free Radicals in Biology* (vol 4). New York, Academic, 1980, pp 2–47.

15. Flohe L: Glutathione peroxidase brought into focus, in Pryor WA (ed): *Free Radicals in Biology* (vol 5). New York, Academic, 1982, pp 223–254.

16. Witschi H: Environmental agents altering lung biochemistry. *Fed Proc* 1977; 36: 1631–1634.

17. Ganther HE, Kraus RJ: Oxidation states of erythrocyte glutathione peroxidase: isolation of an enzyme-glutathione complex, in Spallholz JE, Martin JL, Ganther HE (eds): *Selenium in Biology and Medicine* (Proceedings Second International Symposium). Westport, Conn, AVI, 1981, pp 54–69.

18. Spallholz JE: Selenium: what role in immunity and immune cytotoxicity?, in Spallholz JE, Martin JL, Ganther HE (eds): *Selenium in Biology and Medicine.* Westport, Conn, AVI, 1981, pp 103–117.

19. Reddy K, Tappel AL: Effect of dietary selenium and autoxidized lipids on the glutathione peroxidase system of gastrointestinal tract and other tissues in the rat. *J Nutr* 1974; 104: 1069–1078.

20. Wilkins JF: Haemoglobin oxidation in whole blood samples from sheep in relation to glutathione peroxidase activity. *Austral J Biol Sci* 1979; 32: 451–456.

21. Chiu D, Lubin B, Shohet SB: Peroxidative reactions in red cell biology, in Pryor WA (ed): *Free Radicals in Biology* (vol 5). New York, Academic, 1982, pp 115–159.

22. Stanbury JB (ed): *The Metabolic Basis of Inherited Disease* (5th edition). New York, McGraw-Hill, 1983.

23. Finean JB, Coleman R, Mitchell RH: *Cellular Functions* (2nd edition). New York, John Wiley and Sons, 1978.

24. Beutler E: Glucose-6-phosphate dehydrogenase deficiency and red cell glutathione peroxidase. *Blood* 1977; 49: 467–469.

25. Winslow RM, Anderson WF: The hemoglobinopathies, in Stanbury JB (ed): *The Metabolic Basis of Inherited Disease.* New York, McGraw-Hill, 1983, pp 1666–1710.

26. Yan YW: The thalassemias, in Stanbury JB (ed): *The Metabolic Basis of Inherited Disease.* New York, McGraw-Hill, 1983, pp 1666–1710.

27. Demopoulos HB, Flamm E, Seligman M, et al.: Oxygen free radicals in central nervous system ischemia and trauma, in Autor AP (ed): *Pathology of Oxygen.* New York, Academic Press, 1982, pp 127–155.

28. Perona G, Guidi GC, Piga A, et al.: In vivo and in vitro variations of human erythrocyte glutathione peroxidase activity as result of cells aging, selenium availability and peroxidase activation. *Br J Haematol* 1978; 39: 399–408.

29. Griffin AC, Lane HW: Selenium chemoprevention of cancer in animals and possible human implications, in Spallholz JE, Martin JL, Ganther HE (eds): *Selenium in Biology and Medicine* (Proceedings Second International Symposium). Westport, Conn, AVI, 1981, pp 160–170.

30. Goodwin WJ, Lane HW, Bradford K, et al.: Selenium and glutathione peroxidase levels in patients with epidermoid carcinoma of the oral cavity and oropharynx. *Cancer* 1983; 51: 110–115.

31. Katz AM, Messineo FC: Lipid-membrane interactions and the pathogenesis of ischemic damage to the myocardium. *Circ Res* 1981; 48: 1–16.

32. Juhlin L, Edqvist J-E, Ekman LG, et al.: Blood glutathione peroxidase levels in skin diseases: effects of selenium and vitamin E treatment. *Acta Dermatol-Venereol* 1982; 62: 211–214.

33. Sinet FM, Merril CR (eds): *Alzheimer's Disease, Down's Syndrome, and Aging.* New York, New York Academy of Sciences Annals, vol 396, 1982.

34. Lott IT: Down's syndrome, aging, and Alzheimer's disease: a clinical review, in Sinet FM, Merril CR (eds): *Alzheimer's Disease, Down's Syndrome, and Aging.* New York, New York Academy of Sciences Annals, vol 396, pp 15–27.

35. Patterson D, Jones C, Scoggin C, et al.: Somatic cell genetic approaches to Down's syndrome, in Sinet FM, Merril CR (eds): *Alzheimer's Disease, Down's Syndrome, and Aging.* New York, New York Academy of Sciences Annals, vol 396, pp 69–81.

36. Sinet PM: Metabolism of oxygen derivatives in Down's syndrome, in Sinet FM, Merril CR (eds): *Alzheimer's Disease, Down's Syndrome, and Aging.* New York, New York Academy of Sciences Annals, vol 396, pp 69–81.

37. Hoffer A: Oxidation-reduction and the brain. *J Orthomolec Psychiatr* 1983; 12: 292–301.

38. Armstrong D, Koppang N, Ryder J (eds): *Ceroid-Lipofuscinosis (Batten's Disease).* Amsterdam, Elsevier/North-Holland, 1982.

39. Pecora P, Shriftman MS: *A Study of Insulin, Fatty Acids and Other Metabolites in Psychiatric and Normal Control Populations.* Monroe, NY, Monroe Medical Research Laboratory, 1983 (unpublished).

40. Rimland B: *Infantile Autism: The Syndrome and its Implications for a Neural Theory of Behavior.* New Jersey, Prentice-Hall, 1964.

41. Michelson AM: Clinical use of superoxide dismutase and possible pharmacological approaches, in Autor AP (ed): *Pathology of Oxygen.* New York, Academic, 1982, pp 277–302.

42. Yagi K (ed): *Lipid Peroxides in Biology and Medicine.* New York, Academic, 1982.

43. Glavind J, Hartmann S, Clemessen J, et al.: Studies on the role of lipoperoxides in human pathology. 2. The presence of peroxidized lipids in the atherosclerotic aorta. *Acta Pathol* 1952; 30: 1–6.

44. Yagi K: Assay for serum lipid peroxide level and its clinical significance, in Yagi K (ed): *Lipid Peroxides in Biology and Medicine.* New York, Academic, 1982, pp 223–242.

45. Hafeman DG, Hoekstra WG: Protection against carbon tetrachloride-induced lipid peroxidation in the rat by dietary vitamin E, selenium, and methionine as measured by ethane evolution. *J Nutr* 1977; 107: 656–665.

46. Dillard CJ, Litov RE, Savin WM, et al.: Effects of exercise, vitamin E, and ozone on pulmonary function and lipid peroxidation. *J Appl Physiol* 1978; 45: 927–932.

47. Hafeman DG, Hoekstra WG: Lipid peroxidation in vitro during vitamin E and selenium deficiency in the rat as measured by ethane evolution. *J Nutr* 1977; 107: 666–672.

48. Goto Y: Lipid peroxides as a cause of vascular diseases, in Yagi K (ed): *Lipid Peroxides in Biology and Medicine.* New York, Academic, 1982, pp 295–303.

49. Calabrese EJ: *Nutrition and Environmental Health.* Volume 1: The Vitamins. New York, Wiley, 1980.

50. Meerson FZ: *Adaptation, Stress, and Prophylaxis.* New York, Springer-Verlag, 1984.

51. Schenkman JB, Jansson I, Powis G, et al.: Active oxygen in liver microsomes: mechanism of epinephrine oxidation. *Molec Pharmacol* 1979; 15: 428–438.

52. Levine SA, Reinhardt JH: Biochemical pathology initiated by free radicals, oxidant chemicals, and therapeutic drugs in the etiology of chemical hypersensitivity disease. *J Orthomolec Psychiatr* 1983; 12: 166–183.

53. Harlan DM, Mann GV: A factor in food which impairs Na^+-K^+-ATPase in vitro. *Am J Clin Nutr* 1982; 35: 250–257.

54. Boyd MR, Stiko A, Statham CN, et al.: Protective role of endogenous pulmonary glutathione and other sulfhydryl compounds against lung damage by alkylating agents. *Biochem Pharmacol* 1982; 31: 1579, 1583.

55. Pessayre D, Dolder A, Artigou JY, et al.: Effect of fasting on metabolite-mediated hepatotoxicity in the rat. *Gastroenterology* 1979; 77: 264–271.

56. Dickey LD (ed): *Clinical Ecology* (section VI). Springfield, Il, Charles C Thomas, 1976.

57. Goodwin JS, Webb DR: Regulation of the immune response by prostaglandins. *Clin Immunol Immunopathol* 1980; 15: 106–122.

58. Lewis GP: Immunoregulatory activity of metabolites of arachidonic acid and their role in inflammation. *Br Med Bull* 1983; 39: 243–248.

59. Atwal OS, Samagh BS, Bhatnagar MK: A possible autoimmune parathyroiditis following ozone inhalation (Part 2). *Am J Pathol* 1975; 80: 53–68.

60. Levine SA, Kidd PM: Beyond antioxidant adaptation: a free-radical-hypoxia-clonal thesis of cancer causation. *J Orthomolec Psych* 1985; 14(3).

CHAPTER SEVEN

PHOTON COUNTING IN NUTRITIONAL BIOCHEMISTRY

J. W. MEDUSKI, MD, PhD

J. D. MEDUSKI, BS

KHASHAYAR KHAKMAHD, MS

AKBAR AZAD, BS

CLAUDE CRUZ, MS

Any modern textbook of organic chemistry describes compounds in which bonding orbitals are not restricted to two atoms but are spread over three or more atoms. The textbook calls such bonding "delocalized" and states that the molecule in question should be considered a weighted average of the canonical forms. The representation of a molecular structure as a weighted average of two or more canonical forms is called resonance.

For obscure reasons the concept of resonance was considered by Soviet officials in the late 1940s and early 1950s a devious capitalistic plot. Linus Pauling was a prominent chemist of those times who employed the concept of resonance in his work; he therefore was considered persona non grata by official Soviet scientific opinion.

In the early 1940s, I learned the concept of resonance while translating into Polish the book *Mesomerie und Tautomerie: Gleichgewicht und Resonanz* by Berndt Eistert.* In 1951, a Soviet scientist's attack on Pauling during a conference in Zakopane evoked my polite but negative response. As a result, the Russian suggested to the Polish organizers of the conference that I was a "potential deviationist susceptible to capitalist influences." That was my first "involvement" in Pauling's activities—a modest but memorable one.

*The first-person comments are those of the senior author, who presented the oral version of this paper at the symposium honoring Dr. Pauling.

I later followed Pauling's publications on vitamin C and cancer with an obvious interest. This was largely because I published in 1949[1] my work showing that rats able to resist the carcinogenic activity of 1,2:5,6-dibenzanthracene were also able to maintain liver ascorbic acid at a normal level, although their liver glutathione was elevated.

Pauling's scientific activities are not restricted to chemistry, however. He battles war, diseases, and hunger, the curses of civilization. Why do I also call this side of Dr. Pauling's activities a scientific one? To explain, I quote Bernal, the crystallographer: "Science in one aspect is ordered technique; in another, it is a rationalized mythology." We are grateful to Pauling the scientist for his methodologic and theoretical achievements, and also for his attempts to translate his "rationalized mythology" into the reality of a peaceful, healthy, and happy mankind.

WHAT IS CHEMILUMINESCENCE?

The "nonmythological" part of this paper deals with the phenomenon of chemiluminescence, which has recently been used as a tool in nutritional biochemistry. *Luminescence* is a term describing processes that produce light. We can classify luminescence on the basis of the source of excitation energy. I will focus on chemiluminescence and its application to biochemistry, especially to nutritional biochemistry.

Chemiluminescence is the chemical production of light. Energy of a chemical reaction promotes product molecules to an excited state. Decay back to the ground state is then accompanied by the emission of energy in the form of light. Bioluminescence, a special case of chemiluminescence, deals with chemical reactions occurring in vivo. (Fluorescence is a different phenomenon; it is caused not by the energy of a chemical reaction but by the energy of incident radiation.)

Luminescence has long fascinated mankind. In Western civilization, Aristotle described the luminescence of dead fish in *De Anima* (384–322 BC). In 1668 Robert Boyle first described fungal and bacterial luminescent systems. In these systems, he said, (1) light is generated without perceptible heat, (2) chemical agents may inhibit the luminescence, (3) luminescence depends on air (today we would say oxygen), (4) extinction of light by evacuation is reversible, and (5) only a small amount of air is needed for maximal brightness of luminescence.

In 1821, Macaire suggested that organic compounds may be involved in bioluminescence of glowworms. DuBois later (1885, 1887) applied biochemical methods to the investigation of bioluminescence. Beijerinck (1889) first used bioluminescence for analytical purposes: he employed luminescent bacteria to detect minute amounts of oxygen. McElroy (1947) discovered the involvement of ATP and magnesium in firefly luminescence. Today, international conferences on bioluminescence demonstrate the viability of this field of study.

Chemiluminescent reactant
+
Other reactants
↓
Key intermediate
↓
Electronically excited state
↓ ↓
Energy transfer acceptor | Light + ground-state product
↘ ↗
Excited acceptor

Figure 7.1 The series of events involved in chemiluminescence.

Aspects of chemiluminescence that are not necessarily biological have practical import as well. In 1877, Radziszewski provided the first example of chemiluminescence in the aqueous phase of solution. Since then, the chemiluminescence of lophine, pyrogallol, esculin (a glycoside from horse chestnut bark), uric acid, asparagine, luminol, and lucigenin have been described. Today many chemiluminescent systems of the liquid, gas, and solid phases are known.

Chemiluminescent reactions are still considered uncommon. In most other reactions, energy is released as heat via vibrational excitation of ground-state product. Even when electronically excited states are produced in a reaction, most of them decay via nonradiative processes. The chemical energy necessary for chemiluminescent reactions comes from several sources: (1) decomposition of peroxides, (2) singlet oxygen reactions, (3) ion-radical reactions, and (4) chemically initiated electron exchange. Of particular interest is the participation of free radicals, i.e., molecules having one or more unpaired electrons. Free radicals are generally produced in vivo during homolytic oxidations by removal of a hydrogen atom or an electron. Radicals can also be produced, however, in photolytic reactions, by absorbing light and undergoing photochemical decomposition.[2, 3]

The most biologically important free radicals are oxyl radicals, that is, those species in which an unpaired electron is located on an oxygen atom. The molecule of oxygen itself in its ground state is paramagnetic and has two unpaired electrons; it is a biradical. Oxyl radicals are experimentally accessible via chemiluminescence; they luminesce upon recombination. Zachariasse[4] extended the earlier observations of Stauff and Lohmann,[5] who noted that the reactions in which oxygen is consumed (or evolved) emit light.

A chemiluminescent reaction is usually a multistep process (Figure 7.1). Theoretically, a single molecule of chemiluminescent reactant could produce one electronically excited molecule which could decay to emit one photon of light. However, in practice the efficiency is less; the quantum yield (the ratio of number of emitted photons to number of reacting molecules) is about 1 percent.

METHODOLOGY OF CHEMILUMINESCENCE DETECTION

The low efficiency of chemiluminescence reactions necessitates sophisticated instrumentation for its analysis. Originally, liquid scintillation counters were used for measurements of chemiluminescence.

Our laboratory was the first (1972) to use photon counting for chemiluminescence measurements in biochemistry (specifically nutritional biochemistry).[6] This method of measuring light by single photon detection was first applied to astronomical photometry. We became acquainted with the process by chance and were able to adapt it to our biochemical purposes. This method provides optimum signal-to-noise ratio for quantum limited signals, wide linear dynamic range, and high-speed digital processing capability without the need for analog-to-digital conversion.

The photon counter utilizes a photomultiplier tube (we have been using gallium arsenite photocathode) and associated digital pulse-counting equipment. We are counting single photon events and not time-averaged signals. Event counting is accomplished by a digital synchronous computer. With our instrument, counting rates in excess of 85 MHz are attainable. The counter output is recorded by a Sanborn 150 preamplifier and a strip-chart recorder calibrated and linearized before each series of runs.

Recently, several commercial luminometers (photon counters) have become available. Various models include automatic samplers, microprocessors, temperature control of samples, automatic or manual injection, and a range of sensitive photomultipliers. Quick-flow attachments to a photon counter, first described by us in 1981, are now widely used.

ANALYTICAL APPLICATIONS OF CHEMILUMINESCENCE REACTIONS

Although the chemiluminescent process has been known for many years, the application of chemiluminescent materials as analytical reagents is a more recent development. Advantages of the analytic applications of chemiluminescence as compared with radiotechniques are sensitivity, specificity, speed, low cost, and uncomplicated waste disposal.

The simple procedure involves reaction of the analyte with the excess of luminogenic reagent. The progress of the reaction is recorded as the chemiluminescent intensity as a function of time. If the kinetics of the reaction are of the first order with respect to the analyte, the rate of change of chemiluminescent intensity (in photons per second) as the analyte is consumed can be related to analyte concentration.

In addition to the analysis of direct reactants (catalytic or inhibitory in a chemiluminescent reaction) photon counting can be used to measure oxidizing agents (e.g., hydrogen peroxide), thus expanding the range of analytes. It is possible, for instance, to measure H_2O_2 in the presence of excess chemiluminescent reagent and a catalyst. Because many enzymes produce H_2O_2, it has become possible to measure these enzymes or their substrates by means of photon counting. Some applications include the analysis of serum and urinary glucose, vitamin B_{12}, Cr^{13}, cytochrome C, ferritin, hematin, hemoglobin, hypoxanthine, lactate dehydrogenase, myoglobin, NADH, and uric acid. The use of chemiluminescent labels (luminol, isoluminol, luminol derivatives, and lucigenin derivatives) attached to proteins or to haptens made it possible to carry out luminescence immunoassays.

EXPERIMENTAL RESULTS

Preliminary Studies

Our own experiments using the chemiluminescent technique arose out of our interest in the reactions of molecular oxygen in vivo. Preliminary results of our studies led to the following generalizations:[6–8]

1. Every investigated mammalian cell contains lipid peroxides in, *caeteris paribus,* reproducible quantities. These peroxides seem to be normal, strictly controlled, intermediary metabolites of cytomembrane systems.
2. During the intermediary metabolism of these lipid peroxides, there is chemiluminescence detectable with a photon-counting system.
3. As a result, all investigated normal eukaryotic cells are able to emit light under special conditions.
4. This light emission can be studied in subcellular preparations (mitochondria and microsomes) and can be enhanced using Fe^{2+}.
5. The eukaryotic cells that contain metabolically controllable lipid peroxides and produce light also contain essential fatty acids (methylene-interrupted polyunsaturated) in which the double bonds have the divinyl methane arrangement: (—CH═CH—CH2—CH═CH—).
6. These essential fatty acids can bind dioxygen on the methylene carbon between two double bonds without the disruption of the continuity of the carbon chain.

Our initial results were obtained with the Hamamatsu photomultiplier, which has a spectral response range of 160 to 650 nm. When we obtained similar results in an all-quartz optical path and in a borosilicate glass we concluded that the range 160 to 300 nm is of minor importance in chemiluminescence studies. We subsequently conducted studies dealing primarily with the visible range of about 300 to 650 nm, as described below.

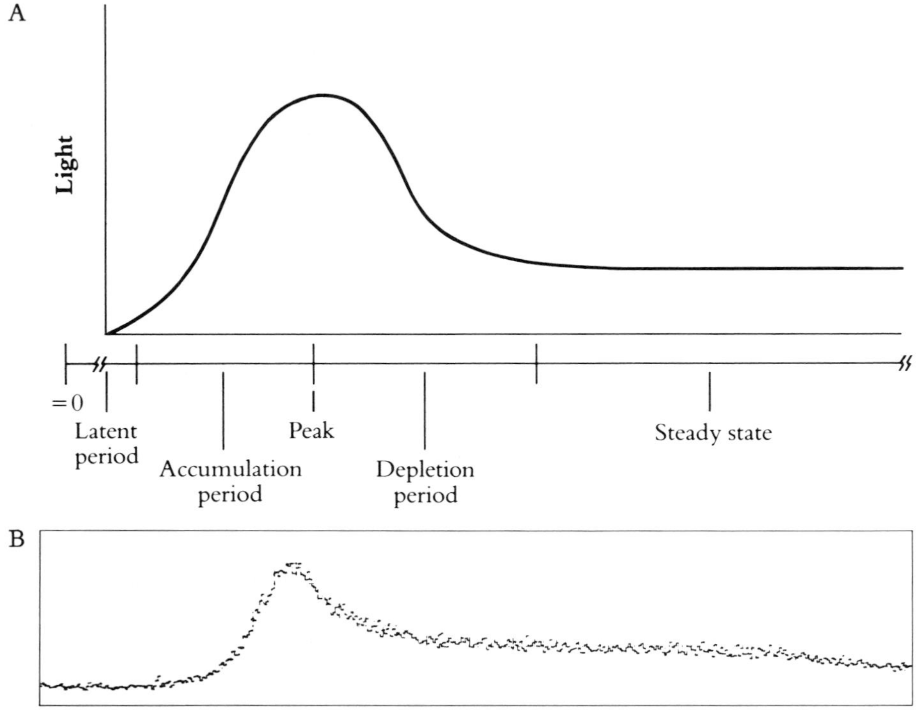

Figure 7.2 (A) Nomenclature of the photochemical event. (B) Experimental recording of a sample of 1.25-ml normal rat liver mitochondria suspended in a 1.645-ml sucrose medium, to which 0.105 ml of ferrous ammonium sulfate was added.

Later Studies

Our subsequent studies began with a sampling period of 1 continuous second, starting about 10 seconds after mixing the ingredients, until the steady-state period was reached. A sample (final volume, 3 ml) consisted of 1 to 8 mg of microsomal or mitochondrial proteins from male Sprague-Dawley rats. The subcellular fractions were prepared immediately before use and were suspended in a medium of the following composition: 35 m*M* KCl, 30 m*M* $MgCl_2$, 0.25 *M* sucrose, and 0.05 *M* K_2HPO_4/KH_2PO_4 buffer, pH 7.4. Immediately before counting, a specified quantity of freshly prepared ferrous ammonium sulfate was added (usually 4 m*M* starting solution). The resulting response curve became the basis for evaluating our experiments (Figure 7.2).

We plotted counts per second versus time, thus obtaining a derivative curve; we evaluated time-to-peak (seconds) and the peak amplitude (counts per second). We integrated our curve, determining the area within specified time limits (usually from the end of the latent period to the beginning of the steady state) (counts). We

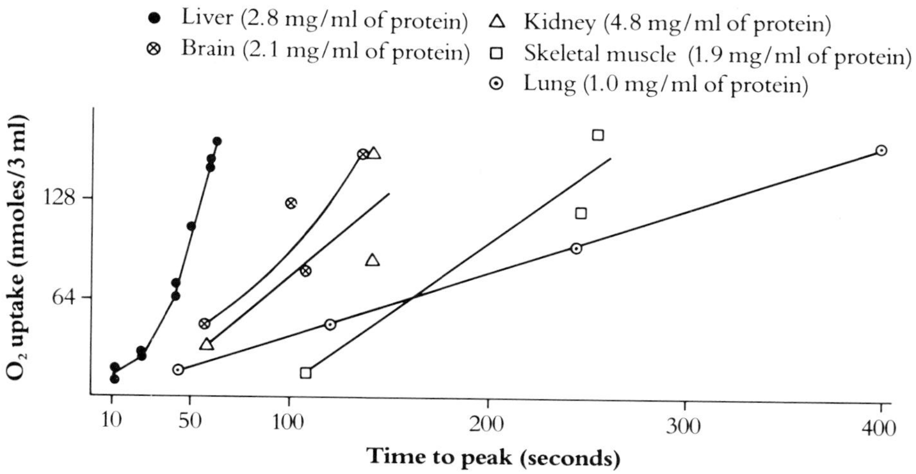

Figure 7.3 Oxygen uptake by rat mitochondrial preparations.

conducted peroxide assays and oxygen-uptake assays concurrently with photon-counting runs, using our own lipid peroxide determination micromethod and an oxygen electrode system (J. W. Meduski and J. D. Meduski, unpublished).

The comparative studies of subcellular (mitochondrial and microsomal) preparations from various rat organs elucidated the general metabolic role of essential fatty acids in mammalian metabolism.[9] The supply of dioxygen in mammals involves three stages: (1) dioxygen transport by the blood, (2) movement of dioxygen from capillaries to the cellular interior, and (3) the collision of dioxygen with electrons in mitochondria. The second stage had been considered a passive diffusion process. We found, however, that the cytomembranes (microsomes, mitochondria) of various organs bind dioxygen reversibly. The decreasing sequence of the binding ability is liver, brain, kidney, heart, skeletal muscle, and lung (Figures 7.3, 7.4, and 7.5). This behavior corresponds to the decreasing hypoxic condition in venous capillaries of these organs,[11] and implies greater essential fatty acid (EFA) concentration in the less-oxygenated tissues, to facilitate diffusion of dioxygen.

If EFAs facilitate dioxygen binding, then the cytomembranes of the corresponding organs of EFA-deficient rats would have strongly diminished ability to bind dioxygen. This in fact we found in further experiments. The mitochondrial and microsomal preparations from livers of EFA-deficient rats were obtained from Sprague-Dawley outbred rats kept on an EFA-free diet during one year. The onset of EFA deficiency was revealed by classical physical signs and confirmed by subsequent autopsies and gas chromatography determination of 18:2-ω-6 and 20:4-ω-6 fatty acids in the rats' livers. We propose that the reactions of molecular oxygen with essential fatty acids of cytomembranes occur as in Figure 7.6. The result of the facilitation of diffusion of oxygen from capillaries to intracellular mitochondrial sites could be summarized as in Figure 7.7. The result is an increase in oxygen

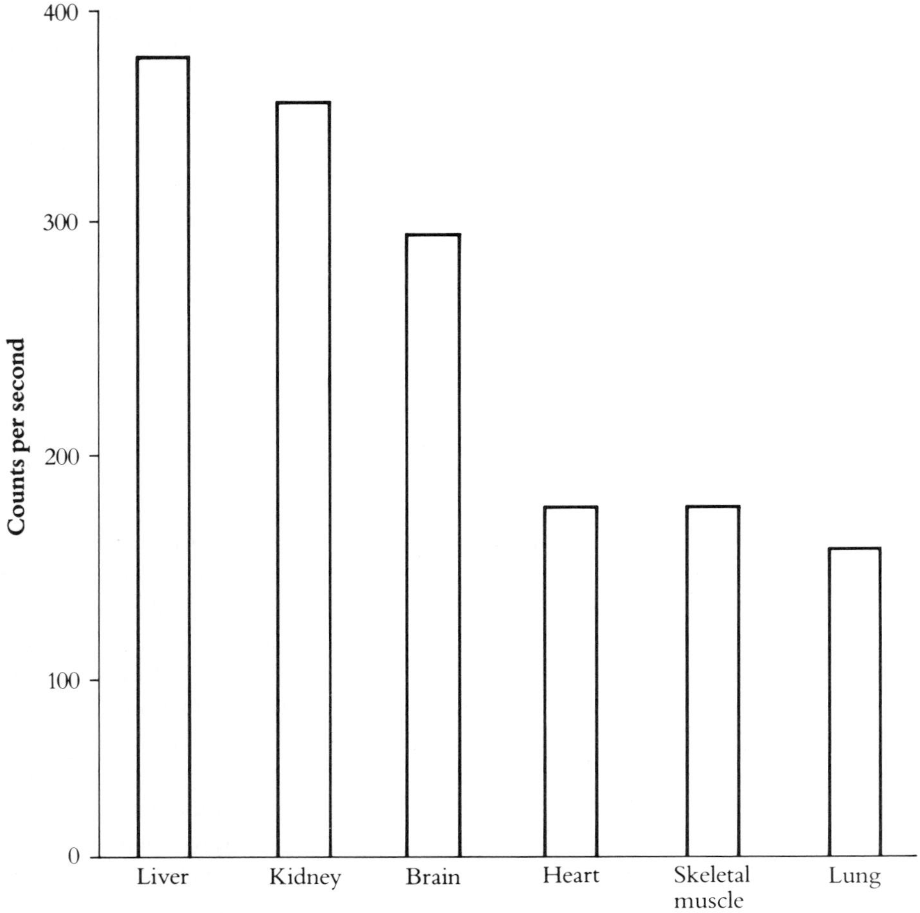

Figure 7.4 Light emission of mitochondrial preparations from six different rat organs. The peak amplitude was measured. Suspensions were adjusted to the same protein content (2 mg/3 ml). In all cases $[Fe^{2+}] = 6.67 \times 10^{-4}$.

concentration at mitochondrial sites.[12]* Of special interest is a clinical observation in support of our theory on facilitation of dioxygen transport. It has been ob-

*Our experiments indicate that oxygen-fixing sites involve unsaturated fatty acid chains of membrane lipids rather than cytochrome P-450 as suggested by these authors. We reject the "classical theory" and adopt a model essentially that of the "Bucket Brigade" by Scholander (*Science* 1960; 131: 585).

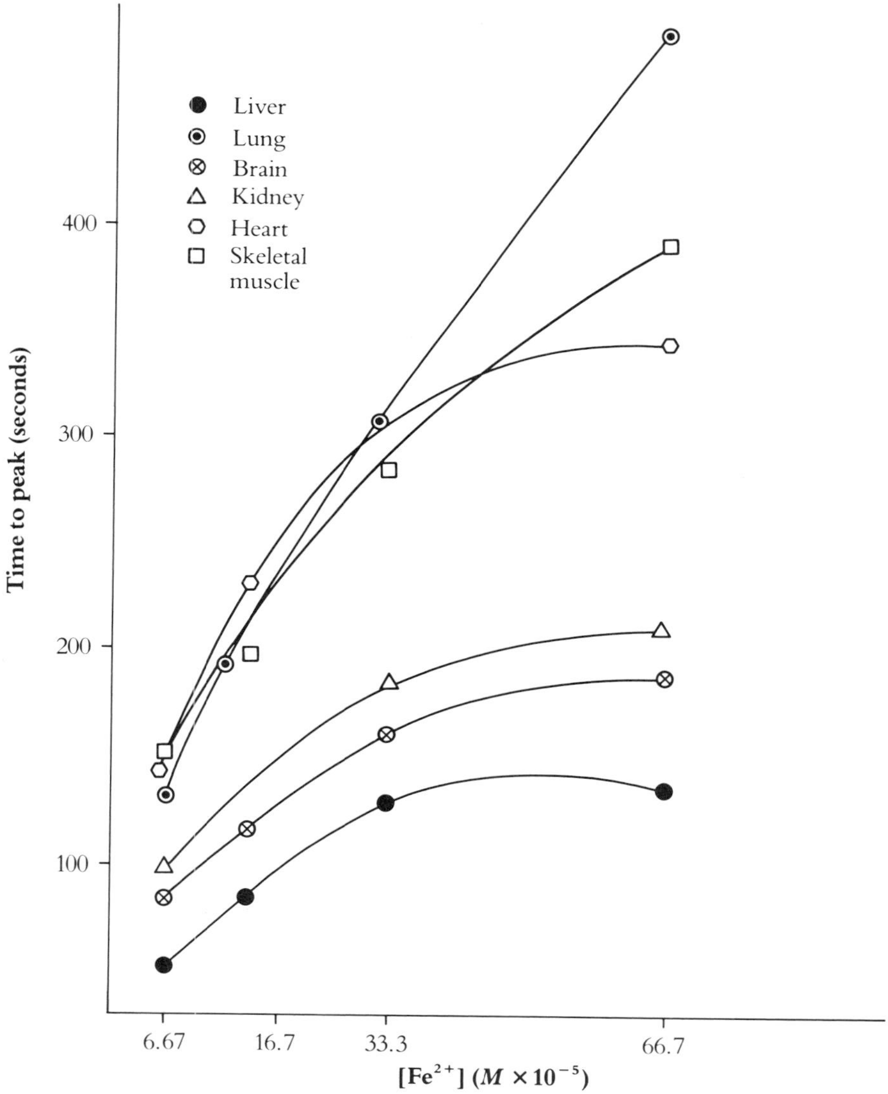

Figure 7.5 Light emission of mitochondrial preparations from six different organs. Suspensions were adjusted to the same protein content (2 mg/3 ml).

served[13] that hypoxia in coronary heart disease could be prevented by increase of EFA in tissues of individuals through an increase in dietary EFA. The link between EFA and prevention of hypoxia could be explained only by our theory.

A

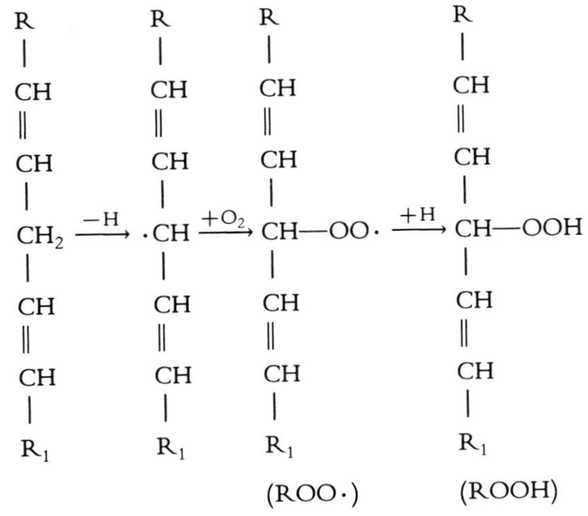

B $$ROOH + ROO\cdot \longrightarrow ROO^{+} + OH^{-} + RO\cdot$$

or in vitro

$$ROOH + Fe^{2+} \longrightarrow RO\cdot + OH^{-} + Fe^{3+}$$

Then, depending on availability of ROOH,

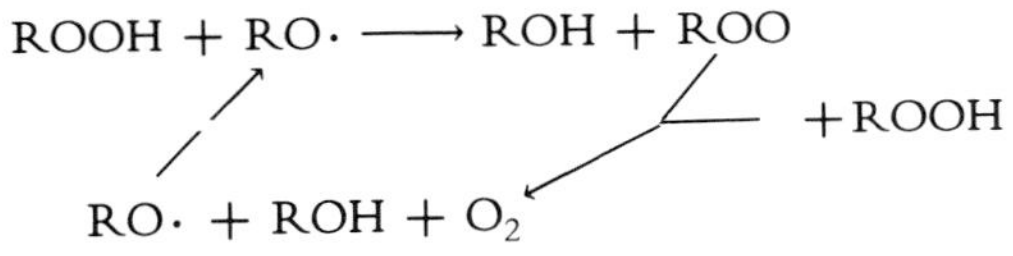

until [ROOH] decreases.

Figure 7.6 Reaction of molecular oxygen with essential fatty acids. (A) Formation of hydroperoxides. (B) Release of dioxygen from a hydroperoxide (ROOH) situated on methylene C, activated by the adjacent double bonds.

CONCLUSIONS

Our results can be summarized as follows:

1. The structure of cytomembranes in a tissue reflects the dioxygen level of this tissue.
2. Stage two of the dioxygen supply in mammals is a facilitated diffusion process.
3. This process is aided by essential fatty acids in what appears to be their basic role in mammals.

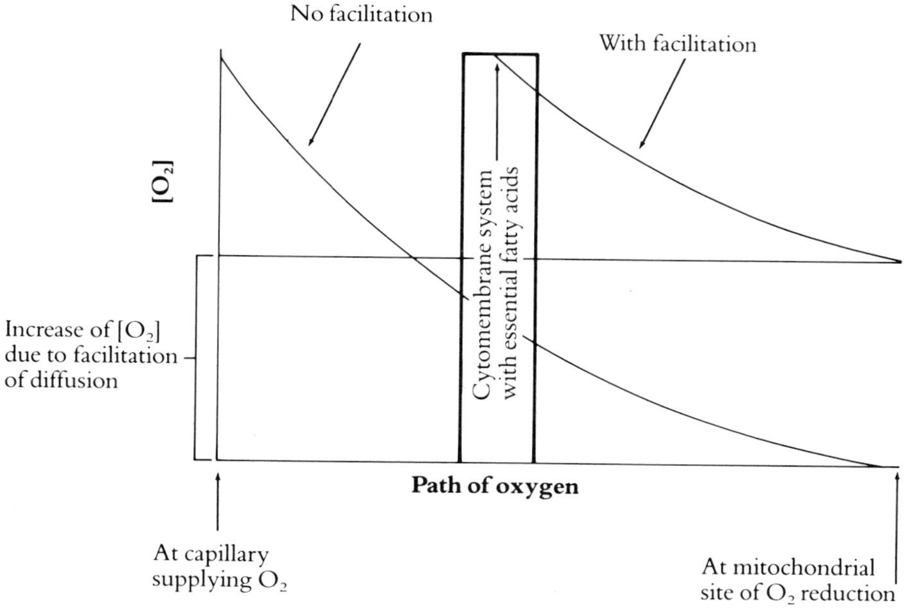

Figure 7.7 Biological role of facilitated diffusion of dioxygen aided by reversible binding of dioxygen by essential fatty acids, in the reaction of molecular oxygen with essential fatty acids.

In our studies on fatty acid peroxides using measurements of chemiluminescence and peroxide and dioxygen determinations, we made some remarkable observations. In addition to adjustment of dioxygen inflow into the cells, screening of the dioxygen species entering the cellular environment (singlet versus triplet oxygen), and participation in certain bioprocesses (metabolism of prostaglandins, hydroxylations, or regulation of the saturation level of biomembranes), essential fatty acyl residues maintain a *nascent surface of biomembranes.* Comparing, appropriately today, a surface of a cellular particulate material to a surface of a crystal, we should realize that reactivity of a crystal surface decreases as the surface "ages" through interactions among neighboring chemical groups. The basis of the continuity of cellular integrations is an ability of surfaces of the particulate systems of a cell to "rejuvenate": to be able to continue to interact with the cytosol. In this "rejuvenation" process, essential fatty acyls reacting with dioxygen seem to play a basic role. (As a corollary, one would predict that powerful antioxidants (e.g., BHT) would be harmful as well as unnecessary in living systems, as they would hinder interaction between EFAs and dioxygen.)

1. $[EFA] + [Fe^{2+}] \xrightarrow{K_1} [EFA\cdot] + [H] + [Fe^{3+}]$
   $K_1 = 0.1 \times 10^{-3}\ \mu M^{-1}\ s^{-1}$
2. $[EFA\cdot] + [O_2] \xrightarrow{K_2} [ROO\cdot]$
   $K_2 = 0.01\ \mu M^{-1}\ s^{-1}$
3. $[EFA\cdot] + [ROO\cdot] \xrightarrow{K_3} 2[ROOH] + h\nu$
   $K_3 = 0.18 \times 10^{-1}\ \mu M^{-1}\ s^{-1}$
4. $[ROO\cdot] + [ROO\cdot] \xrightarrow{K_4} 2[ROOH] + h\nu$
   $K_4 = 0.18 \times 10^{-1}\ \mu M^{-1}\ s^{-1}$
5. $[ROO\cdot] + [H] \xrightarrow{K_5} [ROOH]$
   $K_5 = 0.01\ \mu M^{-1}\ s^{-1}$
6. $[ROOH] + [Fe^{2+}] \xrightarrow{K_6} [RO\cdot] + [Fe^{3+}] + [OH^-]$
   $K_6 = 0.83 \times 10^{-3}\ \mu M^{-1}\ s^{-1}$
7. $[ROOH] + [RO\cdot] \xrightarrow{K_7} [ROH] + [ROO\cdot]$
   $K_7 = 0.005\ \mu M^{-1}\ s^{-1}$
8. $[ROOH] + [ROO\cdot] \xrightarrow{K_8} [ROH] + [O_2] + [RO\cdot]$
   $K_8 = 0.001\ \mu M^{-1}\ s^{-1}$
9. $[Fe^{2+}] + [O_2] + [H^+] \xrightarrow{K_9} [Fe^{3+}] + [HO_2\cdot]$
   $K_9 = 0.15 \times 10^{-13}\ \mu M^{-1}\ s^{-1}$
10. $[Fe^{2+}] + [EFA\cdot] \xrightarrow{K_{10}}$ RH complex
    $K_{10} \geq 0.02\ \mu M^{-1}\ s^{-1}$

Figure 7.8 Reactions in the interaction of essential fatty acids with molecular oxygen.

MATHEMATICAL APPENDIX

We devised a mathematical model of the chemiluminescent event to support our postulated mechanism of interaction of EFA with molecular oxygen. To do this we had to assume that the reactions listed in Figure 7.8 took place in our preparation.

The reaction rates used were approximated from available literature[14–16] and our own results. Using these 10 reactions and their reaction rates we wrote a set of governing differential equations to be solved simultaneously using simple Euler-Cauchy method and a digital computer (PDP-11).[16] The rate of light production was plotted over 15 minutes and the curve was similar in shape to those found experimentally.

The following initial conditions were used to solve the differential equations: we started with 74 μg and 21 μg of EFA per milligram of rat liver mitochondrial or microsomal protein, respectively. The initial oxygen concentration was taken to be 0.5 μmole in 3 ml.

Incremental concentrations of Fe^{2+} ranging from 0.2 μmole/ml to 4 μmole/ml were added to the suspension. The experiment was run for 15 minutes. The average molecular weight of EFA was assumed to be 287 daltons and that of the proteins to be 70,000 daltons.

The differential equations were derived as follows: according to the rate laws for the two reactions below with rate constants K_1 and K_2, we can write a rate of change for C as follows:

$$A + B \xrightarrow{K_1} C + D$$
$$C + E \xrightarrow{K_2} F + G$$
$$\frac{d[C]}{dt} = +K_1[A][B] - K_2[C][E]$$

In this equation [+] means production and [−] means usage of the chemical. Keeping the above in mind, we can write similar differential equations for the 10 reactions listed in Figure 7.8. We need to write the rate of changes for the reactants only. Therefore, we obtain the eight differential equations in Figure 7.9. Also following the same general rules one can write the rate of light production, d(hν)/dt, as

$$\frac{d(h\nu)}{dt} = K_3[EFA\cdot][ROO\cdot] + K_4[ROO\cdot]^2$$

These nine differential equations were solved simultaneously and numerically using simple Euler-Cauchy method.

1. $\dfrac{d[EFA]}{dt} = -K_1[EFA][Fe^{2+}]$
2. $\dfrac{d[O_2]}{dt} = -K_2[EFA][O_2] + K_8[ROOH][ROO\cdot] - K_9[Fe^{2+}][O_2]$
3. $\dfrac{d[Fe^{2+}]}{dt} = -K_1[EFA][Fe^{+2}] - K_6[ROOH][Fe^{2+}] - K_9[Fe^{2+}][O_2] - K_{10}[Fe^{2+}][EFA\cdot]$
4. $\dfrac{d[EFA\cdot]}{dt} = K_1[EFA][Fe^{+2}] - K_2[EFA\cdot][O_2] - K_3[EFA\cdot][ROO\cdot] - K_{10}[Fe^{2+}][EFA\cdot]$
5. $\dfrac{d[H]}{dt} = K_1[EFA][Fe^{2+}] - K_5[H][ROO\cdot]$
6. $\dfrac{d[ROO\cdot]}{dt} = K_2[EFA\cdot][O_2] + K_7[ROOH][RO\cdot] - K_3[EFA\cdot][ROO\cdot] - K_4[ROO\cdot]^2 - K_5[ROO\cdot][H] - K_8[ROOH][ROO\cdot]$
7. $\dfrac{d[ROOH]}{dt} = 2K_3[EFA\cdot][ROO\cdot] + 2K_4[ROO\cdot]^2 + K_5[ROO\cdot][H] - K_6[ROOH][Fe^{2+}] - K_7[ROOH][RO\cdot] - K_8[ROOH][ROO\cdot]$
8. $\dfrac{d[RO\cdot]}{dt} = K_6[ROOH][Fe^{2+}] - K_7[ROOH][RO\cdot] + K_8[ROOH][ROO\cdot]$

Figure 7.9 Differential equations for the reactions listed in Figure 7.8.

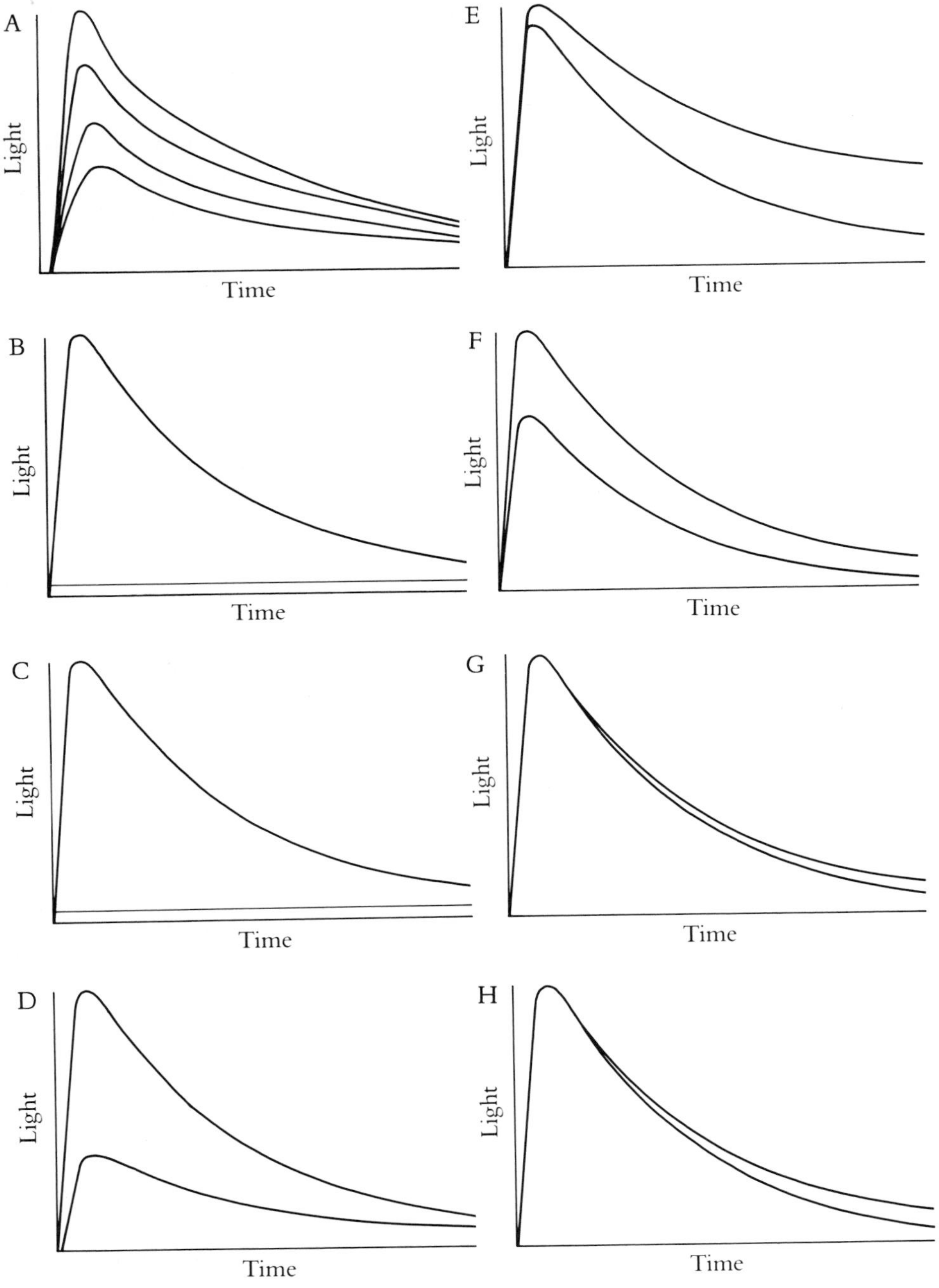
A
Light
Time
E
Light
Time
B
Light
Time
F
Light
Time
C
Light
Time
G
Light
Time
D
Light
Time
H
Light
Time

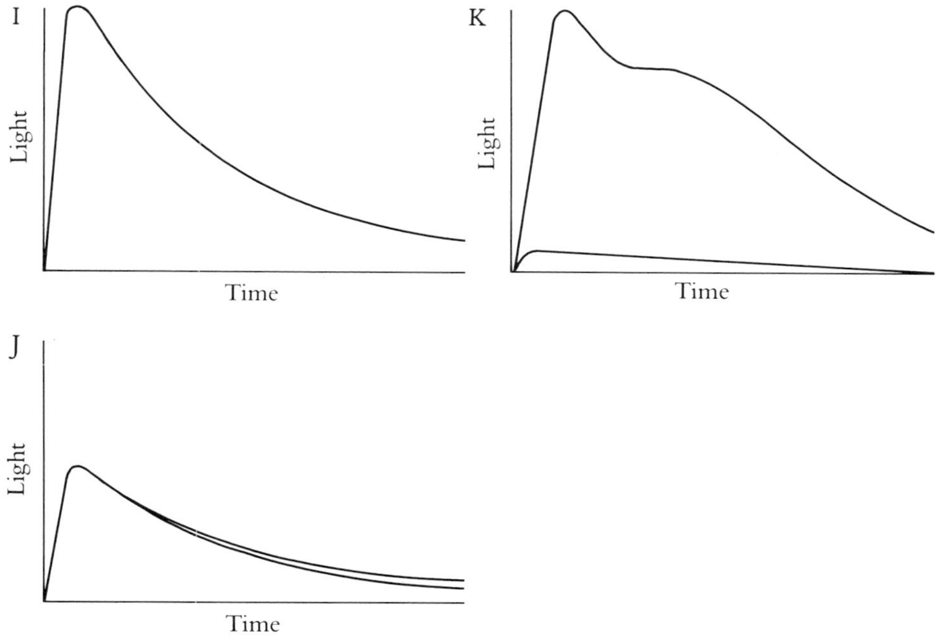

Figure 7.10 Graphic representation (tracings of computer printouts) of results of mathematical modeling. For explanation see text. Reference curves are included on some of the graphs.

The graphic presentation of the mathematical modeling results gives figures that agree with the experimental data. Plotting rate of light production as a function of time for four different concentrations of Fe^{2+} shows that the increase of Fe^{2+} in the mixture causes a decrease in time to peak, a higher peak value, and a faster decay in the depletion period (Figure 7.10A, family of curves).

The subsequent graphs (Figure 7.10B–K) show effects of each of the 10 reactions considered (Figure 7.8) on the rate of light production. As seen on Figure 7.10B, C (lower lines) there is no light production without the first two reactions present. The third reaction affects the peak and decay in the depletion period, as seen on Figure 7.10D (lower curve). In Figure 7.10E (upper curve), the effect of the fourth reaction is shown. This reaction increases both time to peak and peak value; a slight change in decay is also noted. The effect of the fifth reaction is to decrease the time to peak and the peak value itself. The depletion period is also smaller. This is obvious in Figure 7.10F (lower curve). The sixth and seventh reactions slow down slightly the decay of the rate of light production (Figure 7.10G, H; lower curves).

The eighth reaction does not significantly change the shape of the light production curve (Figure 7.10I). The ninth reaction leads to a slightly faster decay and a lower peak of light production (Figure 7.10J).

With the tenth reaction absent, the shape of the light production curve is completely different (Figure 7.10K). The curve peaks and then returns to a lower plateau, which is sustained for a few seconds and then starts to decay. This phenomenon has been observed with high concentrations of Fe^{2+}.

REFERENCES

1. Meduski JW: The ascorbic acid and glutathione content of the livers of rats with sarcomata induced by 1,2:5,6-dibenzanthracene. *Br J Can* 1949; 3: 559.

2. Thacher HC Jr: Unstable chemical species, free radicals, ions, and excited molecules. *Ann NY Acad Sci* 1957; 67: 447–670.

3. Slater TF: *Free Radical Mechanisms in Tissue Injury.* London, Pion, 1972.

4. Zachariasse KA: *Chemiluminescence from Radical Ion Recombination.* Amsterdam, Holland, Vrije Universiteiet te Amsterdam, 1972.

5. Stauff J, Lohmann F: Chemiluminescence specra of several inorganic oxidation reactions. (Germ.) *Z Physikal Chem NF* 1964; 40: 123–126.

6. Meduski JW, Abbott BC, Wen SC, et al.: Investigations of membrane lipid peroxides through ultraweak chemiluminescence. Proceedings of the Pacific Slope Biochemistry Conference, Riverside, Univ. of Calif. Press, 1974, p 34.

7. Meduski JD, Meduski JW, De La Rosa J: A novel mixing apparatus for studies of chemiluminescent reactions, in DeLuca MA, McElroy WD (eds): *Bioluminescence and Chemiluminescence.* New York, Academic, 1981, pp 715–719.

8. Meduski JW, Abbott BC, Wen SC, et al.: Oxygen and the ultraweak chemiluminescence of biomembranes of the rat. *Biophysical J,* 1975; 15: 2.

9. Meduski JW, Abbott BC, Wen SC, et al.: Role of mammalian cytomembranes in the intracellular availability of oxygen. Presented at the Tenth International Congress of Biochemistry. Hamburg, Germany, July 25–61, 1976.

10. Meduski JW, Abbott BC, Meduski JD: Physiological aspects of the differences in the ability of mammalian cytomembranes to interact with molecular oxygen. *Federation Proc* 1977; 26.

11. Schuchhardt S: Comparative physiology of the oxygen supply, in Kessler M, Bruley DF, Clark LC Jr, et al. (eds): *Oxygen Supply.* Baltimore, University Park Press, 1973, pp 223–229.

12. Longmuir IS, Sun S, Soucie W: Possible role of cytochrome P-450 as a tissue oxygen carrier, in King TE, Mason HS, Morrison M (eds): *Oxidases and Related Redox Systems,* Proc 2nd International Symp (vol 2). Baltimore, University Park Press, 1973, pp 451–461.

13. Turpeinen O: Role of diet in the primary prevention of coronary heart disease. *Adv Exp Med Biol,* 1972; 26: 207–211.

14. Vladimirov YA, Gutenev PI, Kuznetsov PI: Mathematical modeling of chain oxidation kinetics of biomembrane lipids in the presence of iron (2+) ions. *Biofizika* 1973; 18(6): 1024–1030.

15. Anbar M, Neta P: A compilation of specific biomolecular rate constants for reactions of hydrated electrons, hydrogen atoms, and hydroxyl radicals with inorganic and organic compounds in aqueous solution. *Int J Appl Radiat Isot* 1967; 18(7): 493–523.

16. Kochi J. (ed): *Free Radicals* (vol 1). New York, Wiley-Interscience, 1973, p 628.

17. Kreyszig E: *Advanced Engineering Mathematics,* 4th ed. New York, Wiley, 1979, pp 792–798.

18. Vladimirov YA, Archakov AI: *Perekisnoe Okislenie Lipidov Biologicheskikh Membranakh (Peroxidative Oxidation of Lipids in Biological Membranes).* Moscow, Nauka, 1972.

PART II

NUTRITION AND HEALTH

CHAPTER EIGHT

VITAMIN C AND CANCER CACHEXIA: THE CARNITINE CONNECTION

EWAN CAMERON, MB, ChB, FRCS (Glas), FRCS (Edinb)

Lassitude, weariness, muscle fatigue, exhaustion, and apathy are the classic prodromal symptoms of scurvy, as recounted in all historical writings on the subject. We read, again and again, of entire crews being so prostrated by loss of energy that they cannot man their ships, all prior to the appearance of flagrant scurvy. Such symptoms to a greater or lesser degree are also the dominant features of cancer cachexia, and are even more pronounced in what I have termed the "cancer plus cancer-treatment syndrome." This describes the all-too-familiar clinical picture of the listless, exhausted patient who has endured not only cancer itself, but the stress of major surgery, perhaps followed by heavy radiation or prolonged courses of toxic chemotherapy.

Individuals suffering from prescurvy or cancer have at least one important biochemical feature in common: both groups have significantly depressed levels of tissue and circulating ascorbate. Our own studies in Scotland have confirmed that, even at diagnosis before treatment has been instituted, cancer patients have significantly lower ascorbate reserves than noncancerous hospital admissions drawn from the same general population (Table 8.1). There are not enough estimations to present them in tabular form, but our scattered data indicate that the assaults of major surgery, radiation, and chemotherapy—individually or sequentially—deplete the already diminished ascorbate levels even further. Thus, many patients with the "cancer plus cancer-treatment syndrome" have values well within the scorbutic range. I have explained elsewhere why such patients never develop the flagrant manifestations of classic scurvy.[1]

"I feel so much better, doctor, so much stronger!" Many of my cancer patients have made this type of remark spontaneously, 5 to 7 days after supplemental ascorbate intake began, and continued to repeat it regularly throughout the remaining

Table 8.1 Comparison of plasma and leukocyte ascorbate levels in nonwasted cancer patients at diagnosis, and the levels found in routine surgical admissions without malignant disease

Category	No. of subjects	Estimation	Mean values	Standard deviation	Maximum recorded	Minimum recorded
Hospital patients without cancer	166	PAA*	0.529	0.376	1.87	0.00
		LAA†	24.573	10.636	53.70	7.00
Noncachectic cancer patients at diagnosis	117	PAA	0.348	0.285	1.66	0.00
		LAA	14.778	7.364	37.00	0.00

*PAA = plasma ascorbate in mg/dl (noncancer/cancer $p < 0.0001$)
†LAA = leukocyte ascorbate in $\mu g/10^8$ WBC (noncancer/cancer $p < 0.0001$)
From: Cameron E, Sheen M: Some observations on ascorbate metabolism in cancer patients. In press.

weeks, months, or years of their illness. Indeed, a few of my advanced cancer patients receiving ascorbate supplementation assumed levels of physical activity they would not have even considered before their cancers were diagnosed and that were quite unbelievable considering the advanced stage of their illness. I can clearly recall three remarkable examples: (1) the working engineer in his late fifties (with multiple skeletal metastases from renal adenocarcinoma) who managed to reduce his golf handicap by two strokes, through assiduous practice evenings and weekends; (2) the retired schoolteacher in his midsixties (with both hepatic and pulmonary metastases from colonic cancer) who took up jogging for the first time; and (3) the retired railway stationmaster then in his seventies (with disseminated pancreatic cancer) energetically splitting logs for friends and neighbors, including my own household.

Although such responses are gratifying to the attending physician, until now I could offer no explanation for such apparently remarkable improvements in vigor, energy, and general well-being. Indeed, in our ascorbate/cancer publications of the last decade, Dr. Pauling and I have never focused attention on the likes of our trio of golfer, jogger, and log-splitter, for fear of attracting incredulity that might damage our credibility. It must be emphasized that that remarkable trio showed a quite exceptional response to supplemental ascorbate; nevertheless, the great majority of my cancer patients on ascorbate experienced some degree of improvement in physical strength and well-being. Almost paradoxically, this symptomatic response seemed increased in those with the more advanced disease. This welcome therapeutic response surely had a biochemical explanation.

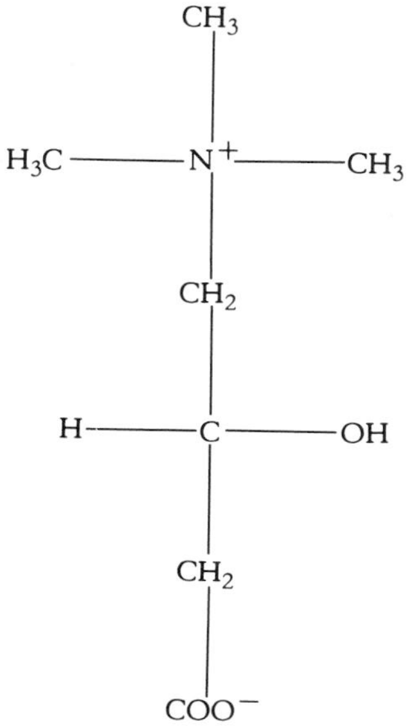

Figure 8.1 Chemical structure of carnitine.

CARNITINE, AN ESSENTIAL CARRIER MOLECULE

The answer lies in the molecule carnitine, as revealed in the important work being carried out by Dr. R. Emlyn Hughes in the Department of Nutritional Biochemistry at the University of Wales Institute of Science and Technology, in Cardiff.[2]

"I feel so much better, doctor, so much stronger!" Many of my cancer patients have made this type of remark spontaneously, 5 to 7 days after supplemental ascorbate intake began, and continued to repeat it regularly throughout the remaining

Carnitine [β-hydroxy-γ-(trimethylamino) butyric acid] has the chemical structure shown in Figure 8.1. It is widely distributed throughout all muscular tissues, including cardiac muscle. Its main function, indeed probably its only function, is to act as a carrier molecule essential to transport the long-chain fatty acids through the mitochondrial inner membrane into the mitochondria, where they are oxidized to provide energy.[3] This mechanism of mitochondrial long-chain fatty-acid oxidation is the major source of muscle energy requirements.[4, 5]

It has been estimated that about one-fifth of the daily human carnitine requirement is obtained from the diet, particularly from red meat. The other four-fifths of the daily requirement are synthesized endogenously in the liver.[6, 7]

The crucial breakthrough in our own clinical observations came with the discovery by Hughes[2] that ascorbate is an essential cofactor for the biosynthesis of carnitine in mammals, as had earlier been demonstrated in molds by Horne and

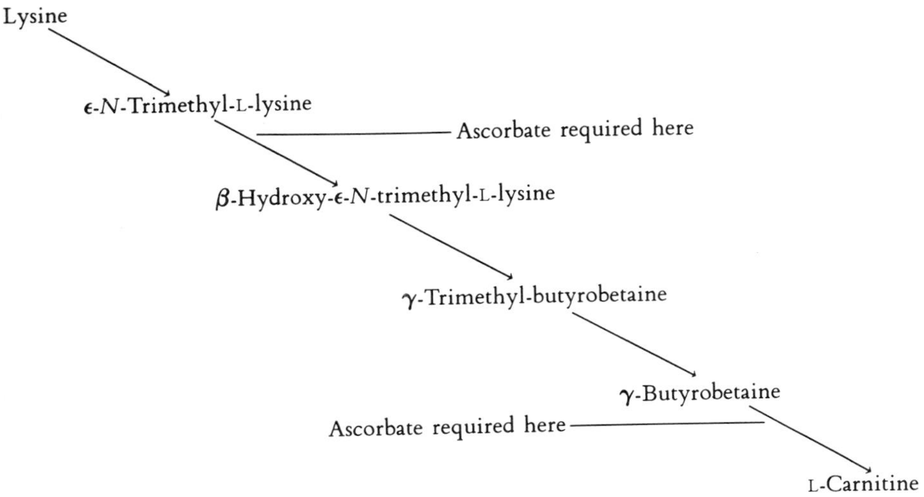

Figure 8.2 Conversion of lysine to L-carnitine involves at least two steps for which ascorbate is an essential cofactor.

Broquist.[8] According to Hughes, the biosynthesis of carnitine from its precursors lysine or methionine involves, among others, two essential hydroxylation steps (the conversion of ε-*N*-trimethyl-L-lysine to β-hydroxy-ε-*N*-trimethyl-L-lysine, and the conversion of γ-butyrobetaine to L-carnitine), with ascorbate as the essential cofactor for both steps (Figure 8.2). Thus we have a biochemical pathway that accounts for the finding that a shortage of ascorbate would result in diminished carnitine biosynthesis, producing in time symptoms of progressive muscle weakness, lassitude, and fatigue, with loss of weight from muscle atrophy due to disuse.

THE WORK OF HUGHES

As Hughes points out in his excellent review,[2] the latter symptoms were precisely those recognized as warning prodromal symptoms in all the classic historical writings about scurvy. His conclusion that such symptoms were due to diminished carnitine synthesis (and hence to reduced muscle carnitine and a progressive reduction in the ability of muscle tissue to oxidize fatty acids for energy) seems unarguable. To prove his thesis, he studied two groups of guinea pigs, one given enough dietary ascorbate to maintain tissue saturation, the other on an ascorbate-restricted diet so as to maintain only 12 percent saturation. It should be noted that the latter degree of restriction did not produce such evidence of scurvy as failure to thrive, renal hypertrophy, skin changes, or hemorrhagic tendencies. At sacrifice, the carnitine content of the muscles of the animals of the restricted group was less than half the concentration found in the controls.

Hughes pointed out that current Recommended Daily Allowance levels for ascorbate (determined by one experiment on a small group of volunteers conducted more than 25 years ago[9]) are sufficient to protect the great majority of the population against scurvy. Nevertheless he concluded that the optimal level may be much greater, and that many of the population at large may be in a state of chronic fatigue because of suboptimal intakes of ascorbate leading to suboptimal biosynthesis of carnitine.

CLINICAL SIGNIFICANCE

The significance of all this exciting new work to the listless, apathetic, dying cancer patient is clear. It has long been established that cancer patients, especially those with advanced disease, and particularly those who have or are enduring the "cancer plus cancer-treatment syndrome," have low levels of tissue and circulating ascorbate. (Note the large standard deviations in Table 8.1 indicating that, even at diagnosis, many cancer patients have extremely low plasma and leukocyte ascorbate levels, the latter taken to be a measure of tissue saturation.)

A valid assumption is that such cancer patients must also have a significantly depressed rate of carnitine synthesis, which would account for such features of cancer cachexia as listlessness, weariness, lassitude, undue fatigue on little exertion, general malaise, and weight loss from muscle atrophy. It is tempting to speculate that the only other major feature of cancer cachexia, nausea and anorexia often associated with troublesome constipation, could be due to reduced gastrointestinal peristalsis for the same biochemical reason.

The ascorbate-carnitine connection would also account for the dramatic improvement in vigor and well-being many cancer patients claim to experience soon after commencing supplemental ascorbate therapy. This simple form of nutritional support is presumably restoring carnitine-depleted muscles to normal energy and strength.

My colleagues and I at the Linus Pauling Institute for Science and Medicine are about to embark on a series of studies on carnitine metabolism. Having perfected a method of measuring serum carnitine levels, my colleague Dr. Constance Tsao will carry out estimations on samples obtained from a group of cancer patients, and will repeat these estimations at intervals after ascorbate supplementation has been initiated. We anticipate being able to show initially depleted carnitine values being rapidly restored to the "normal" range.

Just as exciting will be an attempt to define exactly the normal range of serum carnitine values, not in the sense of the average range found in the population at large, but rather in the sense of the maximum or optimal levels that can be obtained in healthy people by ascorbate supplementation. As Dr. Pauling points out, many healthy individuals, including himself, experience a sense of increased vigor soon after commencing supplemental ascorbate in the several-gram-each-day range. We plan to study a group of healthy student volunteers and have them ingest increasing daily doses of ascorbate while we monitor their serum carnitine levels. By this approach, we hope to be able to determine the optimal daily intake of ascorbate as indicated by the maximum biosynthesis of carnitine. We are confident that the value will lie well above the official RDA. If our expectations are fulfilled, our findings could have important implications for maximizing good health. For instance, if the differences are great, this finding would have immediate application in improving athletic performance.

Dr. Pauling has suggested that the improved sense of well-being induced by ascorbate in so many cancer patients might be enhanced by furnishing them with supplemental lysine, the carnitine precursor. Dr. Emile Zuckerkandl has speculated that the improved sense of well-being and increased survival time, which we have reported as being the principal effects of ascorbate in cancer patients, may not be separate effects after all; in other words, he suggests that these cancer patients live longer because they feel stronger and indeed are physically stronger as a result of this clearly defined biochemical pathway. These and other suggestions will be studied.

The importance of the lysine-ascorbate-carnitine axis in long-chain fatty acid oxidation has important implications in cardiovascular disease, as well as in cancer. If these fatty acids are not being oxidized at a "normal" rate, it seems likely that they will accumulate in the tissues and the bloodstream; this could explain the hyperlipidemia associated with vitamin C deficiency and the documented success of pharmacological dosages of ascorbate in lowering serum triglycerides.[10] Clinical studies have shown that the administration of carnitine is a valuable therapy for patients with myocardial infarction and ischemic heart disease in whom it improves myocardial contractile efficiency.[11, 12] Presumably, supplemental ascorbate would have a similar (if somewhat delayed) effect by stimulating the biosynthesis of carnitine.

CONCLUSION

To conclude, the milestone discovery by Hughes that ascorbate is an essential cofactor for the biosynthesis of carnitine has important implications for the practice of orthomolecular medicine. We now have a rational explanation for a variety of medical observations, well enough documented, but until now not clearly understood. Observations such as the relief of the severe fatigue experienced as a prodrome to scurvy by ascorbate ingestion and the reversal of symptoms and signs of cancer cachexia by supplemental ascorbate can now be potentially explained. The discovery also provides a rationale for ascorbate in cardiovascular disease, both for reducing serum triglycerides and protecting the muscle of the ischemic heart against cardiogenic shock and arrhythmias. It also explains why many people on inadequate intakes of ascorbate (albeit well above the RDA levels) experience vague ill health and chronic fatigue, and why there is a tonic effect on well-being and vigor enjoyed by even healthy people when ascorbate supplementation is commenced and maintained. It may even offer a simple method of maximizing athletic performance.

Studies on carnitine metabolism, about to commence at the Linus Pauling Institute of Science and Medicine, will explore the many ramifications of this fascinating connection, and may help us to determine, once and for all, the optimal level of ascorbate intake in both health and disease.

REFERENCES

1. Cameron E: Biological function of ascorbic acid and the pathogenesis of scurvy. *Med Hypothesis* 1976; 2: 154–163.

2. Hughes RE: Recommended daily amounts and biochemical roles—the vitamin C, carnitine, fatigue relationship, in Counsell JN, Hornig DH (eds): *Vitamin C (Ascorbic Acid).* London and New Jersey, Applied Science Publishers, 1981, pp 75–86.

3. Bremer J: Carnitine and its role in fatty acid metabolism. *Trends Biochem Sci* 1977; 2: 207.

4. Cederblad G, Bylund AC, Holm J, et al.: Carnitine concentration in relation to enzyme activities and substrate utilization in human skeletal muscles. *Scand J Clin Lab Invest* 1976; 36: 547–552.

5. Borum PR: Variations in tissue carnitine concentrations with age and sex in the rat. *Biochem J* 1978; 176: 677–681.

6. Cederblad G, Lindsted S: Metabolism of labeled carnitine in the rat. *Arch Biochem Biophys* 1976; 175: 173.

7. Karpati G, Carpenter S, Engel AG, et al.: The syndrome of systemic carnitine deficiency. *Neurology* 1975; 25: 16–24.

8. Horne DW, Broquist HP: Role of lysine and ϵ-*N*-trimethyllysine in carnitine biosynthesis. 1. Studies in *Neurospora crassa. J Biol Chem* 1973; 248: 2170–2176.

9. Bartley W, Krebs HA, O'Brien JRP: Vitamin C requirements of human adults. *Medical Research Council Special Report Series No. 280.* HMSO, London, 1953.

10. Ginter E: Marginal vitamin C deficiency, lipid metabolism, and atherogenesis. *Advanc Lipid Res* 1978; 16: 167–220.

11. Thomsen JH, Shug AL, Yap VU, et al.: Improved pacing tolerance of the ischemic human myocardium after administration of carnitine. *Am J Cardiol* 1979; 43: 300–306.

12. Opie LH: Role of carnitine in fatty acid metabolism of normal and ischemic myocardium. *Am Heart J* 1979; 97: 375–388.

CHAPTER NINE

NITRITES, NITROSAMINES, AND VITAMIN C

MELVIN GREENBLATT, MD, FCAP

It is a great honor and pleasure to dedicate this brief account of the relationship of nitrosamines and vitamin C to Dr. Linus Pauling.

It would seem unlikely that any medically important relationship might exist between a class of chemical carcinogens and an antiscorbutic vitamin. Yet, like many chance discoveries, the relationship between nitrosamines, some of which have carcinogenic potential, and vitamin C has engendered one of the most fruitful lines of inquiry in nutritional carcinogenesis research. This short, primarily historical account will summarize some of the highlights of this fascinating story.

CHEMISTRY

Nitrosamines have the general chemical structure

$$R_2N—N=O$$

in which the R (organic) group can be any of a variety of aliphatic, aromatic, or complex organic structures. They are formed in nature and in the laboratory by the combination of nitrous acid (HNO_2) and an amine (R—NH) through a relatively simple chemical reaction involving a nitrous anhydride intermediary:

$$2HNO_2 \rightleftharpoons N_2O_3 + H_2O$$
$$R_2NH + N_2O_3 \rightarrow R_2N—N=O + HNO_2$$

The reaction is pH-dependent with respect to secondary amines, and is further influenced by the basicity of the amine. Strongly basic amines nitrosate less readily. The optimum pH for nitrosation of most secondary amines is 2.5 to 3.5, which translates to hydrogen ion concentrations similar to those in the human stomach. The rate is also influenced by the concentration of the nitrite ion, as in the following equation:

$$\text{Rate} = K[R_2NH][HNO_2]^2$$

Note that the rate of the reaction increases as the square of the nitrite concentration. This fact has important implications when considering the permissible limits of nitrite in food, such as preserved meats. Tertiary amines react more slowly and they are active at higher pH levels, even in basic solutions.[1] It is noteworthy that many therapeutic drugs and agricultural and industrial chemicals are amines.

Nitrosation of amines is further influenced by various chemicals that may retard, accelerate, or even substitute for some of the reactants in the nitrosation reaction. For example, some nitroso compounds, in themselves not carcinogenic (i.e., nitrosohemoglobin or nitrosomyoglobin found in preserved meats), may split off their own nitroso group for transformation of other amines into carcinogenic nitroso compounds. This phenomenon has been called transnitrosation.

HISTORICAL PERSPECTIVE

Nitrosamines, as chemicals, have been known for about 100 years. Magee and Barnes in 1956,[2] reacting to reports of hepatic toxicity in automobile workers using dimethylnitrosamine as a solvent, studied its effect in rat-feeding experiments. They noted malignant tumors (hepatocarcinomas) in rats receiving this compound in their diet. Druckrey et al.[3] soon extended this work to include other types of nitrosamines and other species. They also explored the relationship of chemical structure to carcinogenicity.

Nevertheless, before 1968, nitrosamines were "laboratory carcinogens." They were useful in studying important basic carcinogenic mechanisms but they seemed irrelevant to human carcinogenesis except in restricted industrial situations.

In 1968 a young doctoral student, Johannes Sander,[4] and his collaborators at the University of Tübingen reported that nitrosamines were formed in the stomach of rats fed a mixture of secondary amines and nitrite, and led to development of malignant tumors. His observations were shortly confirmed and extended by Greenblatt et al.,[5] and the significance of the new finding to human carcinogenesis was emphasized by Lijinsky and Epstein.[6]

Since that time the role of nitrosamines as potentially significant human carcinogens has become increasingly apparent. Not only have nitrosamines been identified in processed foods and other ingested or inhaled substances, but there is further evidence for their formation in vivo. That nitrosamines cause colon and urinary bladder cancer in man is suggested by their formation under laboratory conditions similar to those in these organs. Considerable epidemiological evidence indicates the association of nitrite in the diet with the occurrence of gastric and esophageal cancer.[7]

Montesano and Magee[8] demonstrated similar patterns of nitrosamine metabolism in human liver samples and rat liver. Later, Ohshima and Bartsch,[9] using a brilliant experimental model, conclusively demonstrated nitrosamine formation in man and abolition of the reaction by ascorbic acid. It is not surprising that nitrosamine studies have dominated the field of chemical carcinogenesis for the last 15 years.[10]

ASCORBIC ACID AND NITROSAMINES

The observation that ascorbic acid prevented nitrosation of amines was made serendipitously by a chemist, Dr. Larry Wallcave, at the Eppley Institute in Omaha in 1969. In evaluating the nitrosation of oxytetracycline (Terramycin®) he noted that nitrosation occurred when pure analytical grade oxytetracycline was used as the substrate but did not occur when Terramycin® capsules obtained from the hospital pharmacy were substituted. It was learned that ascorbic acid was added to the capsules as an antioxidant by the manufacturer. Further studies showed that ascorbic acid inhibited the nitrosation. This astute observation became the basis for the studies of Mirvish et al.,[11] Greenblatt,[12] and others, showing that ascorbic acid inhibited or abolished nitrosation of amines both in vitro and in various animal systems, including man.

Ascorbic acid blocks nitrosation by competing for nitrite ion. Tannic acid, glutathione, and vitamin E act similarly, although the concentrations of these compounds required approach toxic levels in some cases.

Ascorbic acid is now added to bacon to prevent the formation of nitrosopyrrolidine during cooking. Its use may increase in the field of food technology. Isoascorbic acid, a vitamin C isomer, acts similarly to vitamin C and has the added advantage of producing a pink color in processed meat.

SUMMARY

After many years of use as laboratory carcinogens without apparent bearing to human tumorigenesis, nitrosamines were catapulted into the main stream of experimental carcinogenesis only 15 years ago by the demonstration that these powerful carcinogens could be produced in vivo by the interaction of nitrites and amines, both common chemicals in the human environment. Tumors produced by nitrosamines paralleled those found in man with respect to organ localization and histologic appearance. Nitrosamines were strong carcinogens in all species tested. Epidemiological studies, particularly with human gastric and esophageal carcinoma, demonstrated correlations between environmental levels of nitrites and gastric and esophageal cancer. Finally, ascorbic acid (vitamin C) was found to prevent effectively the formation of these carcinogens.

REFERENCES

1. Mirvish SS: Formation of N-nitroso compounds: chemistry, kinetics and in vivo occurrence. *Toxicol Appl Pharmacol* 1975; 31: 325–351.

2. Magee PN, Barnes JM: The production of malignant primary tumours in the rat by feeding dimethylnitrosamine. *Br J Canc* 1956; 10: 114–117.

3. Druckrey H, Preussmann R, Ivankovic S, et al.: Organotrope carcinogene Wirkungen bei 65 verscheidenen N-Nitroso Verbindungen an BD-ratten. *Z Krebsforsch* 1967; 69: 103.

4. Sander J, Burkle G: Induktion maligner Tumoren bei Ratten durch gleichzeitige von Nitrit und secondaren Aminen. *Z Krebsforsch* 1969; 73: 54.

5. Greenblatt M, Mirvish SS, So BT: Nitrosamine studies: induction of lung adenomas by concurrent administration of sodium nitrite and secondary amines in Swiss mice. *J Nat Canc Inst* 1971; 46: 1029–1034.

6. Lijinsky W, Epstein SS: Nitrosamines as environmental carcinogens. *Nature* 1970; 225: 21–23.

7. Zaldivar R, Robinson H: Epidemiologic investigation on stomach cancer in Chileans: association with nitrate fertilizer. *Z Krebsforsch* 1973; 80: 289–295.

8. Montesano R, Magee P: Evidence of formation of N-methyl N-nitrosourea in rats given N-methylurea and sodium nitrite. *Int J Canc* 1971; 7: 249–255.

9. Ohshima H, Bartsch H: Quantitative estimation of endogenous nitrosation in humans by monitoring N-nitrosoproline excreted in the urine. *Canc Res* 1981; 41: 3658–3661.

10. National Academy of Sciences: *The Health Effects of Nitrate, Nitrite and N-Nitroso Compounds.* Washington DC, National Academy Press, 1981.

11. Mirvish SS, Wallcave L, Eagen M, et al.: Ascorbate-nitrite reaction: possible means of blocking the formation of carcinogenic N-nitroso compounds. *Science* 1972; 177: 65–68.

12. Greenblatt M: Ascorbic acid blocking of aminopyrine nitrosation in NZO/Bl mice. *J Nat Canc Inst.* 1973; 50: 1055–1056.

CHAPTER TEN

NUTRIENTS AND THE IMMUNE SYSTEM

MICHAEL ROSENBAUM, MD

In recent years, there has been a surge of interest in immunology among physicians and scientists. The role of nutrition in the immune response has been investigated for about 60 years. For the first 30 years or so, the literature in this field focused on protein metabolism, including the nutrient cofactors that are associated with protein synthesis, such as zinc, pyridoxine, folic acid, and vitamin A. Subsequently, there was a vacuum in substantive research in this area of nutrition from 1950 to about 1970. A decade ago, Linus Pauling asserted the efficacy of vitamin C in the treatment of the common head cold. His efforts stimulated several studies on the role of ascorbate in immune functions. Since that time, it has been demonstrated that other nutrients have effects on immune functions, including the antioxidants vitamin E, selenium, and beta-carotene, and lipids such as cholesterol, unsaturated fatty acids, and vitamin D.

The literature in this field is expanding rapidly. Several comprehensive review articles on nutrition and its role in immunity have appeared in major journals since 1980. The most ambitious of these reviews was published in the *American Journal of Clinical Nutrition* in 1982 and contained almost 400 references.[1] R. K. Chandra, MD, one of the current leaders in this field, published in 1980 a volume entitled *Immunology and Nutritional Disorders.*[2] In this treatise, Chandra stated: "On a global scale, undernutrition is the most frequent cause of immunodeficiency."

Another pioneer in this field is Dr. Robert A. Good, recently of the Memorial Sloan-Kettering Cancer Center in New York. Dr. Good has stated that "Nutritional factors can exert profound influences on immunity functions and immuno-regulatory mechanisms in mice and rats. . . . We are optimistic that such factors can be exploited and applied to the prevention of diseases of aging and to greatly prolong health in humans."[3]

The immune system is sensitive to the effects of malnutrition. Even subclinical malnutrition may cause pathological changes in immune function, leading Chandra to assert that quantitative measures of immunocompetence may serve as potent indices of nutritional assessment. "The thymus and other lymphoid tissues react to nutritional deficits more rapidly than do most other organs. Nutritional recovery is associated with a gradual return of the thymus histology to normal."[4]

This sensitivity to nutrient flux is understandable, because the immune system is dynamic, and has a rapid turnover. The bone marrow—the source of all immune progenitor cells—weighs about 6 pounds in humans. Approximately 10^{10} neutrophils are released by the bone marrow daily. This remarkable daily production holds true for eosinophils and lymphocytes as well. Therefore, the bone marrow responds very sensitively to nutrient deficiency. The converse is also true. When severely malnourished humans are fed adequately, the immune system may restore itself faster than any other organ system in the body. For example, before any other clinical signs of improvement appear, a formerly low number of T-lymphocyte cells may be restored to the normal range. However, if malnutrition occurs in utero or in early infancy, prolonged or permanent damage to the immune system may result, regardless of attempts at nutrient replenishment.

Human malnutrition generally involves multiple nutrient deficiencies. Beisel et al. have noted, "In generalized malnutrition, it is virtually impossible to define causal relationships between individual nutrients and abnormalities in immune responsiveness."[5] Whereas any single nutrient deficiency (vitamin, mineral, protein, carbohydrate, or lipid) may cause immune aberrations, such isolated deficiencies rarely exist in nature. Consequently, most research efforts to define the effects of single nutrients on immunity have been conducted by artificial means on laboratory animals. For example, in studies on the effects of vitamin B_6 deficiency, an animal may be fed for a prolonged period either a diet deficient in vitamin B_6 or a diet containing a selective B_6 antagonist (deoxypyridoxine). Many of these studies are performed on laboratory animals, usually rodents, the metabolism of which may differ significantly from that of humans. A final drawback to these studies is that they rarely use optimal or orthomolecular doses of nutrients. Most studies test the effects of artificially imposed nutrient deficiencies rather than higher-than-normal doses of vitamins and minerals.

COMPONENTS OF THE IMMUNE SYSTEM

In recent years, the architecture of the immune system has been described in fine detail (Table 10.1). Yet, there is still much to be learned about this highly intricate network. The brevity of this chapter permits only a sketchy overview of its components and the impact of the various nutrients upon its structure and diverse functions.

Cellular Components

The cellular components of the immune system (Figure 10.1) derive from stem cells in the bone marrow. These immune cells may be conveniently divided into two cell types: phagocytes and lymphocytes.

Table 10.1 The immune system: components

Cellular

1. Granulocytes
2. Lymphocytes
3. Macrophages

Humoral

1. Immunoglobulins A, D, E, G, M
2. Complement enzymes

Inflammatory mediators

1. Prostaglandins ("2" series)
2. Leukotrienes
3. Histamine
4. Kinins

Phagocytes. The phagocytic cells are depicted at the bottom left and right of Figure 10.1. The myeloid cells (bottom left) include the neutrophil, eosinophil, and basophil. The neutrophil, and to a lesser extent the eosinophil, possess phagocytic capability. Four major steps are involved in phagocytosis, each of which may be affected by the deficiency or excess of isolated nutrients.

Chemotaxis is the capacity to be attracted to a target area. Motility is included under chemotaxis, and refers to the speed with which the phagocytic cells move to a target area. (As an example of the differing effects of nutrients on the immune response, vitamin C tends to enhance motility, whereas the trace mineral zinc suppresses it.) *Opsonization* refers to the capacity of the phagocyte to adhere to its target. Step three is *engulfment,* or the capacity of the phagocyte to ingest the target. The *phagocytic index* is a test that measures the ability of the white blood cell to ingest carbon particles in vitro. Finally, *cidal capacity* is the ability of the phagocyte to destroy the target. In some situations, white blood cells may engulf a pathogen but do not have the capacity to destroy it. (For example, this phenomenon has been demonstrated during overcolonization of the body by *Candida albicans.*)

Phagocytes utilize a metabolic shift to the hexose-monophosphate shunt, which generates free radicals as hydrogen peroxide (H_2O_2) and superoxide anion. They also contain high levels of the enzyme myeloperoxidase, which generates potent free radicals in order to destroy the ingested matter. From a nutritional standpoint, the phagocytic cell must contain high levels of antioxidants to prevent the cell from being destroyed in the process of phagocytosis. Glutathione and vitamin C are the most plentiful antioxidants in the phagocyte. It has been reported that excessive amounts of vitamin C in the cell may suppress its cidal capacity. Consequently, the phagocyte must carefully regulate its own generation of free radicals in tandem with its level of antioxidants.

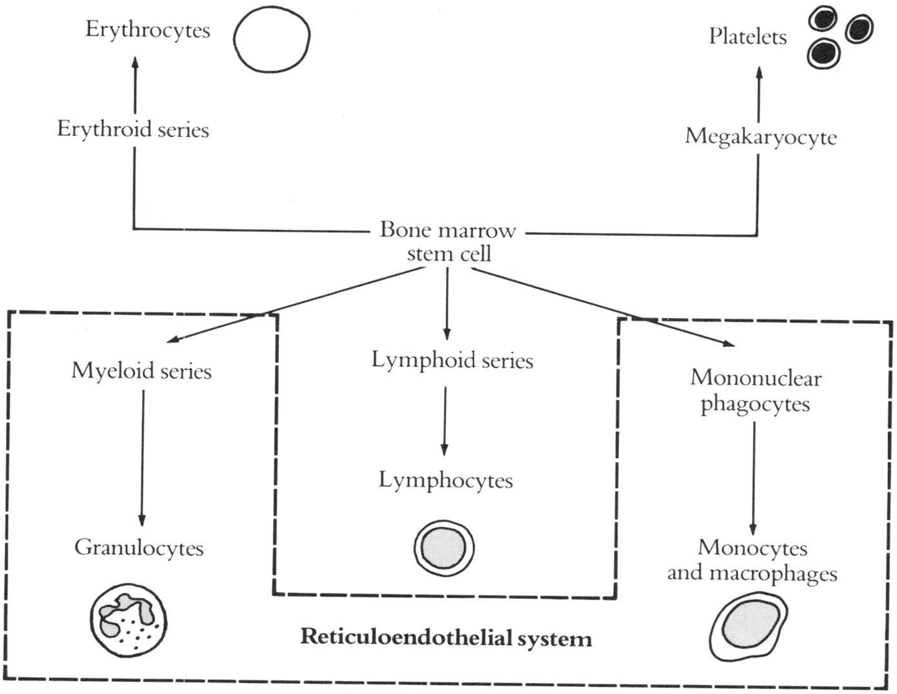

Figure 10.1 Cellular components of the immune system.

The eosinophil is a cell mobilized especially against parasites and allergens. This cell tends to suppress the allergic reaction by secreting histaminases and arylsulfatases, which act to destroy histamine and leukotrienes, respectively, and thereby decrease the inflammatory response.

The monocyte (Figure 10.1, bottom right) is a short-lived circulating phagocyte that differentiates into the macrophage, a cell that may live from months to several years. The macrophage is the "sanitation plant" of the immune system. It is capable of not only engulfing pathogens, but of removing circulating cell debris and aggregations of immune complexes. These cells tend to reside in various organ systems, where they selectively differentiate according to the needs of their host organ. For example, macrophages in the liver are called Kupffer's cells, and those in the lung are termed alveolar macrophages. The macrophage, like the granulocyte, depends on the generation of free radicals to destroy its target matter.

Lymphocytes. The functions of lymphocytes have been defined during the past two decades. There are two types of lymphocytes, T-cells and B-cells, both arising from the bone marrow stem cell. The T-cell differentiates within the thymus and the B-cell matures in lymphoid tissues.

The T-cells serve as the master regulators of the entire immune system. They have the capacity to modulate and orchestrate all immune responses. There are three main types of T-cells: helper T-cells, suppressor T-cells, and cytolytic or effector T-cells. The helper T-cell stimulates the production of B-cells. In addition, it augments the production of other helper cells and of effector cells. Consequently, it promotes lymphocytosis. The suppressor T-cell acts to diminish helper cell activity, thereby preventing excessive immune reaction. Normally there are about twice as many helpers as suppressor cells in circulation. The helper/suppressor ratio tends to increase in autoimmune disorders, and decreases in some types of virus infection and in protein-calorie malnutrition.

The effector T-cells are capable of destroying target cells by destroying the target cell membrane. Certain of the effector cells are responsible for delayed hypersensitivity reactions. The adequacy of this response may be tested conveniently in a doctor's office by intradermal administration of antigen for *Candida albicans.* Localized skin inflammation tends to develop within 24 to 48 hours. The absence of this reaction is called *anergy.* The delayed hypersensitivity reaction is especially dependent on an adequate supply of zinc; hence, a zinc deficiency may cause a spurious anergic response to common sensitizing antigens such as *Candida.*

The B-cell also originates from the stem cell in the bone marrow. Compared to the T-cell, the B-cell has a relatively short life span. It comprises approximately 25 percent of the total circulating lymphocytes. The B-cell matures and differentiates into the antibody-producing plasma cell, found within lymphoid tissues, in lymph nodes and in the spleen.

Antibodies are globulin-type proteins called immunoglobulins (Ig). The five main classes of antibodies are IgA, IgD, IgE, IgG, and IgM. On serum protein electrophoresis, the antibodies comprise the gamma-globulin fraction. IgG is by far the predominant antibody in the circulation. It confers longstanding immunity. The IgM fraction increases during the acute stage of an infection. It is phylogenetically the oldest type of antibody and is a pentamer—five times the size of the units in the other four types of immunoglobulins.

An antibody molecule is composed of a pair of H, or heavy, chains, and a pair of L, or light, chains. These chains are bound together by a series of disulfide bonds which also cause the antibody molecule to fold upon itself in several areas. *From a nutritional standpoint, the importance of sulfur-containing amino acids in antibody formation is evident.* This molecular folding confers a secondary and tertiary structure to the antibody that contributes to its remarkable specificity for antigens.

Secretory Antibodies

The two main *secretory antibodies* are IgA and IgE. Secretory IgA is abundant in saliva and in the mucosal fluids of the respiratory, gastrointestinal, and genitourinary tracts. It is the first line of defense against invading pathogens and food allergens. People who have an absence of secretory IgA tend to be more susceptible to food allergy. Extreme stress as well as vitamin A deficiency can lower the production of secretory IgA, and therefore increase vulnerability to infection.

IgE was discovered in the mid-1960s. It is the so-called reagin antibody, which causes common allergies. It is also mobilized against parasites. There is speculation that common allergens possess a substance similar to that found in parasites. About 15 percent of Americans have excessive levels of circulating IgE. The IgE binds to mast cells and, in the presence of the allergen, causes the mast cell to discharge its histamine and other inflammatory mediators. There may be as many as one-half million IgE molecules on an individual mast cell.

Complement

The complement system tends to amplify many types of immune reactions. Complement consists of a series of enzymic proteins that trigger each other in linear fashion. They are generally identified in the laboratory as C1 through C9. Certain complement fractions have the ability to attract a wide variety of inflammatory cells to a specific region. Complement can also amplify the concentration of inflammatory chemicals in that region, and participates actively in the lysis of foreign or invading cells. Complement has the ability to bind to the B-cell, and to certain antibodies: IgG (IgG1 and IgG3) and IgM. It is not involved in IgE-mediated or allergic reactions.

Immune Complexes

The immune complex consists of antigen bound to specific antibody, usually in the presence of complement. These complexes may form large aggregates in the circulation, and are measurable in the laboratory. They serve as one index of an ongoing inflammatory reaction. There is now evidence that food allergens may be a component of some circulating immune complexes.

LABORATORY MEASUREMENT OF IMMUNE STATUS

Since the unfortunate advent of acquired immune deficiency syndrome (AIDS), there has been a surge of clinical interest in laboratory assessment of immune competence. Clinical laboratories now routinely offer immune profiles. Both quantitative and functional assays are available, although the functional measurements are available mostly in research laboratories. The quantitative assay can provide, for instance, the concentration in blood of T- and B-lymphocytes, but does not provide information about how these cells will respond to an immune challenge.

T- and B-cells

Assessment of T-cells includes the following measurements: (1) total lymphocyte count (includes both T- and B-cells), (2) total T-cells, (3) helper T-cells, (4) suppressor T-cells, (5) helper/suppressor T-cell ratio (H/S), and (6) null cells (immature, undifferentiated T-cells). Many of the above measurements have been refined by the recent introduction of monoclonal antibody technique. Unfortunately, the suppressor cells still cannot be routinely separated from the T-cytolytic cells. This fact limits the usefulness of the helper/suppressor ratio.

Functional capacity of T-cells is evaluated by several means. First there is *delayed dermal hypersensitivity* (DDH), or skin challenge with antigens such as *Candida* or purified protein derivative (PPD). This provides a functional measurement of effector T-cell activity, provided that the local skin zinc level is adequate. *Mitogen T-cell studies* utilize various plant substances called lectins in the laboratory to stimulate lymphocyte blastogenesis. The two most commonly used substances are phytohemagglutinin (PHA), which stimulates T helper cells, and concanavalin-A (CON-A), which stimulates T suppressor cells. When a patient's lymphocytes are exposed to radioactive thymidine, the ability of the lymphocyte to respond to the mitogen is measured by the radioactive uptake by the cell, which indicates nucleic acid synthesis. (Macrophages must be present for this reaction to occur.)

Another measurement involves *lymphokine production.* T-cells have the capacity to secrete small proteins called lymphokines, which exert influence on multiple immune activities. There are many kinds of lymphokines, such as transfer factor, interleukin-2, and macrophage activating factor. T-cells also synthesize and release interferons, which have potent antiviral properties. Several of these lymphokines can now be measured, serving as a functional T-cell assay.

T-cell function is also referred to as cell-mediated immunity (CMI). Noncellular immunity, which is related to circulating antibody and complement levels, is called humoral immunity. Humoral immunity is evaluated by the following methods.

One method is to *quantitate B-cells.* The B-cell may be recognized by its surface coating of immunoglobulins. It also contains cell surface receptors for complement. Neither of these markers is present on the T-cell. Unfortunately, there is no easy way to measure functional B-cell activity in humans because there is no specific in vitro mitogen response as there is in animals. Animals may be challenged with an antigen following a baseline measurement of the antibody level to that antigen. A subsequent injection of the same antigen (sheep erythrocytes or the toxin of a pathogen like tetanus or diphtheria) should raise the level of specific antibody to that antigen. However, it is unfeasible to challenge humans in this manner.

It is also possible to measure *serum immunoglobulin* levels. Individual levels of IgA, IgD, IgE, IgG, and IgM are now readily obtainable at the clinical laboratory. Clinical laboratories also usually offer assays for *total serum complement* (CH-100 or CH-50), and measurements of specific complement (C-3 and C-4). There are two main complement pathways: the classic pathway, which utilizes C-4, and the alternative pathway which does not. C-3 is a major complement intermediary for both pathways. Specific levels of C-1, C-2, and C-5 through C-9 can be obtained through reference laboratories.

Circulating Immune Complexes

A variety of measures of immune complexes are available in ordinary laboratory immune profiles.

Assays of Phagocytic Competence

The routine complete blood cell count (CBC) provides the total white blood cell count and includes the polymorphonuclear leukocyte (PMN), eosinophil, and monocyte levels. Laboratories specializing in immune studies can also measure phagocyte motility in a chemotaxic chamber.

Immune Hormonal and Chemical Mediators

Hormones produced by the thymic cortex are measurable in reference laboratories. The most important are thymosin α-1, thymopoietin, thymic humoral factor, and FTS (thymulin) (a nine amino-acid peptide stimulated by the trace element zinc). Mast cells and platelets release a variety of inflammatory chemicals that generally increase local vascular permeability and cause swelling in the affected area, and induce local smooth-muscle spasm and sometimes pain and itching. Mast cells and platelets release histamine and serotonin. Mast cells, in addition, release inflammatory prostaglandins and leukotrienes. It is of value in the immune profile to measure serum histamine, serotonin, and prostaglandin F_2-α.

NUTRIENTS AND THE IMMUNE SYSTEM

Protein-energy Malnutrition

Protein-energy malnutrition (PEM), also called PCM (protein-calorie malnutrition), is the most frequent cause of acquired immune deficiency in humans. PEM was one of the first subjects to be studied in regard to impaired immunocompetence. The effects of PEM on immunity have received enormous scientific attention, although the condition is difficult to define; PEM encompasses a broad spectrum of malnutrition that may range from subclinical symptoms to the opposite extremes of marasmus and kwashiorkor. PEM occurs frequently in impoverished countries and primarily affects children and the elderly. Diverse nutrient deficiences may occur, which makes it difficult to establish clear-cut nutrient cause-and-effect relationships.

Primary PEM is the result of a lack of adequate food intake. Secondary PEM is due to factors that impair the utilization of food, such as malabsorption, emesis, or diarrhea. Oftentimes, primary and secondary PEM coexist. Primary PEM generally involves a deficiency in essential amino acids and associated nutritional cofactors that support protein synthesis. These include zinc, pyridoxine, and folic acid. It affects people whose diet consists mainly of carbohydrate foods like grains and legumes. There generally also is a deficiency in total calories.

Young children are most at risk because of their enhanced requirement for nutrients. Affected children fail to thrive, and they tend to be short, underweight, and subject to infection. Generally unhygienic living conditions complicate the situation. If the child can avoid infection, he or she may survive, but tend to manifest chronic fatigue, irritability, and poor mentation. The presence of infection, producing anorexia, vomiting, or diarrhea, increases the extent of malnutrition.

Several gradations of PEM are recognized. "Mild to moderate" refers to a 10 to 25 percent weight loss below the standards for that culture. "Moderate" characterizes individuals with weight loss of 25 to 40 percent. Greater than 40 percent weight loss is "very severe." If the protein deficiency is severe, kwashiorkor may result. It is characterized by hepatomegaly and generalized edema.

General laboratory findings include anemia, serum iron and folate deficiencies, low levels of visceral serum proteins, and diminished plasma amino acids, with especially low levels of tyrosine and the branched-chain amino acids. Serum levels of vitamins and minerals that depend on protein carriers may also be diminished.

Subclinical PEM

PEM is not limited to third world countries. There is a surprising prevalence of mild PEM in the United States. George Blackburn recently stated: "There is clinically significant PEM in many acute care hospitals, reaching over 15 percent of the patient population. Many patients enter the hospital with marginal PEM due to poor diet and chronic disease with its attendant anorexia and malabsorption. Add to this the stress of being in a hospital and the stresses of surgery and infection, which induces a catabolic state. This stress causes protein catabolism and may shift a patient into negative nitrogen balance."[6] Blackburn recommends the following tests on patients at risk for marginal PEM: serum transferrin, albumin and prealbumin, and tests of DDH.

PEM and Immune Functions

Although the nutritional deficiencies in PEM are not always consistent, a number of clear-cut effects on immune function have been described. For instance, cell-mediated immunity is depressed and there is a marked reduction in thymosin secretion. The thymus tends to be smaller and weighs less than usual. Along with thymic involution, there occurs a marked depletion of mature lymphocytes.

The lymph nodes and spleen manifest a more selective cell reduction, particularly in those areas of high T-cell population. The number of circulating T-cells is reduced, but the total lymphocyte count may occasionally be normal. This may be explained by an actual increase in the number of circulating null cells, which are immature T-cells. The null cells originate from the bone marrow, and because of reduced output of thymosin, these cells may accumulate without maturing, thereby causing a paradoxically normal blood lymphocyte count.

The indices of cell-mediated immunity tend to be uniformly depressed. DDH is decreased and the output of T-cell lymphokines is depressed (MIF, or macrophage inhibition factor, is the lymphokine usually measured). Homograft rejection, a normal function of T-effector cells, is also depressed. There is evidence that in children with PEM, the helper T-cells are reduced proportionately more than the suppressor cells, thereby resulting in a sometimes marked lowering of the helper/suppressor ratio. In a study by Chandra,[7] six children under 18 months of age had an average helper/suppressor ratio of 0.87. This is about half the normal level. Four to eight weeks following nutritional replenishment, the H/S ratios were shown to be in the normal range. There is also a marked depression in the functional response of T-cells in vitro to mitogens, especially PHA.

Humoral Immunity. Surprisingly, many quantitative measurements of humoral immunity remain unchanged or may be increased under conditions of PEM. Serum levels of immunoglobulins are normal, and there may be marked increases in antibodies in cases of repeated infections of malnourished individuals. IgE is often markedly elevated during parasitic infections. Therefore, the blood level of antibodies by itself may provide what would seem to the clinician to be a normal humoral immune response. However, the functional antibody response to direct antigen challenge is generally reduced (especially if the antibody response is dependent on the helper T-cell). Furthermore, there is a quantitative reduction in secretory IgA over most mucosal surfaces. In summary, serum antibody levels are usually normal, but secretory IgA levels are much reduced.

Phagocytes. The number of white blood cells and neutrophils in the blood may be normal in malnourished individuals. Phagocyte chemotaxis and the ability to engulf bacteria and fungi may be normal. However, there is marked reduction in the cidal capacity of the phagocytes. This abnormality may be reversed after a few weeks of nutritional repletion.

Miscellaneous Immune Factors in PEM. Reductions in other generalized, nonspecific immune functions increase the susceptibility to infection in PEM. Among these are decrease in mucosal integrity and function of cilia; reduction in the level of lysozymes in blood, tears, and saliva; and decreased interferon production.

In summary, PEM results in a depression of immune functions, particularly of the cell-mediated type. Antibody levels in the blood may be normal, but are often functionally inadequate. Secretory IgA production, the first line of immune defense, is often markedly reduced. Phagocytes have less ability to destroy their ingested prey.

PEM is not confined to impoverished nations. As Blackburn stated,[6] the problem is rampant in acute care hospitals throughout the western world. Mild to moderate PEM may be commonplace in the ghettos of the inner cities of the United States, where impoverished children are often treated repeatedly with antibiotics for recurrent infections. A concerned physician may be misled by the presence of normal serum antibodies in these children, whereas testing for cell-mediated immunity and secretory IgA would be more appropriate and may often indicate the need for nutrient replenishment.

One might suspect a similar pattern of immunity depression to occur in patients with anorexia nervosa. However, a recent study in the *American Journal of Clinical Nutrition* showed that immune competence is preserved until weight loss becomes profound.[8] At the University of Pennsylvania, 22 consecutively admitted patients with anorexia nervosa had incidence of infections similar to normal controls. All patients had normal visceral protein levels. Of the patients, 6 were anergic; these 6 were below 60 percent of their ideal body weight. This study unfortunately did not evaluate the serum zinc levels of these patients. The anergic response may well correlate with serum zinc better than with most other nutrient parameters.

ZINC, VITAMIN B_6, AND FOLIC ACID

These three nutrients are grouped together because they share the common role of stimulating nucleic acid and protein synthesis.

Zinc

Zinc is a potent immunostimulant. Zinc deficiency occurs commonly in PEM and seems to be the primary reason for the depression of T-cell immunity in malnutrition. Its critical role in PEM was discovered by comparing cell-mediated immunity in humans with PEM with that of laboratory animals with artificial PEM. In many laboratory species PEM actually *increases* cell-mediated immunity. Hansen et al.[9] explain this discrepancy as follows: "Much of the cell-mediated immunodeficiency seen in PEM syndromes in humans appears to be attributable to concomitant deficiencies in the intake of zinc. This deficiency does not exist when the circumstances of PEM are produced in the laboratory." In early experiments, laboratory animals were provided a diet containing adequate zinc but low protein, which contrasts sharply with the circumstances of human malnutrition.

Isolated zinc deficiency occurs in a rare breed of Dutch Black cattle that genetically are unable to absorb zinc. Aside from the usual dermatological signs of zinc deficiency, these cattle manifest a profound depression of T-cell immunity with extreme susceptibility to infection. Zinc treatment often brings complete remission.

A similar condition occurs in human infants afflicted with acrodermatitis enteropathica. These children exhibit skin lesions, alopecia, and severe growth retardation, as would be expected with severe zinc deficiency. They are also extremely susceptible to infection. Autopsies have revealed thymic involution; an extreme lack of lymphocytes is seen on histologic examination, and T-cells have decreased mitogen responses. These children also demonstrate markedly diminished DDH responses. However, as with PEM, many of these children have normal levels of serum antibodies.

Children suffering from malnutrition almost always have low levels of serum zinc. Golden et al.[10] found that the thymic involution that occurs in PEM is reversible when children are treated with zinc supplements.

Most zinc deficiency in human populations is acquired, and there have been reports that the average American diet is borderline in zinc content. Children and pregnant women are particularly at risk because zinc is necessary to support rapid growth.[11] Factors that contribute to zinc deficiency are high phytate-containing fiber diets (because of the tendency to consume large amounts of bran in the diet), cadmium toxicity (a common pollutant in tap water), and alcohol abuse. Zinc deficiency also occurs commonly in patients on long-term TPN (total parenteral nutrition) and in patients with cancer (e.g., Hodgkin's disease is often associated with low serum zinc regardless of dietary zinc intake). It is not surprising that Robert Good remarked, "Greater attention to zinc and other trace elements should be paid by physicians in the many pathologic situations they encounter—not the least of which is malignant disease."[12]

Zinc is required as a cofactor to at least 80 human enzymes. Some of the more important enzymes are carbonic anhydrase, which is necessary for carbon dioxide transport in the blood, alkaline phosphatase, carboxypeptidase, alcohol dehydrogenase, superoxide dismutase, and several enzymes supporting protein synthesis, including DNA and RNA polymerases.

The Effects of Zinc on Immune Competence. As has been pointed out, zinc deficiency may result in atrophy of the thymus gland and reduction in circulating mature T-cells. Consequently, zinc deficiency can impair many parameters of cell-mediated immunity, including DDH, homograft rejection, and lymphokine production. There may be a significant reduction in the level of total T-cells and in the helper/suppressor ratio. As in PEM, the null cells increase. Also, thymosin levels decrease, especially thymosin FTS.

Zinc and the Delayed Dermal Hypersensitivity Reaction. Golden et al.[13] have dramatically demonstrated that local application of a zinc ointment before DDH testing with *Candida* antigen can prevent the expected anergic response in children with PEM. Thus, even local application of zinc, which could not affect the thymus gland, produces a normal skin test in severely malnourished children. These children must have previously been sensitized to *Candida,* but could not express the reaction by skin challenge. It would seem vital to use this technique in skin testing for tuberculosis in malnourished patients.

Zinc and the Mitogen Response of T-cells. A major quality of zinc is its capacity to promote the mitogen T-cell response to antigen challenge. According to Good,[14] zinc is the only known naturally occurring lymphocyte mitogen to be found in the body.

Zinc and Humoral Immunity. Zinc has much less effect on humoral immunity than on other immune functions. It does affect antibody production that is directly dependent on the helper T-cell.

Zinc and Phagocytic Activity. Although zinc is a potent stimulant of T-cell–mediated immunity, it has the opposite effect on neutrophils and macrophages. Zinc has been repeatedly shown to inhibit the motility, chemotaxis, and phagocytic ability of activated neutrophils and macrophages. In contrast, macrophages and neutrophils from zinc-deficient animals and humans exhibit *peak* phagocytic ability. Thus, supplementation of zinc produces a double-edged sword: whereas it improves T-cell immunity, it decreases phagocytic immunity. It is of interest that the individual leukocyte contains about 25 times as much zinc as does a single red blood cell. Perhaps zinc may be present in such abundance in white blood cells in order to hinder excessive phagocytic activity.

Serum zinc decreases during bacterial infections. A protein called leukocyte endogenous mediator (LEM), which is produced by phagocytes, causes zinc and iron to pass from the blood circulation into the liver. (Serum zinc also is lowered by surgery or burns.) LEM increases serum ceruloplasmin during infections and generalized inflammation. The system seems to increase serum copper as it lowers serum zinc. This phenomenon raises serious questions about the proper administration of supplemental zinc in various immune disorders. It would seem beneficial to give zinc to correct T-cell immunosuppression, but it may be deleterious to administer zinc when there is a danger of bacterial infection, as may occur following burns or surgery. In the latter conditions, a depressed cell-mediated immunity may coexist with a bacterial infection.

The body seems to maintain a circulating zinc homeostasis; this balance should not be challenged with large, inappropriate doses of zinc in the presence of acute or chronic bacterial infections. This principle may also apply to the treatment of chronic *Candida* infection, in which the macrophage and neutrophil play a key role in the immune response. In the treatment of candidiasis, a high serum zinc therefore possibly may interfere with therapeutic success.

In summary, zinc is a potent stimulator of T helper cell immunity and T-cell–dependent humoral immunity. However, zinc markedly inhibits all the parameters of the phagocyte response.[15]

Vitamin B_6 (Pyridoxine)

Pyridoxine is similar to zinc in its effects on the immune system. It too is necessary for nucleic acid and protein synthesis. It is not surprising, therefore, that vitamin B_6 and zinc seem to potentiate each other's effects in nutritional medicine. Isolated pyridoxine deficiencies cause more profound effects on immune system functions than deficiencies of any other B vitamin.[1]

Vitamin B_6 deficiency is artificially induced in animals by the competitive inhibitor deoxypyridoxine. In laboratory animals, vitamin B_6 deficiency consistently impairs T-cell–mediated immunity. There is diminished DDH to *Candida* and PPD challenge. There is also prolongation of skin graft survival. The size and weight of the thymus decrease, and there is oftentimes a lymphopenia. This lowering of the blood lymphocyte count is usually not observed with zinc deficiency.

As would be expected, antibody responsiveness to antigen challenge is consistently diminished. Phagocyte chemotaxis is depressed.

Pyridoxal 5-phosphate is necessary to restore the immune responsiveness in all parameters listed. Therefore, riboflavin (vitamin B_2), which is needed for the formation of pyridoxal 5-phosphate, would also seem to be necessary.

Unfortunately, there is no apparent literature concerning the effects on immunity of megadoses of pyridoxine. Research on this question is needed.

Folic Acid

Folate deficiency leads to both cellular and humoral immune suppression in animals and humans. Of laboratory animals tested, rats and guinea pigs are the most susceptible to these effects. There occurs a diminution in the size of the thymus, and a lymphopenia. DDH is depressed, as is the mitogen T-cell response to antigen challenge, indicating both a quantitative and functional depression of cell-mediated immunity. These effects are also noted in humans suffering from megaloblastic anemia due specifically to folic acid deficiency. These defects are reversed by folic acid supplementation. The neutrophils exhibit normal motility and bactericidal activity, although the nuclei become hypersegmented.

OTHER NUTRITIONAL AGENTS

Pantothenic Acid

This B vitamin is so ubiquitous in nature that its dietary deficiency is a rarity. Artificially induced deficiency of pantothenate in animals yields one particular immune response defect: reduced antibody formation to specific antigen challenge with bacteria or viruses. Pantothenic acid seems to promote the release of antibody from the plasma cell. In combined pantothenic acid and vitamin B_6 deficiencies, there occurs a significant drop in the level of circulating antibodies.

Vitamin B_{12}

Vitamin B_{12}, or cobalamin, functions along with folic acid in the synthesis of hemoglobin. It also acts to increase the synthesis of methionine, and it possesses methylating activity. It has been particularly difficult to study the effects of vitamin B_{12} deficiency in laboratory animals because the deficiency cannot in fact be induced in a laboratory setting. In humans, the researcher must find patients with untreated pernicious anemia who have normal folic acid levels, an uncommon situation. Therefore, there are limited significant data on the in vivo effects of vitamin B_{12} on immunity.

The *Journal of Clinical Immunology* carried in 1982 a report on the in vitro effects of vitamin B_{12} on human T-cells.[16] The authors reasoned that vitamin B_{12} may play an important role in immune regulation because of its positive effect on the restoration of nerve damage. The nervous system and the immune system are similar in respect to their adaptability to external stimuli. This prompted the authors to test the effects of methyl B_{12} on the lymphocyte transformation of T helper and T suppressor cells. The results of their experiments are not entirely clear. Vitamin B_{12} had an immunomodulating effect—it could stimulate both helper and suppressor cell activity—but its effect varied considerably, based on its concentration and the specific concentrations of the T-cells. The authors concluded that vitamin B_{12} possesses immune regulatory activity which is, as yet, not clearly defined.

Vitamin C (Ascorbic Acid)

Linus Pauling, by his publication of *Vitamin C, the Common Cold and the Flu,* has generated tremendous scientific interest and controversy about the effects of ascorbate on the immune response. The enthusiastic interest and involvement of the general public in this subject has served as a stimulus to the scientific community. In the past decade, many revealing studies have been performed, although controversy about the effects of vitamin C on immune competence still abounds. It is unfortunate that few of these studies have employed the megadoses of vitamin C recommended by Dr. Pauling. Most studies utilized less than 1 g/day of vitamin C. However, the extensive research performed at this "low" level of vitamin C administration has been enlightening. Many authors agree that vitamin C supplementation produces a reduction in the severity and duration of symptoms of upper respiratory viral illness. At the relatively low doses of vitamin C employed, the results are usually described as modest but definite. Orthomolecular physicians generally use 10 g/day or more to effect a significant reduction in the symptoms of bacterial or viral illness. The greatest effect is noted when megadoses of vitamin C are begun at the early stages of the illness.

Phagocytic Function. The present consensus of scientific opinion is that vitamin C exerts its therapeutic effect via its stimulation of phagocytic functions (Table 10.2). Vitamin C administration has no apparent effect on the structure of the thymus or other lymphoid tissues, and lymphocyte counts remain the same. In the scorbutic animal, there is no apparent involution of the thymus or other lymphoid tissues; however, homograft rejection is impaired.[17] Vitamin C deficiency or supplementation seems to have little effect on the humoral immune system; blood antibody levels generally remain the same, although exceptions have been reported.[18]

Macrophages and neutrophil cells contain high levels of vitamin C. As previously mentioned, the phagocyte has several properties that contribute to its pro-

Table 10.2 Biological effects of vitamin C (ascorbic acid) administration

Vitamin C	Deficiency	Excess
Susceptibility to infection	Increased	Reduced
Antibodies	Same	Same or ↑
Neutrophils		↑ Chemotaxis Possible ↑ bactericidal activity
Macrophages	↓ in size and motility	↑ Chemotaxis
Thymosin		Possible ↑
Interferons		Possible ↑

tective effects. These are motility (both spontaneous and secondary to challenge by a pathogen), opsonization (the ability to adhere to its target cell), ingestion of the pathogen, and finally destruction of the pathogen. Ascorbic acid seems to have its most pronounced effect on stimulating both spontaneous and purposeful motility of PMNs and macrophages. It has no demonstrable effect on opsonization or ingestion. There is controversy as to its effects upon the cidal capacity of these cells. Some studies indicate that it potentiates destruction of pathogens, and other studies seem to indicate either no effect or a lessening of bactericidal properties.

Anderson[19] investigated the effects of increasing doses of vitamin C on neutrophil chemotaxis in healthy volunteers. Participants were given 1 g/day of vitamin C for a week, following which their neutrophils were tested in a chemotaxis chamber. During the second week of the study the subjects received 2 g/day of vitamin C, and during the third week 3 g/day of vitamin C. Neutrophil motility was observed weekly.

After one week of 2 g/day vitamin C, phagocyte motility increased three- to fourfold. At 3 g/day vitamin C there was a modest further stimulation of neutrophil chemotaxis.[19]

Boxer et al.[20] reported that ascorbate will restore chemotaxis and bactericidal activity to the leukocytes of subjects with Chediak-Higashi syndrome, a condition in which the neutrophils have markedly lower than normal motility. Vitamin C at a dosage of only 200 mg/day is capable of stimulating neutrophil motility in this situation. However, this treatment is not always effective in this rare disease.

It is notable that vitamin C raises the concentration of cyclic GMP within the phagocytic cell. The neutrophils of patients with the Chediak-Higashi syndrome have high cyclic AMP prior to the administration of vitamin C. It would seem that the salutary effect of vitamin C on the neutrophil and macrophage is related to its stimulation of intracellular cyclic GMP. Vitamin C has also been observed to stimulate the hexose-monophosphate shunt in these cells. This effect would increase the production of hydrogen peroxide, which is responsible in part for the bactericidal effects.

Phagocytic cells also contain myeloperoxidase, which iodinates the ingested pathogen. Some investigators have suggested that megadoses of vitamin C inhibit the myeloperoxidase system, but this finding is not consistent.

In summary, the greatest effect of vitamin C on the phagocyte is on its spontaneous and purposeful motility, and to a lesser extent on its bactericidal and fungicidal capacity.

Antiviral Activity. Ascorbic acid does not seem to have a direct antiviral effect in vitro. Nonetheless, it does influence immunity against viruses. Leukocyte vitamin C is rapidly depleted during virus infections. Vitamin C has recently been shown to have a stimulatory effect upon lymphocyte transformation, indicating an effect on cell-mediated immunity. A 1979 report demonstrated that ascorbic acid can reverse the depression in lymphocyte mitogen response caused by influenza virus.[21] Anderson et al.[19] confirmed this finding in a study in which the daily dosage of vitamin C was increased weekly by 1 g over a 3-week period. They found a marked increase in the mitogen lymphocyte response to both PHA and CON-A. The effect was most dramatic at 1 g/day vitamin C. At that dose, the mitogen response was generally increased two to three times, with no substantial changes with higher doses of ascorbate.

The enhancement of T-cell function by vitamin C might produce another antiviral effect, the release of interferons. Several authors reported this effect in fibroblasts and lymphocytes stimulated by poly-IC both in vitro and in vivo.[22, 23]

There seems to be increased danger of virus spreading as a result of aspirin. This phenomenon occurs in Reye's syndrome in children and in the shedding of virus in the nasopharyngeal area during viral rhinitis. In this regard, it is of interest that aspirin has an anti-vitamin C effect: it increases the urinary loss of vitamin C and decreases its uptake by leukocytes.

Vitamin C and Cancer. Pauling and Cameron reported a positive therapeutic effect in the treatment of cancer with vitamin C, 10 g/day.[24] Such a beneficial effect is understandable in terms of the vitamin's physiologic role in the immune response. The macrophage is now thought to play a critical role in the body's defense against tumors. That cell can be attracted to tumor cells, ingest them, and process their antigens for presentation to the T-lymphocyte. The effect of vitamin C in stimulating macrophage motility and T-cell transformation would increase the antibody response to tumor; it would also promote an increase in T killer cells which attack and destroy tumor cells, provided the immune system can recognize the tumor cells as foreign. Consequently, high-dose vitamin C therapy for cancer patients has some theoretical basis.

Fat-Soluble Vitamins

Vitamin A. Vitamin A enhances nonspecific resistance to a wide variety of infectious organisms. This protection is probably related to stimulation of epithelial and connective tissue growth. Vitamin A acts to preserve the integrity of skin and mucous membranes, making it more difficult for offensive agents to penetrate into the body's interior. The presence of vitamin A is also required for the production of lysozymes in tears, saliva, and sweat.

Aside from this nonspecific resistance, vitamin A stimulates directly both cell-mediated and humoral immunity. Laboratory animals with induced vitamin A deficiency (few studies use humans) demonstrate thymic and lymphoid tissue atrophy, with occasional lymphopenia. The T-cell mitogen response is often depressed, as is the secondary antibody response to infectious agents, including bacteria, viruses, and fungi. Thus, the vitamin A–deficient animal is consequently immunosuppressed. With the addition of vitamin A, immune function is restored.

Few studies with megadoses of Vitamin A have been attempted. Cohen et al.[25] administered daily doses of 300,000 to 400,000 IU for one week following extensive surgery* in an attempt to reverse immunosuppression. Control and vitamin A–treated individuals did not differ with respect to age, sex, diagnosis, length of operation, type of anesthetic, or number of blood transfusions. Patients were tested 1 day prior to surgery, 1 day after, and 7 days following surgery for functional T-cell activity and monocyte activity. At the seventh day following surgery, the vitamin A–treated group exhibited heightened T-cell activity, whereas the control group displayed the expected immunosuppression. There were no significant changes in either group in monocyte activity. The authors concluded: "When compared with untreated patients after operation, the results of these tests indicate that vitamin A is capable of blocking the depression of immune function associated with operation and acting as an immunostimulant in man."[25]

There was no evidence of vitamin A toxicity during the week of megadose treatment, given in the form of the acetate (orally in the majority of cases) in three divided doses per day. Unfortunately, the study provided no information about other parameters of immune function, such as complement levels, circulating immune complexes, or quantitative helper and suppressor lymphocyte levels.

*Surgery often produces an immunosuppression that may last 3 to 4 weeks; it is associated with decreases in cell-mediated immunity and in the function of macrophages and neutrophils. Cohen et al. point out that after surgery in which tumors are found to be unresectable, tumor growth often increases and the patient's clinical condition deteriorates. This effect may be due to a combination of stress caused by the surgery itself and that due to the anesthesia, which has been noted on occasion to depress resistance to infection.

Cohen et al. also point out that vitamin A has been shown to reverse the immunosuppression usually caused by corticosteroid hormones. It would be worthwhile to do additional experiments of this type, employing a variety of stressful conditions, for it seems that vitamin A may be protective against the immunosuppressant effects of extreme stress. This study also supports the general safety of short-term megadose vitamin A therapy.

Results of another recent study demonstrated the protective effects of vitamin A and provitamin A (beta-carotene) on the formation of chromosome breaks and oral cancer.[26] Administration of vitamin A (100,000 units per week) and beta-carotene (300,000 units per week) was associated with a threefold decrease in the proportion of buccal squamous cells with chromosome breaks in Filipinos who were chewing betel nut and tobacco leaf. Filipinos who chew these items exhibit a high rate of oral cancer.

Vitamin E (α-tocopherol). Vitamin E, a known antioxidant, is found primarily in cell and organelle membranes. It is believed to protect membranes against lipid peroxidation by chemical free radicals and may protect against thromboembolic disorders. Some tocopherols seem to increase fertility in laboratory animals. These biological effects of vitamin E are well known. However, the immunostimulant property of vitamin E, including the protection it affords against infection, is a subject on which most physicians and the general public are largely ignorant.

Numerous investigations have reported that the addition of moderate amounts of vitamin E to animal feed enhances humoral antibody responses to pathogen challenge. One of the first and classic experiments was conducted in 1974 by Heinzerling,[27] who reported that a three- to sixfold increase in vitamin E over normal dietary intake in chickens provided a two- to threefold increase in antibody titers against challenge with *E. coli.* Similar results have been obtained with mice challenged with a virulent strain of pneumococcus, guinea pigs challenged with an encephalitis virus, and mice inoculated with tetanus toxoid. These immunostimulatory effects are magnified if vitamin E is given together with a modest increase in dietary selenium. A prominent researcher in this field, William Beisel, concludes that, "the administration of α-tocopherol in amounts somewhat in excess of minimal recommended doses has an often beneficial effect on host resistance in a variety of test animals."[1]

It is of interest that researchers have consistently used excessive doses of vitamin E in their studies rather than creating the usual deficiency of the nutrient being tested. If the immunological effect does pertain to humans, it would surely indicate the need to raise the recommended daily allowance (RDA) for vitamin E in this country.

Vitamin D. In the past few years, the biological role of vitamin D has been expanded beyond its effects on mineral metabolism. Vitamin D receptors have been found in the hypothalamus of the brain, with the suggestion that this vitamin may play a role in hormonal regulation by the pituitary gland. Vitamin D is similar in structure to steroid hormones, and is itself considered to function as a hormone.

Vitamin D may play a role in immunoregulation. Receptor sites for vitamin D are present on normal human monocytes and malignant lymphocytes, and on activated T- and B-cells. A recent article from the Scripps Clinic indicates that vitamin D suppresses the output of interleukin-2 (IL-2) from human lymphocytes.[28] These cells from normal adults were cultured with the mitogen PHA in the absence and presence of vitamin D. The IL-2 content of the media was measured; those containing vitamin D displayed reduced IL-2 activity, which was dependent on the concentration of vitamin D. Only the dihydroxy metabolite of vitamin D had this potent inhibitory effect; pure cholecalciferol was without measurable effect.

IL-2 has a potent stimulatory effect on the formation of helper T-cells, effector T-cells, and antibodies. Thus, the reduction of IL-2 is immunosuppressive. The sudden appearance of vitamin D receptors on activated T-cells and their usual occurrence on malignant lymphocytes might function as a mechanism to prevent excessive lymphocyte proliferation.

It is not surprising that vitamin D is immunosuppressive in light of the fact that it is a steroid hormone. Corticosteroids and progesterone are also immunosuppressive. The evidence in this article "adds a new link to the relation between the endocrine and the immune systems as exemplified by the immunosuppressive action of corticosteroids."[28] To the physician, this information would caution against the prescription of vitamin D supplements in patients with an existing immunosuppression, although such patients might well have fewer vitamin D receptors on their lymphocytes.

Progesterone

Progesterone is also a steroid hormone, and it too is immunosuppressive. In concentrations of 10 to 15 μg/ml in vitro, it reduces the T-cell mitogen response. In concentrations of 50 to 200 μg/ml, it may cause prolonged survival of skin grafts, demonstrating a substantial reduction in cell-mediated immunity. It is important for physicians to recognize this property of progesterone, which has enjoyed recent popularity in dosages of approximately 800 mg/day as a treatment for premenstrual syndrome.

IRON, SELENIUM, AND OTHER TRACE MINERALS

Iron

As a clinical issue, iron deficiency is commonplace in menstruating women and in malnourished children throughout the world. It is one of the most likely forms of single micronutrient deficiency to occur in the absence of any other accompanying form of malnutrition.[1]

Table 10.3 Immune function and mineral deficiency

	Iron	Zinc	Magnesium
Host resistance	↓	↓	↓
Lymphoid tissue	↓ Mitochondria	↓	↑
Lymphocyte counts	↓	↓ % of T-cells	
DDH	Slight ↓	↓	
Neutrophils			↑ Numbers

The body maintains a careful homeostasis of iron levels, for it is critical to avoid both deficiency and excess of this trace mineral. Both iron deficiency and iron excess can cause immune dysfunctions, and both conditions increase the danger of infection with microorganisms.

Iron Deficiency. A deficiency of iron would tend to decrease the delivery of oxygen (and hence its utilization) by all cells of the body. Cells of the immune system undergo rapid turnover, and therefore have a relatively high oxygen demand. The deleterious immune effects of iron deficiency (Table 10.3) depend on the severity of the deficiency and its duration. There usually occurs an atrophy of lymphoid tissues and an accompanying lymphopenia. Some studies report a decline in lymphocyte transformation and DDH, or in antibody responsiveness; others report no changes at all. Most researchers agree that serum antibody levels remain normal. In terms of phagocyte function, there is a strong consistent finding: the bactericidal activity of phagocytes is impaired.

Iron Excess. Overabundance of body iron increases host susceptibility to a variety of infections. Most microorganisms (with the exception of lactobacilli) have a critical need for iron to insure their replication. Many bacteria release into their immediate environment siderophores, which chelate available iron for uptake by the bacteria. It is critical for the host to withhold iron from pathogens during an infection. Many mechanisms are used by the host to achieve this result: (1) intestinal absorption of iron is reduced; (2) white blood cells are attracted to the infected area, and secrete lactoferrin which immediately binds iron and prevents its uptake by the bacteria (transferrin is similar in function; breast milk contains transferrin and lactoferrin, and thereby helps to prevent bowel infections in infants), (3) white blood cells also may secrete a chemical called LEM (leukocyte endogenous mediator), which causes an immediate transfer of blood iron into the liver for storage, and (4) LEM also is a pyrogen, and causes a fever; the elevation of body temperature reduces the ability of bacteria to absorb iron.

There is much documentation in the literature on iron supplementation increasing the dangers of sepsis. This problem exists particularly in malnourished individuals in third world countries. A low-protein diet results in a low iron-binding capacity. The addition of high amounts of iron to the diet of a person with a low serum transferrin increases the danger of iron availability to microorganisms. It is especially dangerous to provide injectable iron to such malnourished individuals. It is more appropriate first to raise the level of general nutrition—especially of protein—in order to raise the serum iron-binding capacity, before providing large amounts of supplemental iron.[29]

Magnesium

Magnesium deficiency does not produce any major immunological impairments in humans. Prolonged and severe magnesium deficiency in animals causes overreactivity of the immune system (Table 10.3) with leukocytosis, eosinophilia, and excessive release of chemical mediators by mast cells. The latter causes a rise in serum histamine. It is known that calcium uptake by these cells stimulates their activity; perhaps magnesium is acting by competitively blocking their uptake of calcium.

Selenium

Much of the work on selenium and its effects on immunity has been reported in the Russian and Eastern European literature, and has not been readily available in this country. Only within the past few years has this research provoked similar investigations in western countries.

The Russian literature contends that selenium has an effect on the humoral immune system similar to that of vitamin E. In laboratory animals, sodium selenite administration raises the antibody responsiveness to a variety of antigen challenges. Selenite has generally been found to be more effective in this regard than organic forms of selenium. The combined use of selenite and vitamin E provides a synergistic effect.

Selenium also potentiates the bactericidal functions of phagocytes. Selenium tends to sequester in cells of the reticuloendothelial system (RES), where it increases the capacity of these cells to destroy other cells, including those of tumors. Selenium is thought to stimulate the enzyme glutathione peroxidase. Results of research into the effects of selenium on the immune response should become fruitful in coming years.[30]

Toxic Heavy Metals—Cadmium, Lead, and Mercury

These toxic metals have all been shown to be immunosuppressive in laboratory animals. The degree of impairment depends on the doses that are used and the level of protective nutrients in the diet. Selenium, vitamin C, and natural chelating agents tend to diminish the toxic effects of these metals, which directly inhibit all parameters of immune function, including phagocyte responses, cell-mediated immunity, and humoral immunity. Host susceptibility to microorganisms is increased. It is difficult to extrapolate from animal studies the levels of exposure that would be immunotoxic to man.

OBESITY, DIETARY LIPIDS, PROSTAGLANDINS, AND IMMUNE FUNCTION

Obesity

Obesity is the most common nutritional disorder in industrialized countries. Obesity has a deleterious effect on certain immune functions: it promotes the incidence of infectious illness, and infection-related mortality is increased. These findings are supported by clinical, epidemiologic, autopsy, and laboratory animal experimental findings.[2, 31]

Chandra,[31] studying obese children and adults, showed that approximately one-third of obese subjects had impairment of cell-mediated immunity from several causes and reduced bactericidal capacity of PMNs. The number of T-cells and immunoglobulins remained normal. Chandra pointed out that the obese often have deficient DDH responses. About one out of three had a depression in T-cell mitogen sensitivity. However, the NK-cell activity is often increased. (NK, or natural killer cells, are nonspecific surveillance lymphocytes capable of activation by α-interferon.)

How can these findings be explained? Nutritional deficiencies seem to be responsible for this immunosuppression. Two trace mineral nutrients seem to be involved: iron and zinc. Plasma zinc levels are low in the obese of all age groups, and a low iron level would impair the phagocytic function of PMNs. It is interesting that those obese subjects in Chandra's study who demonstrated impaired phagocytic functions were also the ones who had overt evidence of iron deficiency. The use of iron supplements in these subjects for one month caused the return of normal phagocytic function. Chandra did not find any satisfactory explanation for the iron and zinc deficiencies in the obese.

Cholesterol

Reports about the effects of cholesterol on immunity are conflicting. There is evidence that high-cholesterol diets render laboratory animals more susceptible to infection. Increases of cholesterol in the macrophage have been shown to inhibit its phagocytic ability. There is controversy about whether the serum cholesterol level is significantly related to such effects. Many studies indicate that dietary cholesterol also diminishes cell-mediated and humoral immunity. Most of these studies were performed on laboratory animals that ordinarily do not consume cholesterol.

There is controversy about the immunosuppressive effects of oxidized cholesterol. This form of cholesterol, which is ordinarily generated to some degree in the body and is present in powdered milk and in fried foods, is a potent free radical. According to Humphries,[32] significant levels of dietary or endogenous oxidized cholesterol might compromise the immune system.

Essential Fatty Acids

A deficiency of unsaturated fatty acids inhibits antibody responsiveness, but does not seem to change serum antibody levels. However, high dietary intake of polyunsaturated fatty acids (PUFA) in laboratory animals produces profound immunosuppression, including thymic involution and lymphoid atrophy, with an accompanying depression of cell-mediated immunity and antibody responsiveness to antigen challenge. Allograft rejection is delayed. Some studies also indicate that high PUFA diets cause marked diminution in the ability of neutrophils and macrophages to engulf and destroy bacteria.

Fatty acids capable of being metabolized to arachidonic acid are the most immunosuppressive. The more unsaturated the fatty acid, the greater is its immunosuppressant effect. Linoleic acid possesses two double bonds, whereas arachidonic acid has four. About 80 percent of fatty acids in most vegetable oils are unsaturated, although peanut and olive oil are only about 50 percent unsaturated.

It is not clear what dietary level of PUFA in the human diet is immunosuppressive. More research is needed in this area, since the content of PUFA in the American diet has increased markedly. This increased ingestion of PUFA has been linked to the increase in heart disease among Americans. Do PUFA contribute, through an immunosuppressive effect, to the high incidence of cancer in the western world? Vitale and Broitman claim that diets high in PUFA relative to saturated fat are both immunosuppressive and promoters of tumorigenesis.[33]

Prostaglandins

There is evidence that PUFA inhibit immune function through formation of prostaglandins. In a review article, Goodwin and Webb[34] concluded that prostaglandins E_1 and E_2 depress T-cell–mediated immunity. Administration of these prostaglandins depresses lymphocyte transformation, reduces lymphokines, and lowers T-cell cytolytic activity, thereby lowering the delayed hypersensitivity response. In contrast, aspirin and other prostaglandin-synthesis inhibitors actually augment T-cell immunity and experimentally have contributed to slowing tumor growth. The suppressor T-cell acts to reduce T-cell activity, in part, by excreting PGE_1 and PGE_2. Apparently the suppressor T-cell contains 10 times as much of these prostaglandins in the unstimulated state as does the helper T-cell. The inhibitory effect of PGE_1 and PGE_2 on the immune response is much more marked in elderly people, which may account for the depression in cellular immune function observed in healthy elderly people.[34]

The statements of Goodwin and Webb appear to contradict directly the thesis of David Horrobin, who claims that the PG_1 series of prostaglandins—especially PGE_1—are potent immunostimulants. Horrobin states in *Medical Hypotheses* that PGE_1 plays a major role in the regulation of thymus development, and that T-lymphocytes may require both endogenous and exogenous PGE_1 in order to function adequately.[35] Horrobin thus recommends dietary primrose oil supplements, along with vitamin C, vitamin B_6, and zinc, to increase systemic levels of PGE_1. In support of his hypothesis, Horrobin notes that corticosteroid hormones depress PGE_1 and also result in thymic atrophy. Lithium seems to have a similar effect. Horrobin further states, "There seems to be more PGE_1 in the thymus than in any other tissue, indicating an important role for PGE_1 in T-cell function."

Is PGE_1 an immunostimulant or an immunosuppressant? According to Horrobin, PGE_1 has a biphasic effect, with its stimulating action reversed at high concentrations. In the study in which PGE_1 appeared to be immunosuppressive, relatively high doses of PGE_1 were employed in the research protocol. One might argue that if the dose of PGE_1 had been substantially lowered, PGE_1 would have served a prominent role as an immunostimulant. The problem for the clinician then becomes determination of the appropriate dose of PGE_1 precursor (usually evening primrose oil) to accommodate each patient's unique immune status.

CONCLUSION

The abundance of published research in the hybrid field of immunonutrition leaves no doubt that diet and individual nutrients modulate immune responses. However, the data are still limited in terms of their applications to the treatment of human immune disorders. Much of the research has been conducted on laboratory animals whose nutrient requirements and metabolisms differ from those of man. Often, the artificially induced single nutrient deficiencies that are created have little relevance to human malnutrition. Further, there has been little effort to explore the adverse immune effects of *multiple* nutrient deficiencies or the possible salutary effects of nutrient megadoses.

Nevertheless, some consistent findings have been established in the new field of immunonutrition:

1. In the stimulation of cell-mediated and humoral immunity, key nutrients are vitamin C, vitamin B_6, vitamin A, vitamin E, folate, and zinc. Zinc seems to have the most profound impact on cell-mediated immunity. The therapeutic use of these nutrients is particularly indicated in malnourished children and in the elderly individual with negative nitrogen balance due to poor diet, chronic stress, or the acute stress of surgery.
2. Nutrients involved in the reduction of cell-mediated immunity are polyunsaturated fatty acids (in high doses) and vitamin D. The reduction of cell-mediated

immunity may be important in the treatment of a variety of autoimmune disorders, as well as to protect skin and organ transplants against rejection.

3. For stimulation of phagocytic functions, key nutrients are vitamin C, iron, and selenium. These nutrients may be clinically useful to support phagocytic functions in the treatment of chronic bacterial and fungal infections, especially those associated with malnutrition. (It is important to exercise caution about rapid iron replenishment in patients with protein malnutrition because of the danger of encouraging sepsis.)
4. Zinc is the key nutrient for the reduction of phagocytic function.
5. The toxic heavy metals—cadmium, lead, and mercury—seem to depress most immune functions.
6. Treatment of the elderly may require higher doses of nutrients than those used in young people.

To quote Chandra,[2] "A study of nutrition-immunity interactions is of fundamental physiological importance. The subject has immense public health importance, and the implications of recent data bear upon every medical and biological discipline."

The field of immunology has experienced an information explosion in the past 20 years. Concurrently, the fields of nutritional science and clinical nutrition have also experienced progressive growth. These two burgeoning disciplines—nutrition and immunology—have begun to interact in a manner that may well help to redefine the nature of preventive medicine in the near future.

REFERENCES

1. Beisel W: Single nutrients and immunity. *Am J Clin Nutr* 1982; 35: 416–468.

2. Chandra RK: *Immunology of Nutritional Disorders.* London, Edward Arnold, Current Topics of Immunology Series, No. 12, 1980, pp 1–110.

3. Hansen MA, Fernandes G, Good R: Nutrition and immunity. *Ann Rev Nutr* 1982; 2: 151–177.

4. Chandra RK: Immunocompetence as a functional index of nutritional status. *Br Med Bull* 1981; 37: 89–94.

5. Beisel W, Edelman R, Nauss K, et al.: Single nutrient effects on immunologic functions. *JAMA* 1981; 245(1): 53.

6. Blackburn G: Nutrition assessment in clinical practice. *Postgrad Med* 1982; 71(5): 46–63.

7. Chandra RK: Inducer and suppressor T-cell subsets in PEM: analysis by monoclonal antibodies. *Nutr Res* 1982; 2: 21–26.

8. Pertschuk M, Crosby L, Barot L, et al.: Immunocompetency in anorexia nervosa. *Am J Clin Nutr* 1982; 35: 968–972.

9. Hansen MA, Fernandes G, Good R: Nutrition and immunity. *Ann Rev Nutr* 1982; 2: 159–160.

10. Golden M, Golden B, Jackson A: Effect of zinc on thymus of recently malnourished children. *Lancet* 1977; 2: 1057–1059.

11. Hambidge KM, Walravens P: Zinc deficiency in infants and pre-adolescent children, in Prasad AS, Oberleas D (eds): *Trace Elements in Human Health and Disease,* vol 1. New York, Academic Press, 1976, pp 21–31.

12. Schloen L, Fernandes G, Garofalo J, et al.: Nutrition, immunity and cancer—a review, Part II: Zinc, immune function and cancer. *Clinical Bulletin,* 1979; 9(2): 63–75.

13. Golden M, Golden, B, Harland G, et al.: Zinc and immunocompetence in PEM. *Lancet* 1978; 1: 1226–1228.

14. Hansen MA, Fernandes G, and Good R: Nutrition and immunity. *Ann Rev Nutr* 1982; 2: 165.

15. Chuapil M, Stankova L, Zukoski C: Inhibition of some functions of polymorphonuclear leukocytes by in vitro zinc. *J Lab Clin Med* 1977; 89(1): 135–146.

16. Sakane T, Takda S, Kotani H: Effects of methyl-B_{12} on the in vitro immune functions of human T lymphocytes. *J Clin Immunol* 1982; 2: 101–109.

17. Wilson CWM: Clinical pharmacological aspects of ascorbic acid. *Ann NY Acad Sci* 1975; 258: 355–375.

18. Prinz W, Bortz R, Bregin B, et al.: The effect of ascorbic acid supplementation on some parameters of the human immunological defense system. *Internat J Vit Nutr Res* 1977; 47: 248–257.

19. Anderson R, Oosthuizen R, Maritz R, et al.: The effects of increasing weekly doses of ascorbate on certain cellular and humoral immune functions in normal volunteers. *Am J Clin Nutr* 1980; 33: 71–76.

20. Boxer LA, Watanabe AM, Rister M, et al.: Correction of leukocyte function in Chediak-Higashi syndrome by ascorbate. *N Engl J Med* 1976; 295: 1041–1045.

21. Manzella J, Roberts N: Human macrophage and lymphocyte responses to mitogen stimulation after exposure to influenza virus, ascorbic acid and hypothermia. *J Immunol* 1979; 123(5): 1940–1944.

22. Siegel BV: Enhanced interferon response to murine leukemia virus by ascorbic acid. *Infect Immunol* 1974; 10: 409.

23. Roberts N, Douglas R, Simons R, et al.: Virus-induced interferon production by human macrophages. *J Immunol* 1979; 123: 365.

24. Cameron E, Pauling L: *Cancer and Vitamin C.* Menlo Park, Calif, The Linus Pauling Institute of Science and Medicine, 1979.

25. Cohen B, Gill G, Cullen P, et al.: Reversal of post-operative immunosuppression in man by vitamin A. *Surg Gynecol Obstet* 1979; 149: 658–662.

26. Stich H, Rosin M, Vallejera M: Reduction with vitamin A and beta-carotene administration of proportion of micronucleated buccal mocosal cells in Asian betel nut and tobacco chewers. *Lancet* 1984; 1: 1204–1206.

27. Heinzerling R, Nockels C, Quarles C, et al.: Protection of chicks against *E-coli* infection by dietary supplementation with vitamin E. *Proc Soc Exper Biol Med* 1974; 146: 279–283.

28. Tsoukas C: 1,25-Dihydroxy vitamin D_3: a novel immunoregulatory hormone. *Science* 1984; 224: 1438–39.

29. Weinberg D: Infection and iron metabolism. *Am J Clin Nutr* 1977; 30: 1485–1490.

30. Spallholz J: Selenium: what role in immunity and immune cytotoxocity?, in Spallholz J, Martin J, Gantmer H (eds): *Selenium in Biology and Medicine.* Westport, Conn, AVI, 1981, pp 103–116.

31. Chandra RK: Immune response in overnutrition. *Canc Res* 1981; 41: 3795–3796.

32. Humphries G: Differences in the ability of compactin and oxidized cholesterol, both known inhibitors of cholesterol biosynthesis, to suppress in vitro immune responses. *Canc Res* 1981; 41: 3789–3791.

33. Vitale J, Broitman S: Lipids and immune function. *Canc Res* 1981; 41: 3706–3710.

34. Goodwin J, Webb D: Regulation of the immune response by prostaglandins. *Clin Immunol Immunopathol* 1980; 15: 106–122.

35. Horrobin D: The nutritional regulation of T lymphocyte function. *Medical Hypotheses* 1979; 5: 969–985.

CHAPTER ELEVEN

HORMONES, FORMONES, AND GORMONES

JOHN E. MORLEY, MD

ALLEN S. LEVINE, PhD

The concept of chemical messengers or "hormones" was first recognized with the pioneering studies of Bayliss and Starling[1] in 1902 when they demonstrated that perfusion of the intestine with acid resulted in pancreatic secretion, and that injections of crude extracts of duodenal mucosa produced a similar stimulation of the pancreas. The classical definition of a hormone is "any substance normally produced in the cells of some part of the body and carried by the blood to distant parts, which it affects for the good of the organism as a whole."[1] With the increasing recognition that many hormones act locally as well as at distant sites, Brugi[2] has operationally described hormones as "chemical messengers which are dissolved in extracellular fluid and carry information between cells." Recent studies have suggested that we may have to modify further our concept of what a hormone is and how it reaches its site of action.

FOOD HORMONES: FORMONES

Animal steroid hormones modulate growth and development of plants. Plants, furthermore, synthesize their own steroid hormones.[3] Hops, for instance, have been shown to have intrinsic estrogenic activity.[4] The most dramatic example of a steroid plant hormone producing effects in animal species is seen in the case of truffles. Truffles grow underground in Europe, and the accepted way of finding them is to hunt them with muzzled boars. The boars smell out the truffles' location because truffles contain 5-androst-16-ene-3-ol,[5] which is the pheromone produced by the sows when in heat.

Over the last decade a number of peptide hormone-like substances have been isolated from food. These include opioid peptide-like substances, thyrotropin-releasing hormone-like peptides, melanocyte inhibitory factor, and a luteinizing hormone-releasing hormone-like (LHRH-like) substance. We have suggested that these food hormones be called *formones,*[6] and accumulating evidence suggests that these formones may have important effects after ingestion. The first formone to be identified was the LHRH-like substance from oat leaves (*Avena sativa*), isolated by a group of Japanese workers.[7] As an aside, this suggests that there may have been more meaning to the old adage "sowing your wild oats" than our ancestors could have dreamed of when they first coined the expression!

A peptide with thyrotropin-releasing hormone (TRH) immunocharacteristics has been isolated by our group[8] and by Ivor Jackson in Boston.[9] This peptide was shown to differ from true TRH by chromatographic techniques and also, unlike TRH, which is a potent releaser of prolactin, it has been shown to be a prolactin inhibitory factor.[8] TRH is highly resistant to degradation by gastrointestinal enzymes,[10] and high doses of orally administered TRH can produce thyroid-stimulating hormone (TSH) and prolactin release.[11] This suggests that the TRH-like peptide in alfalfa may also be capable of producing systemic effects. As both alfalfa[12] and thyroxine[13] lower cholesterol, Malinkow[14] postulated that the hypocholesterolemic effect of alfalfa may be due to thyroid stimulation. However, in a controlled trial in monkeys he could not show that alfalfa-induced low plasma cholesterol levels were secondary to induced hyperthyroidism. A more likely and potentially significant role of the TRH-like peptide in foodstuffs is unmasked by the observation that TRH is distributed throughout the gastrointestinal tract[15] and has potent effects on gastric acid secretion,[16-18] pancreatic secretion,[19] and gastrointestinal tract motility.[17]

The sequence Pro-Leu-Gly has been shown to be formed by enzymatic digestion of α-gliadin[20] and also occurs in κ-casein.[21] This sequence is similar to that found in melanocyte-stimulating hormone release-inhibiting factor (MIF), Pro-Leu-Gly-NH_2. MIF enhances dopaminergic activity in the central nervous system after oral administration;[22] doses of 50 mg have produced EEG changes in normal subjects,[23] and 75 mg has induced behavioral changes in depressed subjects.[24] Mycroft et al.[20] have calculated that up to 150 mg of the MIF-like tripeptide might be formed daily, assuming normal adult intakes of the foods containing MIF. The possibility that elaboration of this peptide from foodstuffs affects the central nervous system deserves further attention.

EXORPHINS

Because some schizophrenics may improve when treated with a gluten-free diet,[25, 26] and endogenous opioids (endorphins) have been postulated (probably erroneously) to play a role in the pathogenesis of schizophrenia,[27] workers at the National Institutes of Mental Health decided it would be worthwhile to determine if gluten contained opiate-like substances. They demonstrated that peptic digestion of a variety of dietary proteins, such as casein and wheat gluten, had opiate-like activity in both receptor assays and bioassays.[28] These compounds were called exorphins in analogy to the endogenously derived opiate-like materials. The peptides responsible for the opioid properties of β-casein hydrolysates (β-casein is a constituent of milk) have been isolated and sequenced.[29-32] Their N-terminal amino acid sequence is Tyr-Pro-Phe-Pro, which differs from the N-terminal sequence of the endogenous opioid peptides, i.e., Tyr-Gly-Gly-Phe (e.g., enkephalins, β-endorphin, and dynorphin). These "β-casomorphins" have been shown to produce naloxone-reversible analgesia following intracerebroventricular administration in rats.[33] Whether these exorphins can produce central effects after ingestion is debatable, but Hemmings and coworkers[34, 35] have demonstrated that after feeding radiolabeled gliadin to rats, labeled peptides, which still reacted with antigliadin antibodies, were present in appreciable amounts in blood and tissues of the animals, including the brain. There is also preliminary evidence that β-casomorphins can be generated in the intestine after ingestion of milk or milk products, and that these opiate-active compounds are taken up into the circulation.[36] This is not surprising in view of the fact that the N-terminal of these exorphins is highly resistant to peptidases.[29] Studies using a variety of bioassays and receptor assays have shown that these substances appear to be specific morphine receptor (μ) ligands, as opposed to the enkephalins that bind preferentially to the delta (Δ) receptor.[37, 38]

Results of studies in dogs by Schusdziarra et al.[39] indicate that intragastric instillation of digested gluten elicits a more rapid and notably greater rise in postprandial peripheral vein insulin and glucagon levels than do equivalent amounts of undigested gluten. Concomitant intragastric administration of 4 mg of naloxone hydrochloride reduces the insulin response to the digested gluten test meal, suggesting that the effect of digested gluten is secondary to activation of the opiate receptor. Further studies by the same group[40] showed that both casopeptone, which contains the opiate-like casomorphins, and synthetic β-casomorphins stimulate insulin release, and this effect can be reduced by opiate receptor blockade. Infusions of β-casomorphin also have been shown to potentiate glucose–amino acid–induced insulin release in dogs.[36]

We recently completed a study on the effects of exorphins on gastrointestinal function, hormonal release, and appetite in humans.[41] Hydrolyzed gluten produced a naloxone-reversible prolongation of intestinal transit time. This was associated with a similar naloxone-reversible increase in plasma somatostatin-like activity. Because somatostatin is recognized as an agent capable of inhibiting bowel motility,[42] we suggested that the exorphin effect on intestinal transit time could have been mediated through the increase in somatostatin. Unlike results in the dog, exorphins yielded no effects on carbohydrate metabolism in humans.

In addition, exorphins do not appear to be responsible for the meal-associated increase in cortisol. Although several studies have suggested a role for endogenous opioid peptides in appetite regulation,[43-45] we disappointingly could not show an exorphin effect on appetite, either as measured by total calories ingested or by rating on a satiety scale. Our studies suggest that the potential role for food-derived exorphins in the pathogenesis or therapy of diseases associated with abnormalities of gastrointestinal motility (such as irritable colon) needs to be explored.

The recent report of a nonpeptide, opiate-like substance in coffee beans suggests a further complexity in our understanding of the interaction of food substances and physiological function.[46]

GORMONES

Although some evidence suggests that small food hormones (formones) may be absorbed intact and produce systemic effects, it seems more likely that their role is to produce local effects on the gastrointestinal tract. The presence of intraluminal endogenous hormones is well recognized. There are reports of luminal gastrin,[47, 48] somatostatin,[49] secretin,[50] VIP,[51] substance P,[51] cholecystokinin,[52] motilin,[52] gastric inhibitory peptide,[52] and secretin.[53] We suggest that in keeping with the use of the term *formones* for food hormones, these gut luminal hormones should be called *gormones*. Shinsky et al.[54] have shown that intestinal motility can be altered after luminal infusion of cholecystokinin; specific gastrin receptor sites have been demonstrated on both the serosal and mucosal sides of parietal cells;[55, 56] and exogenous heptadecapeptide gastrin instilled into the stomach of healthy subjects stimulates acid secretion.[47] These studies strongly support a role for gormones in the regulation of gastrointestinal function. Further, we feel that the presence of gut (luminal) hormones with intrinsic activity provides circumstantial evidence for a potential physiological role for formones as exogenous regulators of gastrointestinal activity.

CONCLUSION

There is a strong case for the existence of formones (food hormones) that regulate physiology predominantly through interaction with gastrointestinal luminal receptors. It is axiomatic that all food hormones need not produce beneficial effects on the gastrointestinal tract. An example is found in frog skin, an extremely rich source of peptides such as bombesin and caerulein. These peptides produce marked gastrointestinal effects, leading to nausea, vomiting, and diarrhea. As such, these skin peptides (dermones?) have become teleologically important as preservers of the frog species. Few predators are prepared to choose foods that produce nausea, diarrhea, and vomiting.

With the introduction of the concept of formones, we can expect to see more clearly developed studies to clarify the interaction between our physiology and the foods we eat. In addition, we can expect to see a new series of popular diet books espousing the virtues of low- or high-exorphin diets, or both. Which, if any, of these formones will prove useful for weight reduction, or for any other purpose, remains to be seen. In conclusion, having introduced the word *formone* into the English language, we have but one fear: at some future date we will tune into our television set to hear the Madison Avenue slogan, "A formone a day trims your form!"

REFERENCES

1. Bayliss WM, Starling EH: Croonian lecture: The chemical regulation of the secretory process. *Proc R Soc London* 1904; 73: 310–324.

2. Brugi H: General aspects of endocrinology, in Labbart A (ed): *Clinical Endocrinology: Theory and Practice.* New York, Springer-Verlag, 1974, pp 1–26.

3. Geuns JMC: Plant steroid hormones—what are they and what do they do? *Trends in Biochemical Science* 1982; 7: 7–9.

4. Fenselan C, Talalay P: Is oestrogenic activity present in hops? *Food Cosmet Toxicol* 1973; 11: 597–603.

5. Claus R, Hoppen HO: The boar pheromone steroid identified in vegetables. *Experientia* 1979; 15: 1674–1675.

6. Morley JE: Food peptides: A new class of hormones? *JAMA* 1982; 247: 2379–2380.

7. Fukushima M, Watanabe S, Kushima K: Extraction and purification of a substance with luteinizing hormone-releasing activity from leaves of *Avena sativa. Tohoku J Exp Med* 1976; 119: 115–119.

8. Morley JE, Mayer N, Pekary AE, et al.: A prolactin inhibitory factor with immuno-characteristics similar to thyrotropin releasing factor (TRH) is present in rat pituitary tumors (GH3 and W5), testicular tissue and a plant material, alfalfa. *Biochem Biophys Res Commun* 1980; 96: 47–53.

9. Jackson IMD: Abundance of immunoreactive thyrotropin-releasing hormone-like material in the alfalfa plant. *Endocrinology* 1981; 108: 344–346.

10. Masson MA, Moreau O, Debuire B, et al.: Evidence for the resistance of thyrotropin-releasing hormone (TRH) and pseudo-hormone, pyroglutamyl histidyl-amphetamine, to degradation by enzymes of the digestive tract in vitro. *Biochemie* 1979; 61: 847–852.

11. Staub JJ, Girard J, Mueller-Brand J, et al.: Blunting of TSH response after repeated oral administration of TRH in normal and hypothyroid subjects. *J Clin Endocrinol Metab* 1978; 46: 260–263.

12. Cookson FB, Fedoroff SR: Quantitative relationships between administered cholesterol and alfalfa required to prevent hypercholesterolemia in rabbits. *Br J Exp Pathol* 1968; 49: 348–351.

13. Malinkow MR, McLaughlin P, Naito HK, et al.: Effect of alfalfa meal on shrinkage (regression) of atherosclerotic plaques during cholesterol feeding in monkeys. *Atherosclerosis* 1978; 30: 27–43.

14. Malinkow MR: Hypocholesterolemic effect of alfalfa meal in monkeys is not due to thyroid stimulation. *Proc Soc Exp Biol Med* 1983; 169: 110–112.

15. Morley JE, Garvin TJ, Pekary AE, et al.: Thyrotropin-releasing hormone in the gastrointestinal tract. *Biochem Biophys Res Commun* 1977; 79: 314–318.

16. Dolva O, Hanssen KF, Berstad A: Thyrotropin-releasing hormone inhibits the pentagastrin stimulated secretion in man: a dose response study. *Clin Endocrinol* 1979; 10: 281–286.

17. Morley JE, Steinbach JH, Feldman EJ, et al.: The effects of thyrotropin-releasing hormone (TRH) on the gastrointestinal tract. *Life Sci* 1979; 24: 1059–1066.

18. Hutton SW, Morley JE, Parent MK, et al.: Thyrotropin-releasing hormone (TRH) suppresses gastric acid output in patients with Zollinger-Ellison syndrome and systemic mastocytosis. *Am J Med* 1981; 71: 957–960.

19. Gullo L, Labo G: Thyrotropin-releasing hormone inhibits pancreatic enzyme secretion in humans. *Gastroenterology* 1981; 80: 735–739.

20. Mycroft FJ, Wei ET, Bernardin JE, et al.: MIF-like sequences in milk and wheat proteins. *N Engl J Med* 1982; 307: 895.

21. Mercier JC, Grosclaude F, Ribadeau-Dumas B: Amino-acid composition and sequence of bovine kappa casein. *Neth Milk Dairy J* 1973; 27: 313–322.

22. Plotnikoff NP, Minard FN, Kastin AJ: DOPA potentiation in ablated animals and brain levels of biogenic amines in intact animals after prolylleucylglycinamide. *Neuroendocrinology* 1974; 14: 271–277.

23. Itit M, Laudahn G, Herman WM: *Psychotropic Action of Hormones.* New York, S Karger, 1974.

24. Kastin AJ, Olson RD, Schally AV, et al.: CNS effects of peripherally administered brain peptides. *Life Sci* 1979; 25: 401–411.

25. Dohan FC, Grasberger JC: Relapsed schizophrenics: Earlier discharge from hospital after cereal-free milk-free diet. *Am J Psych* 1973; 130: 685–688.

26. Singh MM, Kay SR: Wheat gluten as a pathogenic factor in schizophrenia. *Science* 1976; 191: 401–402.

27. Guillemin R: Biochemical and physiological correlates of hypothalamic peptides. The new endocrinology of the neuron, in Reichlin S, Baldessarini RJ, Martin JB (eds): *The Hypothalamus.* New York, Raven, 1978, pp 155–194.

28. Zioudrou C, Streaty RA, Klee WA: Opioid peptides derived from food proteins: the exorphins. *J Biol Chem* 1979; 254: 2446–2449.

29. Brantl V, Teschemacher H: A material with opioid activity in bovine milk and milk products. *Naunyn Schmiedebergs Arch Pharmacol* 1979; 306: 301–304.

30. Brantl V, Teschemacher H, Henschen A, et al.: Novel opioid peptides derived from casein (β-casomorphin). *Hoppe Seylers Z Physiol Chem* 1979; 360: 1211–1216.

31. Henschen A, Lottspeich F, Brantl V, et al.: Novel opioid peptides derived from casein (β-casomorphins). II. Structure of active components from bovine casein peptone. *Hoppe Seylers Z Physiol Chem* 1979; 360: 1217–1222.

32. Lottspeich F, Henschen A, Brantl V, et al.: Novel opioid peptides derived from casein (β-casomorphins). III. Synthetic peptides corresponding to components from bovine casein peptone. *Hoppe Seylers Z Physiol Chem* 1980; 361: 1835–1837.

33. Brantl V, Teschemacher H, Blasig J, et al.: Opioid activities of β-casomorphins. *Life Sci* 1981; 28: 1903–1909.

34. Hemmings WA: The entry into the brain of large molecules derived from dietary protein. *Proc Roy Soc Lond* 1978; 200: 175–192.

35. Hemmings C, Hemmings WA, Patey AI, et al.: The ingestion of dietary protein as large molecular mass degradation products in adult rats. *Proc Roy Soc Lond* 1977; 198: 439–453.

36. Schusdziarra V, Schick A, DeLaFuentl A, et al.: Effect of β-casomorphins and analogs on insulin release in dogs. *Endocrinology* 1983; 112: 885–889.

37. Brantl V, Teschemacher H, Blasig J, et al.: Opioid activities of β-casomorphins. *Life Sci* 1981; 28: 1903–1909.

38. Chang K-J, Killian A, Hazum E, et al.: Morphiceptin (NH_4-tyr-pro-phe-pro-$CONH_2$): a potent and specific agonist for morphine (μ) receptors. *Science* 1981; 212: 75–76.

39. Schusdziarra V, Henrichs I, Holland A, et al.: Evidence for an effect of exorphins on plasma insulin and glucagon levels in dogs. *Diabetes* 1981; 30: 362–364.

40. Schusdziarra V, Holland A, Schick R, et al.: Modulation of post-prandial insulin release by ingested opiate-like substances in dogs. *Diabetologia* 1983; 24: 113–116.

41. Morley JE, Levine AS, Yamada T, et al.: Effect of exorphins on gastrointestinal function, hormonal release and appetite. *Gastroenterology* 1983; 84: 1517–1523.

42. Arimura A: Recent progress in somatostatin research. *Biomed Res* 1981; 2: 233–257.

43. Morley JE: The neuroendocrine control of appetite: The role of the endogenous opiates, cholecystokinin, TRH, gamma-amino butyric acid and the diazepam receptor. *Life Sci* 1980; 27: 355–368.

44. Morley JE, Levine AS: The role of the endogenous opiates as regulators of appetite. *Am J Clin Nutr* 1982; 35: 757–761.

45. Morley JE, Levine AS, Yim GKW, et al.: Opioid modulation of appetite. *Neurosci Biobehav Rev* 1983; 7: 281–305.

46. Boubik JH, Quinn MJ, Clements JA, et al.: Coffee contains potent opiate receptor binding activity. *Nature* 1983; 301: 246–248.

47. Fiddian-Green RG, Farrell J, Havlichek D Jr, et al.: A physiological role for luminal gastrin? *Surgery* 1978; 83: 663–668.

48. Krawisz BR: Gastric luminal gastrin release in man: effects of calcium and pH. *Gastroenterology* 1978; 74: 1173A.

49. Uvnas-Wallensten K, Efendie S, Luft R: Vagal release of somatostatin into the antral lumen of cats. *Acta Physiol Scand* 1977; 99: 126–128.

50. Hanssen LE, Hanssen KF, Myren J: Immunoreactive secretin is released into the duodenal juice. *Scand J Gastroenterol* 1978; 13: 79A.

51. Uvnas-Wallensten K: Vagal release of antral hormones, in Bloom SR (ed): *Gut Hormones.* Edinburgh, Churchill-Livingstone, 1978, pp 389–393.

52. Miller LJ, Go VLW: Intraluminal gastrointestinal hormones and their radioimmunoassay, in Glass GBJ (ed): *Gastrointestinal Hormones.* New York, Raven, 1980, pp 863–874.

53. Hanssen LE, Myren J: Intraluminal gastrointestinal hormones and their radioimmunoassay, in Glass GBJ (ed): *Gastrointestinal Hormones.* New York, Raven, 1980, pp 855–862.

54. Shinsky CA, Martin JL, Wolfe MM, et al.: Do gut peptides work solely through an endocrine mechanism? Alteration of intestinal motility after luminal infusion of cholecystokinin. *Clin Res* 1981; 29: 312A.

55. Hedenbro JL, Fink AS, Fiddian-Green RG: Binding of luminal gastrin to canine parietal mucosa in vitro. *Gastroenterology* 1978; 74: 1045A.

56. Hedenbro JL, Fink AS, Fiddian-Green RG: Directions of access to gastrin receptor sites in canine parietal mucosa. *Scand J Gastroenterol* 1978; 13: 84A.

CHAPTER TWELVE

ORTHOMOLECULAR PSYCHIATRY

RICHARD A. KUNIN, MD

Orthomolecular treatment of mental disorders remains in dispute. In particular, no progress has been made towards resolving the controversy over megavitamin therapy for schizophrenia. In the past 10 years no large-scale studies have been carried out and only the persistence of individual clinicians, spurred by therapeutic successes with individual patients, keeps the issue alive.

Progress in orthomolecular medicine has come in other areas of theory and practice: (1) appreciation of orthomolecular actions of almost all vitamins, minerals, and amino acids as well as accessory food substances, (2) recognition of the special importance of ω-3 essential fatty acids, (3) discovery of the important role of antioxidant systems in modulating the effects of metabolic, toxic, and allergic mechanisms of symptom production, and (4) accomplishment of cell and brain tissue grafts.

There is accumulating information to document the vital role that nutrients play in brain function. The information gathered thus far overwhelms our comprehension and is rejected by the many health professionals who still regard nutrient therapy as a dead issue. On the other hand, those engaged in orthomolecular practice have seen beneficial results in treating anxiety, depression, schizophrenia, mania, alcoholism, addiction, neurasthenia, hypochondriasis, learning disorders, and organic brain disorders.

Medical disorders also respond with sufficient frequency to justify calling orthomolecular nutrient therapy the basis of a "New Medicine." Certainly the return of the medical model in the orthomolecular approach heralds a "New Psychiatry." At a time when most conventional psychiatrists are unprepared to offer even a physical examination, when clinical malnutrition stalks medical and psychiatric wards in this nation, and when the public consciousness recognizes the importance of nutrition in health only the orthomolecular physician and psychiatrist are prepared to treat the total person—mind and body—in the context of diet and disease.

PHYSIOLOGICAL RATIONALE FOR VITAMIN THERAPY

"Orthomolecular psychiatric therapy is the treatment of mental disease by the provision of the optimum molecular environment for the mind, especially the optimum concentrations of substances normally present in the human body." That 1968 statement by Linus Pauling[1] gave a scientific identity to the role of nutrition in psychiatry, and made nutrient and megavitamin therapies more of a challenge to the scientific establishment of the day.

In a footnote Dr. Pauling admitted that the word *orthomolecular* "may be criticized as a Greek-Latin hybrid. I have not, however, found any other word that expresses as well the idea of the right molecules in the right amounts." Dr. Pauling went on to explain that molecular concentrations influence rates of chemical reaction. He referred to the Michaelis-Menten equation, which shows that reaction rate is in direct proportion to the concentrations of enzyme and substrate.

> The rate of an enzyme-catalyzed reaction is approximately proportional to the concentration of the reactant, until concentrations that largely saturate the enzyme are reached. The saturating concentration is larger for a defective enzyme with decreased combining power for the substrate than for the normal enzyme. For such a defective enzyme the catalyzed reaction could be made to take place at or near its normal rate by an increase in the substrate concentration.

This is one basis for the success of megavitamin therapy.

The existence of localized cerebral deficiency disease is another rationale for vitamin therapy. Pauling predicted that,

> There is the possibility that some human beings have a sort of cerebral scurvy, without any of the other manifestations, or a sort of cerebral pellagra, or cerebral pernicious anemia. . . . The localized deficiency diseases . . . are also molecular diseases, compound molecular diseases, involving not only the original lesion, the loss of the ability to synthesize the vital substance, but also another lesion, one that causes a decreased rate of transfer across a membrane, such as the blood-brain barrier, to the affected organ, or an increased rate of destruction of the vital substance in the organ.

In other words, he proposed that for some persons the cerebrospinal concentration of a vital substance may be grossly low while its concentration in the blood and lymph is essentially normal.

SUPPORT FROM CLINICAL TRIALS

In 1983 CJM van Tiggelen et al.[2] verified this discordance: he noted a normal serum B_{12} but deficiency in the cerebrospinal fluid in 5 of 6 patients with alcoholic dementia, 9 of 12 patients with senile dementia, 8 of 16 patients with organic affective syndrome, and 8 of 10 patients with postpartum depression. Overall, these investigators found normal serum but low cerebrospinal fluid levels of B_{12} in 26 of 45 patients with an organic mental disorder. B_{12} was low in both blood and cerebrospinal fluid in an additional 4 patients. A control group of 12 patients free of depression or dementia all had normal levels of the vitamin in both blood and spinal fluid.

In an extension of the trial, patients received 6 weeks of supplementation with oral B_{12} (cyanocobalamin), 100 μg/day. This therapy was not effective in raising cerebrospinal fluid levels of B_{12}. Only after parenteral administration of B_{12}, 1000 μg twice weekly, did cerebrospinal B_{12} increase. A megadose of the vitamin was necessary in order to obtain therapeutic benefits.

In 1939 Cleckley et al.[3] reported 19 cases of atypical psychotic states responsive to treatment with nicotinic acid, at doses up to 300 mg/day intravenously. Some of these, in which cerebral manifestations were recognized as the first evidence of severe depletion of nicotinic acid in arteriosclerosis, alcoholism, or syphilis, were defined as "cerebral pellagra." In 1941 the authors reported an additional 29 cases whom they treated with doses of nicotinic acid up to 1500 mg/day orally.[4] They reported, "Usually the response to nicotinic acid was prompt, often it was spectacular," and, "A therapeutic trial of nicotinic acid is the only means available by which one can determine whether or not the psychosis is due to avitaminosis."

This breakthrough in the treatment of organic psychoses (and schizophrenia) was almost completely forgotten for the next decade, until the pioneering work of Hoffer, Osmond, and Smythies led to "megavitamin therapy." Dr. Hoffer was Director of Psychiatric Research for the province of Saskatchewan. Dr. Osmond was clinical director of the Weyburn Hospital and, with Dr. John Smythies, had pioneered the theory that oxidized adrenaline in the brain might cause schizophrenia.

Adrenaline is formed by methylation of noradrenaline, and these researchers theorized that niacin, which becomes methylnicotinamide, might compete for methyl groups and thus diminish the formation of brain adrenaline. If so, this would in turn diminish the amount of oxidized adrenaline and thus prevent hallucinations and other symptoms of schizophrenia. Their early research confirmed that adrenochrome and adrenolutin, both derived from oxidized adrenaline, are hallucinogens.[5] Thus encouraged, they proceeded to formally test niacin and niacinamide in schizophrenic patients in the first psychiatric studies to use the double-blind method.

Their first major paper[6] summarized the results in 30 schizophrenic patients treated with or without 3 g/day of niacin or niacinamide. All patients also received barbiturates and electroconvulsive therapy as needed. Phenothiazine drugs were not yet in use. At the end of a year, 3 of 9 placebo-treated patients were well compared to 8 of 10 on niacin and 9 of 11 on niacinamide. The overall recovery rate was 33 percent in the placebo group and 82 percent in the vitamin-treated group.

In 1962 Osmond and Hoffer[7] published a review of 9 years of follow-up on 73 schizophrenics treated with and 98 treated without niacin. In the first 3 years (1952–1955), the niacin group had a 10 percent readmission rate and no suicides. The other group had a 50 percent readmission rate and four suicides. At 3 years the readmission rates equalized, perhaps related to the introduction of phenothiazines.

In a second double-blind study, Hoffer[8] reported a 5-year niacin cure rate of 55 percent (34 of 62) compared to 20 percent (4 of 20) in the placebo-treatment group. This may have been the longest serial, double-blind study ever conducted in psychiatry. Twenty patients were maintained on placebo for the 5 years, while 25 were treated with niacin. In addition, 8 received placebo in the hospital and were discharged on niacin, and 29 were treated in the hospital with niacin and were discharged on placebo. Patients on niacin showed a significant advantage, relapsing only 7 of 118 patient-years. Those on placebo had frequent relapses, equaling 60 of 182 patient-years. Readmission rates during the fifth follow-up year were 50 percent for patients on placebo but only 20 percent for those receiving niacin.

Denson[9] initiated a double-blind study of 36 male schizophrenics treated with electroconvulsive therapy (ECT). Seventeen patients received 3 g niacinamide and 19 patients received placebo for a 5-week period. In a 1-year follow-up, patients in the vitamin-treatment group spent 1810 days in the hospital whereas those in the placebo group spent 3373 days. This averages to 15 and 25 weeks per patient for the vitamin and placebo groups, respectively. Dr. Denson found this to be significant evidence "that nicotinamide therapy can shorten the length of stay in hospital for schizophrenic patients."

In 1964 Hoffer and Osmond[10] stated, in reference to a 10-year follow-up of their initial studies, "No statistical finesse is required to see that the nicotinic acid patients fared much better than the others. Twelve of 16 or 75 percent of the nicotinic acid group did not require readmissions for 10 years, i.e., there has been a 75 percent 10-year cure rate. Ten of 27 or 36 percent of the non-vitamin-treated comparison group were 10-year cures."

A 1966 report[11] compared 128 schizophrenics receiving niacin treatment with 346 others in conventional treatment by psychiatrists who only occasionally used megavitamin therapy. The investigator noted readmission rates of 40 percent in the vitamin group and 50 percent in the other. Although these numbers are not significantly different, the author also found that the vitamin-treated group spent 7422 days in hospital as compared to 54,491 hospital days in the other group, a sevenfold difference. Furthermore, there were six suicides among non-vitamin-treated patients but none among those receiving vitamins.

This study also showed that most *chronic* schizophrenics do not recover with megadose niacin treatment. This observation had first been suggested from the earlier study results and was confirmed in 1955 by O'Reilly.[12] At the urging of Dr. Hoffer, O'Reilly studied the effects of a gram of niacin, three times per day for 8 weeks, given to 11 refractory and deteriorated schizophrenic female patients (5 of these patients had had a lobotomy). The niacin treatment did not produce improvement in schizophrenic symptoms; however, there was some behavioral improvement in comparison with a group of 43 untreated schizophrenic patients (19 with lobotomy). Three niacin-treated patients quadrupled and two tripled their behavior rating scores, and this behavioral improvement was significant. Despite the lack of effect on the schizophrenia per se, all niacin-treated patients improved in sleep and appetite and half were more directable and less combative.

In 1973, Ananth et al.[13] reported that pyridoxine potentiated the therapeutic effects of nicotinic acid in chronic schizophrenics. In their double-blind study, 30 patients were assigned to a group receiving one of three treatments—niacin, pyridoxine, or their combination—for 48 weeks. The authors concluded,

> Of the three indices of therapeutic effects, global improvement in psychopathology scores was seen in all three groups; the number of days in hospital during the period of the clinical study was lower in both the nicotinic acid and the combined group (than the pyridoxine group); and only in the combined treatment group was the daily average dosage of phenothiazine medication decreased. Thus, improvement in all three indices was noted in the combined treatment group.

THE CONTROVERSY

The American Psychiatric Association issued a Task Force Report in 1973 entitled "Megavitamin and Orthomolecular Therapy in Psychiatry." This report found the evidence for megavitamins in the treatment of schizophrenia to be "wanting." It also criticized leaders of the orthomolecular movement for propagation of an "unproved" theory to the lay public.

This report leaned heavily on The Canadian Mental Health Collaborative Studies to support their negative conclusions, although only 4 of 12 studies had actually been completed at that time. The Ananth et al. study[13] was published in 1973, and one of its lead investigators was a member of the task force; yet there is no reference to this paper in the task force bibliography. Furthermore, there is no mention of its positive finding: that even in chronic schizophrenia cases megavitamin therapy, particularly combined niacin and pyridoxine, can prove beneficial. Instead, the APA report refers to Ban and Lehmann[14] to convey the negative opinion that "the overall therapeutic efficacy of combined administration of nicotinic acid and pyridoxine as an adjuvant medication in chronically hospitalized schizophrenic patients is inferior to the overall therapeutic efficacy of the component drugs."

The contradiction between these two quotes from the same authors is baffling. That their results failed to confirm the Hoffer and Osmond studies is not surprising; they did not perform a true replication of the earlier research. In particular they did not use ECT at all in their studies. More important, they did use phenothiazines and at doses that might be considered "megadrug" therapy.

Thioridizine was the preferred phenothiazine in these studies, and it is notoriously sedative. Is there any doubt that high doses of neuroleptic drugs can obscure the sense of well-being that is usually reported by patients on nutrient therapy? As for the reports of negative effects of megadose niacin, these undoubtedly are due to the fixed dose requirements of the research and do not make allowance for skin flush and stomach irritation, both of which are dealt with in orthomolecular practice by individual adjustment of dose in relation to the patient's response.

There is also a question of bias in the task force report: research studies favorable to orthomolecular treatment are omitted from the task force report or interpreted negatively. For example, a large double-blind study by Wittenborn et al.[15] had some intriguing findings in support of the orthomolecular hypothesis; yet here is what the task force said:

> We are left with a sense of puzzlement as to why the results of serious and major attempts to demonstrate the value of nicotinic acid have been so uniformly negative in the hands of independent investigators. Not only have no statistical differences been found, but the possibility of a small subgroup that is responsive in a large heterogeneous group of schizophrenics appears to be minimal because no dramatic individual recoveries have been reported in these studies. If such a subgroup exists, it would consist of those patients with good premorbid interpersonal history such as those found by Wittenborn in a retrospective study. Wittenborn questions the aptness of the term *schizophrenic* for such patients.

The conclusion of the task force is clear: "There was no difference in readmission rate nor in need for tranquilizers . . . a clear failure to replicate any general efficacy of niacin in the treatment of schizophrenia."

Yet, in the next paragraph the task force presents a contradiction favorable to megavitamins. They wrote, "Wittenborn considers his data to be consistent with the possibility that as many as one quarter of his schizophrenic population (those with good premorbid adjustment) might be benefited by the addition of niacin to the psychotropic drug treatment." This is immediately retracted by this negative speculation: "The fact that he finds no significant difference between the total control group and the total vitamin group implies that a fraction of his experimental population may have had their progress impeded by the vitamin addition."

But the fact is that Wittenborn[16] wrote a 2-year follow-up paper that confirmed that 85 percent of the niacin-treated group with positive personality test scores did show treatment benefits from megadose niacin. He found contrary results in the control group. That is, a good pre-illness personality was disadvantageous for the patients on psychotropic medications without niacin.

It is hard to believe that anyone would interpret this study as evidence against megavitamin therapy! Yet, it was the kingpin of the task force report. And 2 years after the task force, Ban and Lehmann[17] were still waxing negative: "the niacin group showed a slight trend in the direction of a lessened sense of responsibility, less self-confidence, and more complaints of not feeling well; and . . . home and community adjustment was more favorable in the control group than in the niacin group. Needless to say, these results are in line with the findings in the CMHA Collaborative Study."

IN SUPPORT OF ORTHOMOLECULAR PSYCHIATRY

Such a blatant contradiction can only be answered by directly consulting the research in question. Wittenborn, for one, conducted his 2-year, double-blind study with 75 male schizophrenic patients, 47 of whom received 3 g/day of niacin and 28 of whom were controls. There were 69 patients available at the 2-year follow-up, and 24 of these had high predictor scores. Of those with high predictors, 12 were on niacin and 12 were on placebo. After 2 years 10 of 12 on niacin were rated as high as their pre-illness score; only 5 of 12 of the control patients scored as well. The author inferred, "Thus, when patients with a good predictor score are considered, there were twice as many with a good outpatient adjustment score in the niacin supplementation group as in the control group." Wittenborn's conclusion speaks for itself with final authority, though it was designed as a hypothesis: "Those patients with conditions diagnosed as schizophrenia who come to treatment with a history of strong interpersonal commitments will respond to niacin supplemental therapy."

The data also showed that among control patients receiving only phenothiazine tranquilizers a good pre-illness personality was relatively disadvantageous. These worsened whereas comparable patients in the niacin group improved. Convinced that this was not a statistical artifact, Wittenborn put forth this possible explanation: "Niacin aids patients with a good premorbid personality by helping them resist a burdening effect of phenothiazine treatment."

The task force report concluded that orthomolecular treatment and megavitamin therapy are ineffective, yet their chief investigator concluded, from the same data, that a large group of schizophrenics do respond favorably to niacin therapy. Specifically, Wittenborn showed that those patients with a good pre-illness personality adjustment can respond favorably to combination treatment with orthomolecular components. Those schizophrenics receiving phenothiazines without niacin are burdened by side effects, including mental torpor, sedation, tremor, rigidity, and akathisia.

The point is that the pillar of the negative task force report ultimately interpreted the data to be positive. He came across in support of the use of niacin in treating schizophrenia. He called for further research into a promising hypothesis, work that has not been done in the ensuing 10 years since the report.

With this in mind, the final paragraph of the task force report undeniably conveys bias. In contradistinction to the actual data at its disposal, the task force report concluded with a pejorative statement that "the massive publicity which they promulgate . . . using catch phrases which are really misnomers like 'megavitamin therapy' and 'orthomolecular treatment' [is] deplorable."

A publication by Hoffer and Osmond[18] entitled "Megavitamin Therapy, in Reply to the American Psychiatric Association Task Force Report" was especially critical of the report's negative bias. Among other things they noted an imbalance in the task force's citations: while omitting half of the reports favorable to vitamin therapy the committee included all 13 unfavorable reports. The authors explained,

> Because the committee ignored so many reports favorable to orthomolecular therapy while paying attention to any negative report, however obscure, it becomes possible to give their bias a mathematical form by using a frequency distribution and the null hypothesis. . . . This shows that the betting odds that the committee surveyed the literature fairly is less than 0.001, or one in a thousand that such a bias occurred by chance alone.

Furthermore, Hoffer and Osmond took issue with some of the negative reports. In response to Wittenborn's conclusion that patients responding to niacin therapy were not really schizophrenic the authors point out that "if this suggestion is accepted seriously, the whole study must be in jeopardy. For who would give a moment's consideration to an investigation in which the chief scientist reports that one third of the patients did not have the illness being studied?" The authors assert that Wittenborn's patients did not include schizophrenic and nonschizophrenic individuals, but rather were of acute or chronic schizophrenic types. This led them to claim:

> As a result, the double-blind study as a whole yielded no significant difference. However, when the groups were purified (made more homogeneous) by using indications which sorted the early from late cases, the differences in the early cases became highly significant. The chronic cases should have been given ECT in combination with vitamin if it had been designed to repeat our original double-blind experiment.

Hoffer and Osmond are particularly critical of the fact that the studies identified as acute many patients who actually were chronic cases, but "newly admitted."

The authors further find fault with the double-blind method in studies of orthomolecular treatment, both ethically and scientifically, for the following reasons: (1) the design assumes that the comparison groups will be equivalent, but psychiatric populations are heterogeneous, (2) it is inappropriate to use short-term treatment for chronic patients, but chronic double-blind experiments are difficult to control so they are seldom used, (3) double-blind conditions not only destroy the placebo effect but induce a negative, antitherapeutic effect into the doctor-patient relationship, and (4) the method has not been proven to work and, in fact, it often gives false-negative results. Thus, despite the scientific importance of the double-blind trial, clinical observation and case studies remain indispensible for the schizophrenic population.

ESTABLISHING CREDIBILITY—A HISTORICAL REVIEW

Most of the major discoveries in this century were accomplished without double-blind trial. In many cases creative thinking established a hypothesis, and statistical methods were used to test the hypotheses under specific conditions. When it is not possible to duplicate the conditions of the original observations, they stand or fall on the basis of their reality and accuracy of description.

Individual patients are not concerned whether a treatment has been validated by double-blind study, but that it works in their case. From this perspective, it is clear that nutrient therapy is helpful to some patients because dramatic recoveries from various forms of mental illness have occurred after orthomolecular intervention. The real issues are, who does it help, at what dose, and why does it work?

The controversy is based in the absolute rejection of the orthomolecular concept by the psychiatric establishment. Practitioners, too busy to study the issues thoroughly, are necessarily cautious about going against the mainstream at a time when malpractice litigation and peer review have become fearsome forces in shaping the behaviors of physicians. Nevertheless, there is credible evidence that nutrient therapy is beneficial in all types of mental disorders. Benefits have been reported not only with megadoses of niacin and niacinamide but with almost all vitamins and minerals.

Vitamin C has proved to be particularly important. VanderKamp[19] and Pauling[20] showed that urinary ascorbate levels were significantly lower in schizophrenic patients than in normal volunteers after loading doses of vitamin C. Experimental ascorbate deficiency caused mood depression—subjectively and as measured by the Minnesota Multiphasic Test—within 10 weeks in studies by Kinsman and Hood.[21] In a study by Kubala and Katz,[22] schoolchildren with vitamin C blood levels below the mean had IQ scores five points lower than those whose vitamin C level was above the mean; supplementation with vitamin C reversed this negative trend.

Milner's double-blind study[23] of ascorbic acid given to 40 chronic psychiatric patients first asserted the psychiatric effects of vitamin C. He studied 34 schizophrenic and 4 manic-depressive patients with an average hospital stay of almost 18 years. Twenty patients received 1 g daily of ascorbic acid and 20 received placebo. Ward observations and psychological tests at 3 weeks showed that "statistically significant improvement in the depressive, manic, and paranoid complexes, together with an overall improvement in personality functioning, was obtained following saturation with ascorbic acid."

VanderKamp found that hospitalized schizophrenic patients benefitted from vitamin C, and they required an average of 40 g/day ascorbate load before spilling over into urine excretion. Large doses of the vitamin yielded a definite improvement: patients socialized more and expressed a feeling of well-being. The author reported that "the anxious, tense facial expression was replaced with a smile and friendliness. They stated that they didn't feel so 'hemmed in,' 'people didn't seem to be so against me,' 'I can now think more clearly.' "

Analgesic and antiaddiction effects have also been observed with megadose ascorbate intake. Cameron and Pauling[24] found that terminal cancer patients required remarkably little analgesic medication when treated with ascorbate doses above 10 g/day. Libby and Stone[25] found that ascorbate greatly attenuated narcotic withdrawal symptoms, and referred to many cases in which the increased well-being was instrumental in successful completion of an acute withdrawal treatment program. Free and Sanders,[26] working in a municipal drug treatment center, confirmed these results and concluded, "the ascorbic acid procedure is slightly more effective than symptomatic medications in alleviating narcotic withdrawal symptoms."

Spector[27] found that ascorbate levels in rat brains doubled after megadose intake of ascorbic acid. And Tolbert[28] found dopamine-blocking effects at megadoses comparable to 20 g or more in humans: rats, with one-sided lesions in the extrapyramidal system, exhibited turning behavior after amphetamine stimulation, which was blocked by haloperidol—and by megadoses of ascorbate.

Rebec et al.[29] confirmed these results, finding that "in standard animal tests, ascorbic acid (AA) enhances the antipsychotic and extrapyramidal actions of haloperidol. . . . Our results point to AA as critical in modulating the behavioral effects of haloperidol. As AA concentrations increase, the response to haloperidol is enhanced."

The nature of the cellular action of megadose niacinamide was discovered by Möhler et al.,[30] who found that benzodiazepine drugs bind to niacinamide receptors in the brain. Intraperitoneal injections of the vitamin cross the blood-brain barrier with only 0.3 percent efficiency so that megadoses of vitamin are comparable to lower doses to the drugs and have similar tranquilizing effects. Recent clinical reports of benzodiazepine efficacy in schizophrenia make this all the more significant.

Other B vitamins (particularly thiamine, pyridoxine, and cobalamin) have also been found useful in the treatment of schizophrenia. Joshi and Eswaran[31] reported results from 60 first-episode, acute schizophrenic patients receiving daily injection of these vitamins for a month—under double-blind conditions. Efficacy was measured as a reduction in number of modified ECT required. There were 48 ECT in the vitamin group and 70 in the placebo group (with one less patient).

Joshi et al.[32] also found that the recovery from schizophrenia was retarded by the injections of thiamine, pyridoxine, or cobalamin. The author theorized that this might be due to "normalization" of postsynaptic neurons, which thus escape from dopamine blockade by phenothiazine as the drug dose is lowered. They advised cautious management of vitamin-treated patients receiving doses of chlorpromazine below 150 mg.

More research clearly is indicated. Joshi and Eswaran note that, "Despite their importance, these neurotropic vitamins B_1, B_6, and B_{12} do not appear to have been well tried in the therapy of schizophrenia."

How about the effects of niacin, which is generally more effective against schizophrenia than is niacinamide? Kunin[33] was first to theorize that the antischizophrenic effect of niacin might be related to its interaction with the prostaglandins. The evidence for this came from the observation that the skin-flush reaction, which is triggered by niacin but not niacinamide, can be prevented by pretreatment with aspirin. Because aspirin is a known inhibitor of prostaglandin formation, an interaction with this hormone system is possible. It is also well known that by increasing the dose of niacin a paradoxic dose at which the flush no longer occurs is eventually reached. In other words, at the larger dose, niacin blocks its own flush, presumably exerting anti-inflammatory activity by altering histamine and prostaglandin (PG) levels.

Schizophrenics are commonly resistant to the niacin flush or require higher doses to induce flush than do normal subjects. Horrobin[34] found that primrose oil, which contains the PGE precursor γ-linolenic acid (GLA), lessens the amount of niacin required to provoke a skin-flush response. He proposed that this could be used as a clinical test of response to therapy. As patients recover from schizophrenia, the flush response to niacin is restored at lower dose.

Horrobin was aware that all antischizophrenic drugs increase prolactin secretion from the pituitary. On further study[35] he found that prolactin stimulates production of PGs of the 1 series. He postulated a role for PG_1 deficiency in schizophrenia and confirmed this by testing the platelets of 20 patients with ADP provocation of PG release. He found that all 20 schizophrenics failed to increase PGE_1, whereas by comparison, 3 normal, 10 depressed, and 8 manic patients all increased PGE_1 up to fivefold, the manics rating the highest. The probability that this occurred by chance is $1:10^7$.

Horrobin proposed that, "The prolactin effect and the platelet studies therefore point to a failure of normal formation of 1 series PGs coupled with normal or perhaps excess formation of 2 series PGs (because of removal of PGE_1 control) in schizophrenics." He speculated that inflammatory diseases such as rheumatoid arthritis (which seldom coexist with schizophrenia) and fevers may produce remission because they generate PG synthesis.

Horrobin further postulated that chronic overstimulation of opiate receptors (by stress and by ingestion of dietary exorphins) might induce dopamine supersensitivity, and thus predispose to schizophrenia. Exorphins are known to be present in wheat and milk, and both are associated with worsening of schizophrenia. Double-blind studies by Dohan[36] and by Singh and Kay[37] demonstrated a 50 percent reduction in hospital recovery time for acute schizophrenics who were removed from wheat and milk. Horrobin proposes that the endorphins exert their influence in part through selectively inhibiting formation of PG_1 while sparing PG_2.

Other stimulators of PGE_1 include zinc, penicillin, and hyperthermia (e.g., sauna). The sauna is the most potent but it is not practical for sustained use. A 6-week test of penicillin V, 300 mg four times per day, showed that eight of ten who started and eight of nine who completed penicillin therapy did not relapse when abruptly withdrawn from phenothiazine. In a confirming study, six chronic schizophrenics who had failed to respond to traditional treatment did not worsen and most improved behaviorally while receiving penicillin and evening primrose oil.

Horrobin proposed a "rational" therapy of schizophrenia. This would include: (1) adequate amounts of PG precursors, (2) adequate amounts of cofactors required for PG synthesis, and (3) a pharmacological agent able to reverse the opiate inhibition of PG_1. Evening primrose oil is the premiere precursor of 1 series prostaglandins, zinc is the cofactor most often deficient (it is required by the δ-6-desaturase enzyme), and penicillin enhances production of PGE_1.

Rudin[38] showed that the ω-3 essential fatty acids (EFA) are an essential substrate for membrane lipids. Furthermore, their deficiency causes damage in every tissue in the body, but particularly in the primate brain where they make up about 50 percent of the lipids. Where Horrobin's research focused on a faulty enzyme, the δ-6-desaturase, Rudin recognized a new class of deficiency disease specific to primates, who share a unique requirement for ultrapolyunsaturated ω-3 EFA found in cold climate vegetable oils and marine oils. He concluded that "it is an assumption that our dominant diseases are unrelated to each other or are merely revealed by our diagnostic acumen and therapeutic success; and that hydrogenating millions of tons of food oils annually, to destroy the rancidity producing ω-3 EFA, is safe for primates."

However, Rudin points out, Fiennes, Sinclair, and Crawford[39] found that six capuchin monkeys became ill on a theoretically complete laboratory diet. The animals received corn oil as their only source of fat and thus received ω-6-linoleic acid but not ω-3-linolenic. This diet had been adequate for laboratory rats but never fully tested in primates.

Crawford and Sinclair had earlier reported[40] "that in 24 mammalian species, both the linoleic and linolenic series acids are structural components of brain, liver, and other tissues, and that the ratio is species and tissue specific." They subsequently found that monkeys receiving corn oil, which is devoid of ω-3 EFA, for 2 years became severely ill. They exhibited a syndrome that was similar to EFA deficiency disease: sparse hair, dry, scaling skin, enteritis, and immune system damage. Two animals were self-mutilating; they gnawed incessantly at their perineums, which became infected, and the monkeys had to be destroyed.

The addition of linseed oil to the monkeys' diet led to partial recovery in a week and almost complete recovery at 2 months. Linseed oil contains 58 percent α-linolenic acid, an ω-3 fatty acid that is not found in corn oil and is not interconvertible into γ-linolenic acid (an ω-6 fatty acid from primrose oil). Tissue samples from untreated animals showed severe fatty infiltration of the liver, adrenals, and

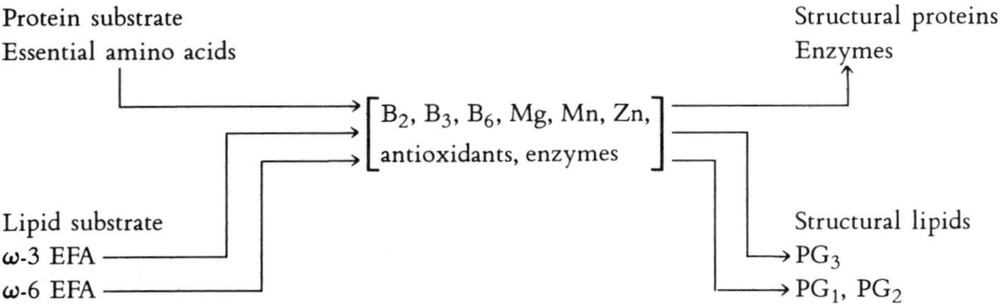

Figure 12.1 Rudin's concept of the fundamental reaction in nutrition.

kidneys (one animal developed rickets) and arrested maturation of lymphocytes in the spleen and Peyer's patches.

The diagram in Figure 12.1 clarifies Rudin's concept of *the fundamental reaction in nutrition.* Rudin views the syndrome of deficiency disease in a biochemical matrix of substrate, catalyst, and modulator, which produce structural and reactant products. Defective or deficient production of cellular constituents, including enzymes, membrane lipids, and prostaglandin hormones, accounts for illnesses.

Most of the illnesses have overlapping symptoms that can be viewed as mixtures of beriberi and pellagra; only the extreme cases look like the "classical" syndromes. The diagram clarifies why similar syndromes may respond in one case to substrate protein or lipid substance and in another to supplemental vitamins or minerals. Now that almost all catalyst-deficiency pellagra (niacin) has been eradicated by food enrichment, Rudin's concept of schizophrenia as a substrate-deficiency pellagra (α-linolenic acid) is quite plausible.

Rudin[41] observed sustained benefits in an uncontrolled pilot study of 12 cases of schizophrenia, manic depressive psychosis, and phobic neurosis. During a 2-year follow-up, patients were treated with 5 to 90 ml of linseed oil. It was interesting that in many instances he found megadose vitamins to cause adverse effects. Others have confirmed these remarkable benefits with individual patients, but the hypothesis has not yet had large-scale clinical trials.

Gilka[42] has authored a well-integrated review of the biochemistry of schizophrenia. Her point of departure is that schizophrenia is commonly due to an inborn error of metabolism, most likely a defect in the tryptophan pathway at the point of activity of the enzyme, 3-hydroxyanthranilate oxidase.

Extensive research has revealed a typical pattern of four basic abnormalities that occur as a result of a defective or deficient enzyme: (1) increased metabolites proximal to the block, (2) decreased metabolites distal to it, (3) increased metabolites via alternate pathways, and (4) increased requirement for vitamins (to deal with the abnormal biochemistry). A load of tryptophan taken by schizophrenic patients exacerbates their symptoms. A similar exacerbation can be induced by methionine or other donors of methyl groups (e.g., betaine or cysteine) especially after pretreatment with monoamine oxidase inhibitors (MAOI). This suggests a relationship between tryptophan metabolites, methylation, and schizophrenia. Do research data fit the pattern of enzyme deficiency in the tryptophan pathway? Does methylation produce psychotogens? Gilka marshalls quite a bit of evidence to the point.

Distal to the blocked enzyme, pyridone is the main urinary breakdown product of niacin derived via the tryptophan pathway. Price, Brown, and Peters[43] gave a standard 2-g tryptophan load and found schizophrenics to have the lowest excretion of pyridone. This suggests a block in metabolism of tryptophan to niacin. Direct measurements have also shown niacin and nicotinamide adenine dinucleotide (NAD) to be decreased in schizophrenics.

Price et al. also found an increase in urinary metabolites from metabolic steps proximal to the enzyme block in schizophrenics: kynurenine, kynurenic acid, acetylkynurenine, *o*-aminohippuric acid, and 3-hydroxykynurenine.

Increased indole metabolites on minor pathways are also found; in particular, a marked increase of tryptamine urinary excretion was observed to precede the peak of psychotic symptoms in the study by Berlet.[44] Due to lack of MAO these indoles are inadequately deaminated and instead are dimethylated into hallucinogenic indoleamines: DMT (*NN*-dimethyltryptamine), bufotenin (5-hydroxy-*NN*-dimethyltryptamine), and 5MeO-DMT (5-methoxy-*NN*-dimethyltryptamine).

Transmethylation is the major alternative to oxidation of amines by MAO and is especially likely to occur when MAO activity is inhibited. The enzyme, *N*-methyltransferase (NMT), is present normally, and it can methylate normal metabolites into their dimethylated derivatives. Hence dimethylated metabolites are found in small quantities in the urine of normal subjects. But they are present more often and in higher concentrations in schizophrenics, especially during acute attacks.

Why the inhibition of MAO? Gilka says MAO enzymes are dependent on high energy bonds—ATP—in mitochondria. Mitochondrial efficiency is, in turn, dependent on NAD and NADP, which are decreased in schizophrenia due to insufficient production of niacin. Hence, the stage is set for dimethylation of metabolites in any blockade of the tryptophan-to-niacin pathway.

Methylation also occurs in the catecholamine pathway. A dimethylated derivative of dopamine, DMPEA (dimethyoxyphenylethylamine) appears in the urine of 90 percent of schizophrenics but only 52 percent of nonschizophrenic patients. Injection into humans causes experimental psychosis but only after pretreatment with MAOI, which makes it an unlikely cause of schizophrenia. It does support, however, the increased methylating activity in many schizophrenics.

Gilka's theory explains an increased requirement for vitamins in schizophrenia. Niacin is needed to make up for the decreased synthesis from tryptophan; thiamine protects the blood-brain barrier and diminishes penetration of psychotomimetic compounds; riboflavin is important in regeneration of MAO activity; ascorbate is needed to maintain the activity of the enzyme, 3-hydroxyanthranilase; and pyridoxine needs are increased to cope with the increased amine intermediates.

A rational treatment according to Gilka is (1) dietary restriction of the inadequately metabolized substrate (i.e., tryptophan), (2) supplementation of the missing product (i.e., niacin), (3) prevention of psychotogenic metabolites (i.e., dimethylated indoles) by restriction of methyl donor foods (e.g., methionine and betaine) and the use of phenothiazines, which inhibit methylation, and (4) increased intake of vitamins B_1, B_2, B_3, B_6, and C.

To detect carriers and to treat them preventively, Dr. Gilka recommends the tryptophan load test with measurement of pyridone and 5-hydroxy-indole acetic acid (5HIAA). Measurement of MAO and 3-hydroxyanthranilate oxygenase levels is also recommended for specific diagnosis.

In a separate thesis Gilka[45] proposed that hyperactivity in children may be tied to an inborn error of GABA metabolism, such that the normal inhibitory processes in the central nervous system are weakened. GABA is formed from glutamic acid and catalyzed by the enzyme glutamic acid decarboxylase (GAD). This enzyme is dependent on pyridoxal phosphate and is vulnerable to oxidation, low-protein diet, salicylates, phenols, and halogen ions, especially chlorine.

Free-radical damage to enzymes and to cell membranes has recently become appreciated as a possible common source of biochemical derangement. Hoffer[46] updated his adrenochrome hypothesis in 1981, emphasizing that oxidized adrenaline not only produces adrenochrome but also liberates a reactive free radical. In fact, all the psychoactive amines yield aminochromes and free radicals as oxidation products, and these intermediates are liable to cause damage, particularly if antioxidant enzymes, vitamins, and minerals are in short supply. The presence of these aminochromes has been confirmed by Galzigna[47] in 1970 and Graham[48] in 1978.

Hoffer has elucidated a number of important biochemical interactions. For example, he clarified that NAD is instrumental in preventing oxidation of adrenaline, thus preventing formation of excess adrenochrome. In the absence of NAD, oxidized adrenaline is irreversibly oxidized to adrenochrome. Any block in the tryptophan pathway can interfere with the production of niacin and NAD; also, niacin is lost in the urine when the diet is high in leucine, and this is reversed by isoleucine;[46] excess glycine also reduces the availability of niacin. All of these factors are known to influence schizophrenia.

Hoffer defends the validity of the adrenochrome theory over either the dopamine or methylation theories of schizophrenia: "Adrenochrome and adrenolutin are hallucinogens. This is an essential element of the adrenochrome hypothesis because it provides an explanation for the clinical symptomatology. The dopamine hypothesis does not provide for such an explanation unless it involves some aminochrome mechanism."[46]

One possible mechanism is the inactivation of catechol-*o*-methyltransferase (COMT) by an aminochrome from dopamine. The lack of COMT causes a shunt of catecholamines into oxidative pathways. Another aminochrome intermediate, this from the oxidation of serotonin, attacks the monoamine oxidase system, thus shunting indole metabolism to the production of toxic methylindoles. All these observations lend further weight to Hoffer's adrenochrome hypothesis.

Graham proposed that auto-oxidation of dopa and dopamine could cause cell injury due to production of free radicals and cytotoxic quinones. Hoffer further offers that niacinamide reduces oxidized adrenaline to adrenalin, and thus prevents cell damage due to formation of aminochromes. Perry[49] suggests that such damage can occur to nerve cells in Huntington's chorea, Parkinson's disease, and schizophrenia. He has found abnormally low levels of antioxidant glutathione enzymes in the substantia nigra of patients with parkinsonism, and from this he recommends that:

> One might very well, at the first signs of parkinsonism, use appropriate free-radical quencher, or appropriate stimulator of glutathione synthesis, and perhaps you could stop the deterioration of the nigrostriatal neurons at the 80 percent mark where first symptoms appear. . . . Another thing to think about is that the L-dopa which physicians are routinely giving to patients with parkinsonism, although it improves symptoms, may actually be exactly the wrong thing to do because it may actually hasten the neuronal death.

Another possible locus of free-radical damage is the choroid plexus. Recall that van Tiggelen found deficiency of B_{12} in the cerebrospinal fluid of patients with depression and organic brain diseases. Free-radical damage to the choroid plexus is one mechanism to account for the blockade of transport of B_{12} from blood to brain. He further proposed that zinc deficiency or, more precisely, excess copper induced by zinc deficiency, could activate free-radical production.

A ROLE FOR MINERALS

Until the early 1970s minerals were not considered important in orthomolecular psychiatry. Megavitamins held center stage until the work of Carl Pfeiffer blazed a trail of understanding of the role of the trace metals manganese, zinc, and copper that has clearly led to progress in treating schizophrenia and depression.

Pfeiffer's orthomolecular roots[50] date to the 1940s when he ran a research ward for chronically unresponsive schizophrenics. He tried therapy for these patients with such familiar substances as pyridoxine, methionine, glutamine, aspartic acid, tryptophan, calcium, magnesium, and cortisone without progress. He did observe that eosinophil counts were so low as to show the physiological state of the schizophrenic to be one of constant stress, which led him to investigate adrenaline and other catecholamines. He injected up to 7 mg IV of pure adrenochrome into volunteers without effect, other than purple urine. This convinced him that catecholamines had little to do with schizophrenia, and he turned his interests elsewhere. Unfortunately, Hoffer had not yet made his discovery[51] that silver ion renders adrenochrome inactive or Pfeiffer's conclusions might have been different. After removing silver contaminants, Hoffer's associate Payza was able to produce and stabilize adrenochrome; Czechoslovakian researchers have subsequently confirmed Hoffer's finding that adrenochrome is a "schizomimetic."

In 1954 Pfeiffer found that arecoline, the cholinergic substance from betel nuts, produced a lucid interval in severe schizophrenics. This led him to test deanol, the amine precursor of choline and acetylcholine, which proved helpful for a small fraction of his patients. Continuing his search for the cause of overarousal in his schizophrenic inpatients, he discovered in 1966 that the chronic male schizophrenic patient had lower-than-normal blood histamine concentration, and that the level rose as the patient improved.

Pfeiffer then tested 72 outpatients and found some with high histamine levels that fell as the patients improved. These patients tended to be depressed and obsessive-compulsive; patients with low histamine levels were more likely to be paranoid and to have hallucinations. Both groups were equal in their degree of thought disorder and overarousal.

In 1968 he began to explore the possibility that storage of histamine in basophils is controlled by the trace elements copper, manganese, and zinc, and by calcium. Copper was found to be high in most patients with low histamine levels. This imbalance could be corrected by giving zinc and manganese supplements, which increase the excretion of copper by competing for absorption.

In 1970 Pfeiffer found that because most of the blood histamine is found in the basophils, the basophil count is a valid indicator of histamine level. This test is less than one quarter the cost of a blood histamine determination and should be routine in the outpatient work-up of schizophrenia and, as we shall see, depression.

In 1974 Pfeiffer[50] confirmed Hoffer and Osmond's report on malvarians, those individuals whose urine gives a pink spot on chromatography with Ehrlich reagent. This pink hue indicates the presence of mauve factor, which can occur in normal persons, especially under stress, and in any type of mental illness. Malvarians as a group have many common features according to the observations of Hoffer:

> They believe that people are watching them more . . . they have visions of people when their eyes are closed. They feel unreal and see others as unreal. There is a mist or fog shutting them away from the world. Many times objects and people as well as their own faces, look strange and therefore they misidentify people. Often they see sparks of light or spots floating before them, and the world may suddenly look dim. They have out-of-the-body experiences.

Hoffer also found the presence of mauve factor was associated with a worse prognosis, requiring longer hospital time and more treatment and carrying less likelihood of recovery.

Hoffer and Osmond[51] reported a positive mauve factor in 90 percent of untreated acute schizophrenics, 75 percent of medicated schizophrenics, 50 percent of chronic schizophrenics, and 35 percent of alcoholics but in only 5 percent of normal individuals. Interestingly, schizophrenics generally are negative for mauve factor when not experiencing psychiatric symptoms.

The mauve factor, also called kryptopyrrole, was identified by Irvine in 1969 as a porphyrin derivative: 2,4-dimethyl-3-ethylpyrrole. Pfeiffer found kryptopyrrole present in more than 30 percent of schizophrenic patients versus only 5 percent of nonschizophrenic controls,[52] an occurrence rate similar to the findings of Hoffer and Osmond.

Pfeiffer and Sohler also found that kryptopyrrole reacts with pyridoxal phosphate and that patients excreting kryptopyrrole simultaneously excreted zinc. Pfeiffer concluded that kryptopyrrole forms complexes with both zinc and pyridoxal phosphate, thus potentially inducing a double deficiency. It is notable that pyridoxine is not affected by kryptopyrrole, making it possible to have normal blood pyridoxine but to be deficient in the activated form of the vitamin. Because of the active excretion of pyridoxal phosphate, doses of B_6 up to 3000 mg are required for treatment, depending on the amount of pyrroluria.

There have been a few reports citing failure to detect pyrroles in the blood of schizophrenics. Gendler et al.[53] were unable to detect kryptopyrrole in urine of schizophrenic, porphyric, or normal subjects, using gas chromatography and mass spectrometry; these methods are less likely to give false-positive results than the paper or thin-layer chromatographic methods of either Irvine or Sohler. However, Gendler depended on freezing as a preservative in his studies, despite the instability of pyrroles. Hoffer[54] is convinced that the samples were inadequately preserved. Hoffer and Pfeiffer both have found ascorbate to adequately stabilize kryptopyrrole for up to 24 hours.

Pfeiffer has suggested that the term *malvaria* be replaced by the term *pyrroluria* to designate patients excreting more than 20 μg of kryptopyrrole per day.[55] The pyrroluric patient's outstanding symptoms are, according to Pfeiffer, perceptual disorders, white spots in the fingernails (meis lines due to zinc deficiency), and failure to recall dreams (dreams recover after treatment with zinc and B_6). These patients also have a rather sweet breath odor and a distinct tenderness in the left upper abdomen.

As a result of his many observations and researches, Pfeiffer derived a classification of schizophrenia based on actual measurement of blood histamine and trace mineral levels as well as urine kryptopyrrole. He has established conclusively that high histamine (histadelia) occurs in 50 percent of the cases, low histamine (histapenia) in 20 percent, and pyrroluria occurs in most of the rest. He has also shown that histadelic patients tend to have low levels of copper and histapenics have high levels of copper. In addition, he has found unsupplemented histapenics to be low in folic acid.

Based on this typology, Pfeiffer has conceived a treatment strategy for dealing with metabolic subtypes of schizophrenia in a more specific way than was heretofore possible. As he sees it, histapenics respond to folic acid, B_{12}, and niacin, which raise histamine, along with zinc and manganese, which lower copper; vitamin C is used to inhibit copper-induced free-radical reactions. Histadelics respond to methionine, which lowers histamine; calcium, which removes it; and phenytoin, which elevates copper. Niacin and folic acid worsen the condition of these patients. Kryptopyrrole excretors (pyrrolurics) respond to repletion of zinc and pyridoxal phosphate, which serve to replace the losses that occur due to excretion of pyrroles complexed with pyridoxal phosphate and zinc.

HEME

It has recently been found that administration of heme reverses symptoms of porphyria. Litman and Correia[56] recently reported that heme deficiency impairs hepatic tryptophan pyrrolase, and this causes elevated tryptophan and 5-hydroxytryptamine (serotonin) turnover in the brain. Sustained elevation of tryptophan causes neuron damage, and this is the means by which porphyric attacks and hepatic encephalopathy produce similar brain lesions. An increase in brain tryptophan leads to increased serotonin, the pharmacological effects of which are similar to acute porphyria: abdominal pain, dysuria, nausea, and psychiatric disturbance.

It is possible that heme may become a helpful adjunct therapy for pyrrole-positive schizophrenics. It is certain that trytophan will affect them adversely. It is even possible that other nutrients, such as bioflavonoids, may aggravate porphyria by stimulating production of heme-containing P-450 enzymes in the liver, thus lowering available heme in the blood. Barbiturates, lead, estrogen, and fasting—anything that interferes with heme synthesis or depletes it—can cause porphyria and pyrroluria as well as mental and physical symptoms.

Pfeiffer's results attest to the heterogeneity of the schizophrenias and this explains why the double-blind niacin studies were doomed to fail from the start: the 20 percent of patients who are histadelic worsen on niacin therapy. Thus, a fixed-dose research in schizophrenic patients will not be productive unless the subtypes are accounted for by patient selection so that specific treatment can be used.

THE ROLE OF METHYLATION

The histamine classifications add critical insight into the role of methylation in schizophrenia and affective disorders. Because histamine is eliminated by methylation, undermethylation interferes with excretion and causes a high blood histamine level. Undermethylation of biogenic amines would occur simultaneously, and this is a likely cause of depression. Indeed, Pfeiffer observed depression to be a salient feature of patients with high serum histamine. He also found that administration of DL-methionine, a methyl donor, lowered blood histamine in depressed and schizophrenic patients within 6 hours.

On the other hand, overmethylation facilitates histamine degradation and results in a low blood histamine level and, as we have seen, the overproduction of hallucinogenic amines. This fits with Pfeiffer's observation that the low histamine schizophrenics are likely to be the hallucinators and are made worse by methionine.

Papaioannou and Pfeiffer[57] proposed that methylation of biogenic amines produces neurotransmitter substances that act to excite brain activity and lift mood as a normal physiological function of neuromodulation. Thus, abnormal states of overmethylation can cause schizophrenia and mania, and abnormal undermethylation can cause depression.

The overmethylation-schizophrenia interaction has been well established. In fact, in one of the Canadian papers,[58] Ananth, Ban, et al. demonstrated that 3 g of niacinamide (a methyl acceptor) was inadequate to antidote the schizophrenogenic effects of 20 g of methionine (a methyl donor). I have not found a paper that studied the effects of a dose of niacinamide adequate to neutralize a 20 g methionine load, which according to Pauling should be 16 g.

Papaioannou surveyed the key research that supports undermethylation in depressive states and overmethylation in mania. She referred to a paper by Mandell and Spooner,[59] who had already conceived of methylated biogenic amines as "chemical modulators of excitability" as early as 1968. They observed activation in human subjects pretreated with a monoamine oxidase inhibitor and then given an indole load. This technique increases production of methylindoles in place of oxidized, deaminated products. The methylindoles include methyltryptamines, as we have seen, and these are among the most potent hallucinogens. When pyrogallol, a depletor of *S*-adenosylmethionine, was given first, activation was prevented. In that *S*-adenosylmethionine is the methyl donor, this lack of activation is due to lack of methylation.

Two sources of deficiency of methylated amines could lead to depression: (1) a dietary deficiency of precursor amino acids tryptophan and phenylalanine or their products norepinephrine or serotonin, or (2) any deficiency of methylated breakdown products of these biogenic amines. Which of these is more likely?

Mendels's review of the literature[60] indicates that precursor amine therapy does not alleviate depression of hospitalized depressed patients, though there are scattered reports of responders to phenylalanine, tyrosine, and tryptophan. Depressive patients who are unresponsive to precursor therapy are likely to be undermethylators—as are the high-histamine depressives. Briggs and Briggs[61] actually found reduced catechol-*o*-methyltransferase (COMT) activity in women with depression, women on oral contraceptives, and women postpartum. High levels of norepinephrine were also found, which implies sluggish methylation to epinephrine, the next metabolic step.

The presence of high levels of norepinephrine in depressed patients surely does not suggest that it is an antidepressant molecule. Furthermore, Wyatt et al.[62] found an 80 percent increase in plasma norepinephrine over normal controls among depressed patients, which fell to normal with clinical improvement. By depleting norepinephrine with α-methyl-l-paratyrosine they could not induce depression. In fact, norepinephrine itself has been found to produce depression, sedation, and stupor.

Papaioannou hypothesizes that excess norepinephrine may compete for receptor sites that otherwise would be occupied by stimulatory methylated amines; or that perhaps norepinephrine, serotonin, other catecholamines, and histamine inhibit the methylating enzyme, *N*-methyltransferase.

Radioactive tracer studies suggest that depression is associated with a defect in utilization of methyl groups. ^{14}C tagged *S*-methylmethionine can be traced by its oxidative end product, carbon dioxide. Hallucinating schizophrenics do not show the normal increase in labelled CO_2 breath excretion after administration of *S*-methylmethionine. The tagged carbon (methyl) is retained and presumably methylates biogenic amines, increasing their transport across the blood-brain barrier and causing psychotic aberrations. On the other hand, depressives show a rapid rise in tagged carbon in the breath, double and triple that of the control subjects, implying excretion rather than utilization of methyl groups.

Another outcome of undermethylation is increased production of noradnamine. Noradnamine is a naturally occurring anabolic product of norepinephrine, and like norepinephrine, it is a sedative and depressant. If norepinephrine is not *o*-methylated efficiently, noradnamine is formed by oxidative deamination. Low levels of COMT have been confirmed in many studies of depression, and MAO has been found to be elevated. This is exactly the combination of enzyme activities that would favor production of noradnamine.

Roberts and Broadley early postulated (1965) that an excess of noradnamine may produce psychotic depression. It is similar in structure to tricyclic antidepressants, which may, in fact, operate by blocking a noradnamine receptor site. They also advanced the hypothesis that a malfunction of methylation would cause depression by shunting metabolism of norepinephrine into oxidative deamination, i.e., noradnamine.

Convincing support for the methylation theory of depression proposed by Papaioannou and Pfeiffer comes from the observation that methylating substances are antidepressant. The antidepressant drug imipramine, for instance, actually increases methylation. Orthomolecular methyl donors are also antidepressant. Injection of *S*-adenosylmethionine, the premier methyl donor, was demonstrably effective in a study by Agnoli[63] in 1976. More recently Lipinski et al.[64] reported that seven of nine depressed patients showed improvement within a few days of treatment with parenteral *S*-adenosylmethionine. A larger clinical trial of this orthomolecular intermediate is now under way.

THE STANDING OF ORTHOMOLECULAR PSYCHIATRY

The variety and complexity of orthomolecular treatments and their relation to demonstrable physiological mechanisms leads us to the realization that orthomolecular psychiatry represents a return to the medical model of mental illness. Osmond and Sigler[65] have written extensively on the important psychological benefits this medical approach brings to patients and their families by restoring to the patient the traditional sickness role, which includes the idea of cooperation with treatment. In addition, families are not confronted with psychodynamically theorized guilt, but are restored to their traditional right to sympathetic concern and appropriate information from the physician. This is particularly important because it has become clear that a supportive family is a positive prognostic factor for schizophrenia.

The medical model provides diagnostic benefits as well, for the process of differential diagnosis is broadened and the examination and testing procedures are more comprehensive than in conventional psychiatry. Several recent studies have shown that the frequency of undiagnosed medical illness in psychiatric patients is higher than had been suspected. Gardner and Hall[66] found that 80 percent of 105 consecutive voluntary admissions to a state psychiatric hospital had at least one previously undetected physical illness that required medical treatment. In 42 percent of the cases, previously undiagnosed medical illnesses were found to be causing the presenting psychiatric symptoms. The psychiatric disorder improved in almost half the patients when the medical illnesses were treated. A combination of history and physical examination, multiple chemistry panel (SMA-34), electrocardiogram, urinalysis, and sleep-deprived electroencephalogram identified over 95 percent of all medical illnesses.

It is usual in orthomolecular psychiatry to perform a medical history and physical examination. Among conventional psychiatrists, more than two-thirds do not physically examine their patients. Many admit that they lack competence in performing physical examinations, and this is a major reason for not doing so. Of course, another reason is that a generation of psychiatrists were taught *not* to examine their patients medically, that this would interfere with the "transference."

The return of the medical model in orthomolecular psychiatry restores the psychiatrist to the role of a complete physician. In addition, the orthomolecular identity confers a sense of respect for medical nutrition, and thus prompts a higher quality of medical care than is currently practiced, even in many general hospitals. In fact several studies[67] have shown that more than half of typical general hospital patients are likely to be suffering from hospital-induced malnutrition and at least a third of them exhibit some iatrogenic symptom due to medication.

Tardive dyskinesia is one of the more interesting examples of iatrogenic malnutrition and toximolecular effects. Kunin[68] has proposed that manganese is chelated and removed from nerve cells by treatment with phenothiazines. This results in localized acetylcholine depletion because the enzyme, choline acetyltransferase, is manganese dependent. Manganese supplementation reverses symptoms within a few days in more than half the cases. Orthomolecular treatment in general prevents the occurrence of dyskinesia. Tkacz and Hawkins[69] found an almost zero incidence in 40,000 cases of schizophrenia treated with phenothiazines combined with orthomolecular therapy.

It is ironic that orthomolecular treatment with manganese, niacin, and other nutrients is required to treat the damage caused by toximolecular treatment. Wurtman's finding[70] that dietary precursors of acetylcholine, such as lecithin and choline, also relieve tardive dyskinesia lends further support for the interpretation that toximolecular damage to cholinergic neurons is fundamental to the dyskinesia.

These researchers coined the term *precursor therapy* based on the many research studies of precursor amino acid-loading effects on brain chemistry. Wurtman found that dietary doses of choline lead to prompt increases in brain choline. He found similar relationships between dietary tryptophan and tyrosine and brain levels of these amino acids, thus claiming the discovery that dietary substances appear in the brain. However, these researchers specifically denied that these events are orthomolecular.

Progress in orthomolecular psychiatry has paralleled progress in neurochemistry, particularly the research into neurotransmitters and neuromodulators. Of the neurotransmitters, acetylcholine, serotonin, norepinephrine, and dopamine have been most heralded, but gamma amino butyric acid (GABA) is implicated in the anxiety disorders and is clearly related both to niacinamide and the benzodiazepines, which share the same receptor. Taurine, glutamic acid, glutamine, choline, inositol, adenosine, and aspartate are among the other recognized transmitters now under scrutiny as therapeutic agents. On the other hand, the physician must keep in mind that dose-dependent nerve cell damage has been observed with aspartate, glycine, L-tryptophan, and monosodium glutamate.

There is now available information to assist in establishing specific diagnosis and treatment of mental disorders. There are laboratory tests to identify nutrient and metabolic factors and at lower expense than was possible even a few years ago. It is possible to measure serum and urine levels of vitamins, minerals, and their related enzymes and urinary metabolites. Hair can be used as a biopsy material for detection of heavy metals, and the recent introduction of amino acid and essential fatty acid profiling promises to open new horizons in clinical practice and research.

OTHER INDICATIONS

Nutrient therapy for agoraphobia as a focal symptom in 23 patients was studied by Abbey.[71] She observed that correction of nutrient deficiency as determined by functional vitamin-enzyme testing yielded dramatic improvement in 19 cases and complete absence of panic in 11. The deficiencies she treated were in B_1 for 7 patients, B_6 for 6, and B_3 for 3; in 3 patients the problem was in B_{12} and in 2 folic acid. Thiamine deficiency, as revealed by a low transketolase activity, was most common. Inadequate phosphorylation of pyridoxine was clearly demonstrated in one case, i.e., tryptophan was significantly elevated before a tryptophan load test and 5HIAA was decreased after. When megadose pyridoxine failed to elicit improvement, administration of preformed pyridoxal 5-phosphate was tried and symptoms resolved.

Hoes et al.[72] found that treatment with megadose pyridoxine plus L-tryptophan was effective in the treatment of hyperventilation syndrome in patients with high urinary excretion of xanthurenic acid. This metabolite indicates a defect in tryptophan metabolism, which is pyridoxine dependent at many steps. Hoes et al. speculated that deficiency of serotonergic neurotransmission is a factor in hyperventilation, citing animal research that demonstrates inhibition of respiration by serotonin during alcohol intoxication and during slow wave sleep. Eight of nine responders had abnormal excretion (too high or too low) of xanthurenic acid after a 5 g tryptophan load, as opposed to none of the nonresponders. This clearly represents progress towards specific orthomolecular treatment rather than nonspecific symptom suppression by tranquilizers or carbon dioxide rebreathing using a paper bag.

Patients with anxiety have been known to be sensitive to lactate since Pitts's report in 1965.[73] Subsequent research has shown that bicarbonate ion is immediately formed after lactate infusion and may be the actual cause of anxiety. The fact that EDTA, which lowers calcium, does not cause anxiety implies that alkalosis plays a greater role than does calcium even though infusion of calcium ion can abort attacks.

Childhood developmental and learning disabilities have been particularly responsive to orthomolecular intervention. Rimland and Calloway[74] reported positive results from a double-blind study in which pyridoxine was used to treat autistic children. A subsequent double-blind study of magnesium supplementation showed similar benefits.

Rimland earlier compared parent and teacher reports[75] on the effects of megavitamin therapy and drug therapy in autism. Though this trial was not double blind, it clearly highlighted the high benefits to risks ratio in orthomolecular treatment. Megavitamin therapy was rated more effective and with significantly less adverse effects than either Ritalin or Mellaril in this study.

Thiessen and Mills[76] compared megavitamin treatment in 24 learning disabled children and 9 controls. Treatments included ascorbate, niacinamide, pantothenic acid, and pyridoxine plus a low-carbohydrate diet. After a year, there was no difference between groups in reading or spelling ability, but there was significant reduction in hyperactivity, nystagmus, and sleep disturbance in the vitamin-treatment group.

In a double-blind study, Harrel[77] treated 16 children with mental retardation or Down's syndrome with megavitamins. Her findings were especially dramatic because the improvements were tangible, including improvement in vision, growth, and IQ test performance. Controversy has raged over these findings and though some reported studies fail to confirm them, Bennet et al.[78] asserted that compliance with nutrient supplements in these failures was not monitored.

Haslam et al.[79] showed that megavitamins are ineffective and have a potential for hepatotoxicity in a study of 41 children with attention deficit disorders. However, they used only four vitamins (niacinamide, pyridoxine, calcium pantothenate, and ascorbic acid). Although a third of the children improved behaviorally in a 3-month period, in crossover placebo comparisons there was no significant difference between children receiving active treatment and those receiving placebo; in fact, the placebo children were less hyperactive and did not have the elevations in transaminase that were seen in almost half the treatment group children.

I find this study inconsistent for several reasons: (1) 29 percent of the children did improve, (2) the fact that there was no difference between vitamin and placebo in crossover studies may be due to the short term—6 weeks—of this part of the study, (3) the elevated transaminase does indicate that the treated children received their vitamins; however, they did not allow for adjustment of doses to avoid toxic effects; and finally (4) this study failed to repeat either the Harrel protocol or the current practice of orthomolecular therapy.

It is remarkable that the pioneering work of Turkel,[80] covering a treatment and observation period of more than 40 years, has been ignored by physicians and rejected by the FDA. This has been carried to the extent that the FDA does not permit shipment of his supplements to Japan, where physicians have corroborated his findings. Turkel has documented significant improvement in 80 to 90 percent of 600 children with Down's syndrome. His before-and-after pictures are more convincing than any statistic could be. Similarly, the Japanese investigators have studied more than 3000 patients in the past 20 years. In the initial study by M. Iida,[81] only 14 of 50 retarded children failed to improve significantly.

The study of Pihl and Parkes[82] deserves mention because of its reliance on hair content of cadmium, cobalt, manganese, chromium, and lithium to identify learning disabled children. Subjects were classified with 98 percent accuracy by discriminant function analysis of these minerals. Cobalt and cadmium together served to predict lead, so lead was not included as a predictor. However there was an almost sixfold higher lead level in the hair of these 31 children compared to 22 normal controls.

It is well known from the studies of David[83] that hyperactivity and learning disability in children without an obvious diagnosis is caused by lead toxicity in at least half the cases. The significant reduction in environmental lead pollution is one of the most positive public health developments in the past decade. This has been accomplished by the passage of hard-won legislation to reduce lead in paint and gasoline.

Medical heroes, such as Herbert Needleman, have provided convincing evidence that low-level lead exposure is more toxic than had originally been believed.[84] The generally recognized toxic blood level has been lowered from 80 μg percent to less than half that, and intellectual impairments are now recognized at under 20 μg percent. The hair test for heavy metals and lead should be a standard procedure in every pediatric evaluation, particularly up to age 6 years.

Many studies confirm the fact that childhood undernutrition, particularly low intake of iron, calcium, and protein, permits greater damage from lead exposure. It is comforting to review Pfeiffer's study[85] of orthomolecular treatment of industrial lead exposure: the administration of zinc and ascorbic acid was followed by a lowering of blood lead in workers in a battery plant—despite continued exposure to lead.

Pyridoxine has demonstrable antilead activity. Regunathan and Sundoresan[86] found that lead reduced rat brain synthesis of GABA and glutamine. However, when pyridoxal phosphate was administered with lead, synthesis of these amino acids was increased over the control level in the cerebellum and brainstem but not cerebral cortex. When given without lead, B_6 increased GABA, glutamic acid, and glutamine in the cerebral cortex as well.

The influence of sugars and chemical food additives on hyperkinesis has been controversial. Connors[87] has produced convincing evidence that sugars increase hyperactivity when eaten alone. However, when taken with a meal, sugar led to an actual improvement in behavior. In normal children Connors found that sugar increased deviant behavior when taken with a high carbohydrate breakfast or no breakfast, but when taken with a protein meal, it had no significant effect. Clinical observations generally indicate that complex carbohydrates are less likely to cause anxiety, depression, or dysperception than are the simple and refined sugars.

Carbohydrate titration, when studied by Kunin,[88] identified an optimal carbohydrate intake in 68 percent of 73 patients. A definite optimal intake range was apparent as well-being and increased energy. Relief of anxiety or depression was most common at an intake of carbohydrate just sufficient to prevent ketosis, i.e., on the average 52 g/day of carbohydrate. Over 80 percent of sedentary patients reported feeling worse with carbohydrate intake greater than 120 g/day. The typical daily intake of carbohydrate in this country today is 300 g. Patients who were active exercisers and joggers comfortably increased carbohydrates to 180 g/day. Carbohydrate titration not only reveals the effects of varying doses of carbohydrates in relation to symptoms of fatigue, irritability, and depression, but it is also a good method of teaching patients about the effects of nutrition and the importance of improving their dietary habits.

Wurtman[89] has demonstrated that carbohydrate exerts significant central nervous system effects by means of insulin alterations on amino acid transport, particularly favoring tryptophan, into the brain. This has been shown to have significant effects on sleep. Acute starvation enhances slow wave sleep and, conversely, a high-carbohydrate diet reduces slow wave sleep and suppresses growth hormone secretion. A diet high in carbohydrates decreases deep, dreamless sleep and increases dreaming, rapid-eye-movement sleep.

Interactions between carbohydrate intake and response of such hormones as insulin, glucagon, growth hormone, and cortisol are well established and explain the symptoms of anxiety, depression, and dysperception lately thought of as "hypoglycemia." Hypoglycemia is actually a misnomer, for it is not a disease but rather a symptom of a number of conditions. It has been attacked as a fad diagnosis by the medical establishment because of the frequency with which it is diagnosed and the lack of correlation between blood sugar levels and symptoms of anxiety and dysperception. Nevertheless, the symptoms often do respond to dietary management. Palm[90] found that substitution of fructose, which is a weak insulin stimulus, for glucose was followed by a decrease in 24-hour urine cortisol excretion. He interpreted this to mean that fructose caused less hormonal stress than did glucose. Treatment of hypoglycemia has varied from the multiple feedings method of Seale Harris to the low-carbohydrate diet plus adrenal cortical-extract of Tintera. However, the carbohydrate titration method remains the most direct and accurate way to determine the individual needs of the patient.[88]

As we look to the future of orthomolecular psychiatry, it is amazing to find that surgical grafts of brain tissue are already having success in laboratory research. Because the brain is immunologically tolerant, grafts are less likely to provoke rejection. Freed et al.[91] found that grafts of substantia nigra produce long-term alteration in the functional status of brain cell receptors, a normalization of postsynaptic dopaminergic receptors, and reduction in behavioral symptoms. Gage et al.[92] observed improved performance in spatial learning tests among aged rats with hippocampal septal grafts. Luine et al.[93] found fetal raphe cell transplants capable of reinnervating the ventromedial nucleus and reversing feminine sexual behavior due to hypothalamic lesions.

The concept of subclinical deficiency has, until recently, been rejected by the scientific establishment. We must credit Dr. Glen Green[94] for his paper on subclinical pellagra, in which he described mental symptoms in patients without frank deficiency of niacin but who responded to treatment with niacin supplementation. Only recently has the medical establishment acknowledged the existence of subclinical deficiency. Gingival dysplasia has been identified as a symptom of marginal vitamin-C depletion, a subclinical deficiency, in a report summarized in JAMA[95] in 1983.

CONCLUSION

To those readers involved in orthomolecular psychiatry, this paper is intended to encourage clinical observation. We must not forget the advice of the nutrition pioneers of a generation ago. James McLester[96] wrote in 1939 that, "The physician who would treat pellagra, and I believe that this holds good in other deficiency states, must not be timid. Whatever is needed, he must have the boldness to give it in large amounts."

Controversy has dogged all orthomolecular studies, from Hoffer to Harrell and from Pfeiffer to Philpott. The fact that some double-blind studies do not confirm orthomolecular claims does not detract from the fact that most clinical observations indicate that these treatments do work. The lack of homogeneity in patient selection makes it almost impossible to draw conclusions from large groups of psychiatric patients treated with subtle agents, such as nutrients.

Reflecting back on all these orthomolecular topics, and we have by no means exhausted all areas of current interest, it is clear that the orthomolecular concept is progressing beyond megavitamins and into a sophisticated biochemical model of health and disease.

Orthomolecular psychiatry has changed and will continue to change because scientific knowledge is changing. But the philosophy remains the same: the therapeutic primacy of substances that naturally belong in the biosystem. Orthomolecules belong in the biosystem, support the metabolic interactions, and are aimed at achieving a therapeutics of optimization. This is a relatively nontoxic approach in contrast to conventional, allopathic psychiatry, which relies almost exclusively on a toximolecular principle, the use of substances that operate by interfering with biological processes. Of course these carry greater toxic risk, and they ignore the potential therapeutic benefits of nutrient therapy.

Despite the many fundamentally important discoveries concerning the function of nutrients in the central nervous system, the orthomolecular concept that molecules normally present in the body are preferable to any toximolecular drug, is still resisted and ignored. Instead the new term in psychiatry is "precursor therapy," meaning the therapeutic use of amino acids and other compounds in optimum concentrations to balance the neurotransmitters. Will the orthomolecular rose smell as sweet by any other name?

I must agree with Dr. Pauling: there is no other word that so well conveys the meaning "the right molecules in the right amounts."

REFERENCES

1. Pauling L: Orthomolecular psychiatry. *Science* 1968; 160: 265–271.

2. van Tigellen CJM, Peperkam JPC, Tertoolen JFW: Vitamin B_{12} levels of cerebrospinal fluid in patients with organic mental disorder. *J Orthomolec Psych* 1983; 12: 305–308.

3. Cleckley HM, Sydenstricker VP, Geeslin LE: Nicotinic acid in the treatment of atypical psychotic states. *JAMA* 1939; 112(21): 2107–2115.

4. Sydenstricker VP, Cleckley HM: The effect of nicotinic acid in stupor, lethargy and various other psychiatric disorders. *Am J Psychiat* 1941; 98: 83–92.

5. Hoffer A: The adrenochrome hypothesis of schizophrenia revisited. *J Orthomolec Psych* 1981; 10(2): 98–118.

6. Hoffer A, Osmond H, Callbeck MJ, et al.: Treatment of schizophrenia with nicotinic acid and nicotinamide. *J Clin Exper Psychopath* 1957; 18: 131–158.

7. Osmond H, Hoffer A: Massive niacin treatment in schizophrenia. Review of a nine year study. *Lancet* 1962; 1: 316–320.

8. Hoffer A: *Niacin Therapy in Psychiatry.* Springfield, Il, CC Thomas, 1962.

9. Denson R: Nicotinamide in the treatment of schizophrenia. *Dis Nerv System* 1962; 3: 167–172.

10. Hoffer A, Osmond H: Treatment of schizophrenia with nicotinic acid. *Acta Psychiat Scand* 1964; 40: 171–189.

11. Hoffer A: The effect of nicotinic acid on the frequency and duration of re-hospitalization of schizophrenic patients: a controlled comparison study. *Int J Neuropsychiat* 1966; 2: 236–240.

12. O'Reilly PO: Nicotinic acid therapy and the chronic schizophrenic. *Dis Nerv System* 1955; 16: 67–72.

13. Ananth JV, Ban TA, Lehmann HE: Potentiation of therapeutic effects of nicotinic acid by pyridoxine in chronic schizophrenics. *Can Psychiat Ass J* 1973; 18: 377–382.

14. Ban TA, Lehmann HE: Niacin in the treatment of schizophrenias, alone and in combination. Presented at the VIIIth CONP Congress, Copenhagen, August 14–17, 1972.

15. Wittenborn JR, Weber ESP, Brown M: Niacin in the long-term treatment of schizophrenia. *Arch Gen Psychiat* 1973; 28: 308–315.

16. Wittenborn JR: A search for responders to niacin supplementation. *Arch Gen Psychiat* 1974; 31: 547–553.

17. Ban TA, Lehmann H: Nicotinic acid in the treatment of schizophrenias. Canadian Mental Health Association Collaborative Study, Progress Report II. *Can Psychiat Ass J* 1975; 20: 103–112.

18. Hoffer A, Osmond H: Megavitamin therapy, in reply to the American Psychiatric Association Task Force Report on Megavitamin and Orthomolecular Therapy in Psychiatry. Regina, Sask, Canadian Schizophrenia Foundation, 1976.

19. VanderKamp H: A biochemical abnormality in schizophrenia involving ascorbic acid. *Int J Neuropsychiat* 1966; 2: 204.

20. Pauling L, Robinson A, et al.: Results of a loading test of ascorbic acid, niacinamide and pyridoxine in schizophrenic subjects and controls, in Hawkins and Pauling (eds): *Orthomolecular Psychiatry.* San Francisco, WH Freeman, 1973.

21. Kinsman RA, Hood J: Some behavioral effects of ascorbic acid deficiency. *Am J Clin Nutr* 1971; 24: 455–464.

22. Kubala AL, Katz MM: Nutritional factors in psychological test behavior. *J Genet Psychol* 1960; 96: 343–352.

23. Milner G: Ascorbic acid in chronic psychiatric patients: a controlled trial. *Br J of Psychiatry* 1963; 109: 294–299.

24. Cameron E, Pauling L: *Cancer and Vitamin C.* Menlo Park, Calif, The Linus Pauling Institute of Science and Medicine, 1979.

25. Libby AF, Stone I: The hypoascorbemia-kwashiorkor approach to drug addiction therapy. *J Orthomolec Psych* 1977; 6: 300.

26. Free VF, Sanders P: The use of ascorbic acid and mineral supplements in the detoxification of narcotic addicts. *J Orthomolec Psych* 1978; 7: 264.

27. Spector R: Vitamin homeostasis in the central nervous system. *N Engl J Med* 1977; 296: 1393–1398.

28. Tolbert LC, Thomas LD, et al.: Ascorbate blocks amphetamine induced turning behavior in rats with unilateral nigro-striatal lesions. *Brain Res Bull* 1979; 4: 43–48.

29. Rebec GV, Centore JM, et al.: Ascorbic acid and the behavioral response to haloperidol. *Science* 1985; 227: 438–439.

30. Möhler H, Polc P, et al.: Nicotinamide is a brain constituent with benzodiazepine-like actions. *Nature* 1979; 278: 563–565.

31. Joshi VG, Eswaran S: Vitamins B_1, B_6 and B_{12} in the adjunctive treatment of schizophrenia. *J Orthomolec Psych* 1980; 9: 35.

32. Joshi VG, Eswaran S, et al.: Vitamins B_1, B_6 and B_{12} in the adjunctive treatment of schizophrenia. Further studies to examine the effect of reduction of chlorpromazine dosage. *J Orthomolec Psych* 1982; 11: 45–49.

33. Kunin RA: The action of aspirin in preventing the niacin flush and its relevance to the antischizophrenic action of megadose niacin. *J Orthomolec Psych* 1976; 5: 89–100.

34. Horrobin DF: Niacin flushing, prostaglandin E and evening primrose oil. A possible objective test for monitoring therapy in schizophrenia. *J Orthomolec Psych* 1980; 9: 33–34.

35. Horrobin DF: Prostaglandin deficiency and endorphin excess in schizophrenia: the case for treatment with penicillin, zinc and evening primrose oil. *J Orthomolec Psych* 1979; 8: 13–19.

36. Dohan FC, Grasberger JC: Relapsed schizophrenics: earlier discharge from the hospital after cereal-free, milk-free diet. *Am J Psychiat* 1973; 130(6): 685–688.

37. Singh MM, Kay SR: Wheat gluten as a pathogenic factor in schizophrenia. *Science* 1976; 191: 401–402.

38. Rudin D: The dominant diseases of modernized societies as omega-3 essential fatty acid deficiency syndrome: substrate beriberi. *Medical Hypotheses* 1982; 8: 17–47.

39. Fiennes RN, Sinclair AJ, Crawford MA: Essential fatty acid studies in primates, linolenic acid requirements of capuchins. *J Med Prim* 1973; 2: 155–169.

40. Crawford MA, Sinclair AJ: Nutritional influences in the evolution of the mammalian brain; in Elliott and Knightt *Lipids, Malnutrition and the Developing Brain,* pp 267–287. Amsterdam, Assoc Scientific Publ, 1972.

41. Rudin D: The major psychoses and neuroses as omega-3 essential fatty acid deficiency syndrome: substrate pellagra. *Biol Psychiatry* 1981; 16: 837–850.

42. Gilka L: Schizophrenia, a disorder of tryptophan metabolism. *Acta Psych Scand Supp* 1975; 258.

43. Price FM, Brown RR, et al.: Tryptophan metabolism in porphyria, schizophrenia and a variety of neurologic and psychiatric diseases. *Neurology* 1959; 9: 456–468.

44. Berlet HH: Endogenous metabolic factor in schizophrenic behavior. *Science* 1969; 144: 311–313.

45. Gilka L: Hyperactivity, learning disabilities, GABA, inborn errors of metabolism and modern environmental factors. *Int J Biosoc Res* 1983; 4: 85–98.

46. Hoffer A: The adrenochrome hypothesis revisited. *J Orthomolec Psych* 1981; 10: 98–118.

47. Galzigna L: Complexes between acetylcholine and catecholamines and their tolerance to mental illness. *Nature* 1970; 225: 1058–1059.

48. Graham DC: Oxidative pathways for catecholamines in the genesis of neuromelanin and cytotoxic quinones. *Molecular Pharm* 1978; 14: 633.

49. Perry T: New biochemical findings relevant to the etiologies of Parkinson's disease, Huntington's chorea and the schizophrenias. Presentation to Orthomolecular Medical Society Symposium, "Linus Pauling and the Roots of Molecular Medicine," May 8, 1983.

50. Pfeiffer CC: Tracking the spoor of the gray behemoths—the schizophrenias. *J Orthomolec Psych* 1977; 6: 165–170.

51. Kahan FH: Out of the quicksands. *J Orthomolec Psych* 1977; 6: 146–147.

52. Pfeiffer CC, Sohler A, Jenney CH, et al.: Treatment of pyroluric schizophrenia (malvaria) with large doses of pyridoxine and a dietary supplement of zinc. *J Orthomolec Psych* 1974; 3: 292–300.

53. Gendler PL, Duhan HA, Rapoport H: Hemopyrrole and kryptopyrrole are absent from the urine of schizophrenics and normal persons. *Clin Chem* 1978; 24(2): 230–233.

54. Hoffer A: personal communication.

55. Pfeiffer CC: Tracking the spoor of the gray behemoths. *J Orthomolec Psych* 1977; 6: 165–170.

56. Litman DA, Correia MA: L-tryptophan: a common denominator of biochemical and neurological events of acute hepatic porphyria? *Science* 1983; 222: 1031–1033.

57. Papaioannou R, Pfeiffer CC: Undermethylation of biogenic amines and psychiatric depression. 10th Collegium Internationale NeuroPsychopharmacologicum, 1976.

58. Ananth JV, Ban TA, et al.: Nicotinic acid in the prevention and treatment of methionine-induced exacerbation of psychopathology in schizophrenics. *Canad Psychiat Assn J* 1970; 15: 3–14.

59. Mandell AJ, Spooner CE: Psychochemical research studies in man. *Science* 1968; 162: 1442.

60. Mendels J, Stinnett JL, et al.: Amine precursors and depression. *Arch Gen Psychiat* 1975; 32: 22–28.

61. Briggs MH, Briggs M: *Experientia* 1972; 29: 278.

62. Wyatt RJ, Cohn CK, et al.: *Arch Gen Psychiat* 1971; 24: 65.

63. Agnoli A, et al.: Effect of S-adenosylmethionine upon depressive symptoms. *J Psychiat Res* 1976; 13: 43054.

64. Lipinski J, Cohen BM, et al.: Open trial of S-adenosylmethionine for treatment of depression. *Am J Psychiat* 1984; 141: 448–450.

65. Osmond H, Siegler M: *Models of Madness, Models of Medicine.* New York, Macmillan, 1974.

66. Gardner ER, Hall RCW: Medical screening of psychiatric patients. *J Orthomolec Psych* 1980; 9: 207–215.

67. Butterworth CE: Malnutrition in the hospital. *JAMA* 1974; 230: 897.

68. Kunin RA: Manganese and niacin in the treatment of drug-induced dyskinesias. *J Orthomolec Psych* 1976; 5: 4–27.

69. Tkacz C, Hawkins DR: A preventive measure for tardive dyskinesia. *J Orthomolec Psych* 1981; 10: 119–123.

70. Wurtman RJ: Nutrients that modify brain function. *Sci Am* 1982; 246(4): 50–59.

71. Abbey LC: Agoraphobia. *J Orthomolec Psych* 1982; 11: 243–259.

72. Hoes MJAM: L-tryptophan in depression and strain. *J Orthomolec Psych* 1982; 11: 231–242.

73. Pitts FN: Biochemistry of anxiety. *Sci Am* 1969; 220: 69–75. Also Pitts FN: *J Clin Psych Monograph,* vol 2, 1, 1984.

74. Rimland B, Callaway E, Dreyfuss P: The effect of high doses of vitamin B_6 on autistic children: a double-blind crossover study. *Am J Psychiat* 1978; 135: 472.

75. Rimland B: *Comparative Effects of Treatment on Child's Behavior.* Publication 34, San Diego, Institute for Child Behavior Research, 1977.

76. Thiessen I, Mills L: The use of megavitamin treatment in children with learning disabilities. *J Orthomolec Psych* 1975; 4: 288–296.

77. Harrel RF, Capp RH, et al.: Can nutritional supplements help mentally retarded children? An exploratory study. *Proc Natl Acad Sci USA* 1981; 78(1): 574–578.

78. Bennett FC, McClelland S, et al.: Vitamin and mineral supplementation in Down's syndrome. *Pediatrics* 1983; 72(5): 707–713.

79. Haslam RHA, Dalby JT, Rademaker AW: Effects of megavitamin therapy on children with attention deficit disorders. *Pediatrics* 1984; 74(1): 103–111.

80. Turkel H: *New Hope for the Mentally Retarded.* New York, Vantage, 1972.

81. M Iida's 1964 report is reviewed in *Medical Tribune*, February 25, 1981, p 1.

82. Pihl RO, Parkes M: Hair element content in learning disabled children. *Science* 1977; 198: 204–206.

83. David O, et al.: Lead and hyperactivity: behavioral response to chelation. *Am J Psychiat* 1976; 133: 1155–1158.

84. Needleman HL, Barrett P: Lead toxicity: deficits in psychologic and classroom performance of children with elevated dentine lead levels. *N Engl J Med* 1979; 300: 689.

85. Papaioannou R, Sohler A, Pfeiffer CC: Reduction of blood lead levels in battery workers by zinc and vitamin C. *J Orthomolec Psych* 1978; 7: 94–106.

86. Regunathan S, Sundoresan R: Incorporation of ^{14}C from glucose into amino acids in brain in vitro. *Life Sci* 1983; 33: 2277–2282.

87. Connors K: Debate sugar, hyperkinesis tie. *Medical Tribune,* June, 1984.

88. Kunin RA: Ketosis and the orthocarbohydrate diet: a basic factor in orthomolecular psychiatry. *J Orthomolec Psych* 1976; 5: 203–211.

89. Wurtman RJ: Nutrients that modify brain function. *Sci Am* 1982; 246(4): 50–59.

90. Palm D: *Diet Away Your Stress, Tension and Anxiety.* Garden City, NY, Doubleday, 1976.

91. Freed WJ, Ko GN, Niehoff DL, et al.: Normalization of spiroperidol binding in the denervated rat striatum by homologous grafts of substantia nigra. *Science* 1983; 222: 937–939.

92. Gage FH, Björklund A, Stenevi U, et al.: Intrahippocampal septal grafts ameliorate learning impairments in aged rats. *Science* 1984; 225: 533–536.

93. Luine V, Renner K, et al.: Facilitated sexual behavior reversed and serotonin restored by raphe nuclei transplanted into denervated hypothalamus. *Science* 1984; 226: 1436–1438.

94. Green RG: Subclinical pellagra among penitentiary inmates. *J Orthomolec Psych* 1976; 5: 68–73.

95. Primate studies indicate that subclinical and acute vitamin C deficiency may lead to periodontal disease. *JAMA* 1981; 246(7): 730. This refers to Alvares O, et al.: The effect of subclinical ascorbic acid deficiency on periodontal health in nonhuman primates. *J Periodont Rsch* 1981; 16: 628–636.

96. McLester J: Borderline states of nutritive failure. *JAMA* 1939; 112: 2110.

CHAPTER THIRTEEN

THE ROLE OF PHOSPHOLIPIDS IN NEUROLOGICAL FUNCTION

JONATHAN E. ROTHSCHILD, MA

Deficits in central cholinergic function may play a role in several pathological states. With the recognition of that fact, researchers are directing increasing attention to the possibility that administration of metabolic precursors of acetylcholine (ACh) may promote its synthesis, availability, and utilization. This therapeutic strategy effectively treats disorders characterized by deficits in the synthesis and metabolism of other neurotransmitters, particularly dopamine. At present, evidence suggests but does not prove that cholinergic deficits are a cause of several clinical illnesses.

The treatment of neurological disorders associated with inadequate cholinergic function is an extension of the "neurotransmitter replacement approach," which originated with the use of levodopa for treatment of Parkinson's disease and was extended to therapy with other neurotransmitters. It was proposed that choline administered parenterally or through foods would increase ACh synthesis. Preliminary studies indicate that oral phosphatidylcholine can raise brain ACh levels, and thus possibly alleviate some neurological motor disturbances and restore cognition and memory. The principle of precursor loading to potentiate neurotransmitter synthesis has gained much support recently, but many theoretical and practical questions remain.

Brain ACh levels are known to be sensitive to plasma levels of choline. ACh levels in the brain are maintained by a complex control system involving end-product feedback inhibition, mass action, availability of energy sources, and rates of nerve stimulation. At present, scientists possess no compelling hypothesis to explain the precursor dependence of ACh on choline. One theory suggests that cholinergic neurons, like those that release serotonin (a transmitter with a rate of synthesis that varies with plasma amino acid levels), may function as "sensors" that inform other brain neurons about the general metabolic state of the organism, as reflected in its plasma choline concentrations. However, neurophysiologists have yet to characterize these metabolic sensors.

Although there is no firm explanation why cholinergic neurons should be "open-loop," clinicians can take advantage of this precursor dependence in order to modify the neurons' functional properties. Physicians specializing in psychiatry and neurology may thereby explore the physiological consequences of enhanced cholinergic tone and treat diseases associated with inadequate release of ACh into synapses.

PHARMACOLOGY

Metabolism and Distribution

Choline is the physiological precursor of ACh. Free choline has been shown unequivocally to enter the brain from the bloodstream, where it is converted to ACh. ACh is synthesized by the combination of choline and acetyl coenzyme A in a reaction catalyzed by the enzyme choline acetyltransferase (CAT).

Within a cholinergic neuron, the highest concentration of ACh and of CAT is present at the nerve endings of the cell. In many respects, the nerve ending is a metabolically independent unit of the neuron.

Absorption and Utilization

Choline in blood is normally derived from two sources: consumption of foods and synthesis in the liver. Most of the dietary choline is in the form of lecithin (phosphatidylcholine), a glycerol molecule covalently bound to one molecule of phosphorylcholine and two molecules of fatty acids. Certain foods, such as egg yolks, liver and soybeans, are rich sources of lecithin.

Serum and plasma levels of choline vary widely, depending on the quantities of choline and lecithin consumed in the diet; this relationship has been demonstrated in both humans and rats. Choline is fairly readily absorbed from the gastrointestinal tract. However, a proportion of choline administered orally to rats or to human patients appears to be converted to trimethylamine and its oxide by intestinal bacteria before absorption takes place.

Despite its essential functions and its presence in the diet, there are several reasons for not classifying choline as a B vitamin. First, choline is present in animal tissues in amounts much greater than those usually associated with the true vitamins. Second, choline has not been found to be a constituent of any cofactor essential for an enzymatic reaction. Finally, choline can be synthesized in the body from serine: (1) serine is first esterified to phosphatidylserine; (2) the phosphatidylserine is decarboxylated to phosphatidylethanolamine (cephalin), which in turn is methylated to form phosphatidycholine (lecithin); and (3) the latter compound is hydrolyzed to liberate free choline. Methionine, in the form of *S*-adenosylmethionine, serves as the methyl donor in the biosynthesis of choline. This pathway is operative in both mammals and microorganisms. Thus, a choline deficiency can be produced in the mammalian organism only as a result of a combined deficiency of choline and methyl donors. This fact becomes of practical significance in considering the therapeutic value of choline.

CHOLINE SYNTHESIS

The brain is apparently unable to make choline de novo. The choline used for the synthesis of ACh and other compounds must be carried to the brain by the bloodstream. The two major factors controlling choline influx into the brain are plasma concentration and blood-brain barrier permeability.

Cholinergic nerve terminals contain little or no free choline, and therefore choline for the synthesis of ACh must be derived from the extracellular fluid. The choline that is transported into cholinergic neurons comes from several places, the most direct of which is from the diet. Foods contain small amounts of free choline as well as large concentrations of choline in a form that is covalently bound.

Choline qualitatively has the same pharmacological actions as ACh but is much less active. The acute toxicity of choline, especially by mouth, is relatively low (about 5 g/kg for rats) in comparison with that of some of its esters and many other quaternary ammonium compounds. The oral LD_{50} for man is estimated to be of the order of 200 to 400 g.

The neuronal choline concentration, the rate-limiting factor in ACh synthesis, is normally controlled by a "high-affinity" choline transport system. Most investigators believe the choline level in the brain can also be raised by increased supply through a "low-affinity" transportation system. Raising brain choline levels increases ACh synthesis or produces a direct choline agonist effect.

Although it had been known for some time that precursor availability may limit ACh synthesis and cholinergic function in vitro, it was not until 1972 that Kunstscherova reported that ACh levels in brain, intestine, and atria were depleted after a 24-hour fast, and could be restored by the administration of choline and glucose or by a single feeding.[1]

The principal objective of recent investigations on choline and lecithin feeding has been to increase brain ACh levels to enhance cholinergic effects. Although a number of early investigators failed to find increased brain ACh after choline administration, the preponderance of evidence from both animal and clinical studies shows that exogenous choline (or lecithin) does increase brain ACh levels.

In initial studies, Cohen and Wurtman gave choline chloride intraperitoneally to rats. Twenty minutes after injection of 60 mg/kg of choline chloride, brain choline levels rose to 223 percent of control values and then declined to base levels at 60 minutes.[2] In an independent study, Haubrich et al. reported similar results showing that choline administration caused parallel increases in ACh release.[3]

Less well known is the effect of lecithin on choline and, particularly, ACh levels in man. The results of the few studies performed indicate that large doses (such as 30 g/day) of lecithin or phosphatidylcholine increase markedly (sometimes three or four times) the levels of plasma choline; the effect is short-lived but may be maintained by repeated dosing.

NEUROTRANSMITTERS IN THE MANAGEMENT OF DISEASE

Parkinson's Disease

It has been proposed that the neurological manifestations of Parkinson's disease may be derived from a disturbance in the balance between inhibitory dopaminergic activity and excitatory cholinergic function in the striatal region. This hypothesis is supported by various observations, including the demonstration that levodopa and anticholinergics improve this disorder.

The improvement of the neurological manifestations of Parkinson's disease is, however, often accompanied by the appearance of choreiform adventitious movements (dyskinesia). As a rule, antidopaminergic agents suppress dyskinesia and diminish levodopa's therapeutic effects, whereas anticholinergic agents may aggravate the levodopa-induced dyskinesia, suggesting that suppression of central cholinergic activity may be involved in the induction of dyskinesia. This is further supported by observations that drugs assumed to increase ACh in central synapses are beneficial in suppressing dyskinesia.

Papavasiliou and Rosal treated seven patients with levodopa-induced dyskinesia with choline chloride and L-α-methyldopa hydrazide, administered in six portions daily, according to a double-blind protocol.[4] Choline chloride dosage was gradually increased to a maximum of 200 to 300 mg/kg/day. Two patients had diminution of levodopa-induced dyskinesia, one exhibited an increase in parkinsonian signs, and two became withdrawn and depressed during choline administration.

Memory

There is much human and animal evidence to support the view that normal function of the cholinergic system is necessary for memory formation. Age-related impairment of central cholinergic neurotransmitter mechanisms is thought to be partially responsible for geriatric memory deficits. The cholinergic hypothesis of impaired memory is supported by corroborative pharmacological, electrophysiological, and neurochemical evidence.

The concept that the central cholinergic system might play a significant role in human memory and cognitive function began to assume neurobiological importance only during the last decade. Previously, a number of anecdotal observations had indicated that anticholinergic drugs were capable of causing profound alterations of human mental function. For example, Jimson weed, a plant containing the anticholinergic agent hyoscine, had been known since the 1600s to induce alterations of thought processes and prolonged amnesia. Early in the 20th century, scopolamine was introduced in obstetrical anesthesia for its ability to interfere with memory. Combined with other medications, it produced "twilight sleep" with amnesia for painful experiences that might occur during its period of effectiveness. Only a few studies on the nature and extent of human memory impairment induced by anticholinergics had been published by the early 1970s.

In addition to these observations in humans, studies carried out during the past dozen years have documented that alteration of learning and memory can be produced in experimental animals by the administration of cholinergically active drugs. Improvement and impairment of these behavioral functions have been demonstrated to result from the administration of cholinergic agonists and antagonists, respectively, depending in part on the time interval between learning and drug administration.

Evidence that the cholinergic system contributes to learning includes the finding that CAT activity is raised in the temporal lobes of animals with high learning ability. Cholinergic mechanisms appear to be involved in short-term memory, and the memory defects associated with human aging are paralleled by the effect of anticholinergic medication.

The involvement of a cholinergic system in memory has been investigated by Deutsch.[5] Anticholinesterases administered to rats were found to obliterate the memory of a habit learned 14 days earlier but to facilitate recall of a nearly forgotten habit learned 28 days previously. The effect of atropine was to depress memory both immediately after the habit was learned and again 28 days later. Deutsch explained these findings by proposing that as a result of learning, the postsynaptic elements (presumably cholinergic) become more sensitive to transmitter up to 14 days and then gradually decline in sensitivity.

The activity of central anticholinergics in causing memory deficits is well recognized. For instance, scopolamine (10 to 15 μg/kg) given to healthy subjects impairs delayed recall of digits. This shows that the capacity to "store" new information is reduced by the centrally acting anticholinergics. Immediate recall of numbers, however, is not significantly affected, indicating that the ability to "register" new information is intact.

Finally, the well-known amnestic action of anticholinergic drugs is in keeping with the notion of cholinergic facilitation of memory. In fact, Deutsch proposed on the basis of his investigations of the action of anticholinesterases on memory that memory storage depends on "cholinergic memory synapses" that change in sensitivity with the progress of the memory process.[6]

Impairment of learning and memory, particularly short-term memory, often accompanies human aging. Choline and lecithin have been fed to demented patients in efforts to improve cognition and memory. In addition, some effort has been made to improve memory in younger, healthy individuals. Accounts of such research in the news media have stimulated public interest in choline and lecithin as dietary supplements. Capacity for memory is prized by individuals of all ages; gradual loss of memory is lamented by the elderly.

There is some disagreement about the relationship between the memory loss observed in persons with mental disorders and the loss in normal elderly persons. One point of view is that senile dementia represents an extreme of the loss of the cholinergic neuronal activity that occurs in normal aging. Others believe that some features of similar degeneration in Alzheimer's disease are unique to that disease. Nevertheless, the rationale of treatment with cholinergic precursors to restore memory is based on the same principle for normal aged as those with mental disorders.

Alzheimer's Disease

In strictest terms Alzheimer's disease refers to a presenility with onset before 65 years; onset after 65 years, the senile form, is called Alzheimer-type disease. However, many investigators believe Alzheimer's disease is a variant of simple senile dementia resulting from common degeneration of the central nervous system with aging. The characteristic features of the disease are the massive formation of senile plaques, granulovascular degeneration, and neurofibrillary tangles. Senile changes, although generally present in the brains of well-preserved elderly persons studied postmortem, are markedly increased in dementia and closely correlated with the degree of dementia.

Alzheimer's disease appears to be associated with a selective, partial degeneration of central cholinergic neurons. There are indications that in Alzheimer's disease the activity of CAT is reduced and that this parallels increasing morphological change which, in turn, correlates with dementia score.

Etienne et al.[7] gave 25 g/day of commercial lecithin (23 percent phosphatidylcholine) to seven patients (42 to 81 years in age, mean age 67 years) for 4 weeks. Three patients responded to treatment. By clinical impression they seemed to understand instructions better, were more cooperative, and displayed less speech rambling. However, the improvement ceased after lecithin was stopped.

Christie et al.[8] compared the effects of choline and lecithin in 11 patients with Alzheimer's disease. Treatment began with 1 g/day of choline chloride and increased over a 4-day period to 5 g/day for 5 days. Three of the nine patients who completed the trial on lecithin showed considerable improvement in speech and topographical orientation.

Peters and Levin gave five patients with Alzheimer's disease physostigmine, lecithin, and a placebo.[9] Neither physostigmine nor lecithin alone gave results comparable to those with the combination.

It is important to note that, as degeneration of cholinergic neurons continues with progression of the disease, the effectiveness of the treatment diminishes.

Tardive Dyskinesia

Tardive dyskinesia is a clinical condition characterized by hyperkinetic involuntary movements, particularly oral grimacing. It commonly develops after prolonged treatment with antipsychotic drugs. Some evidence indicates that cholinergic mechanisms may be involved in this motor dysfunction: a reciprocal relationship between drug-induced parkinsonism and tardive dyskinesia prevails.

Estimates of the prevalence of tardive dyskinesia in large populations being treated with neuroleptic drugs vary widely—from 5 percent to over 50 percent. This broad range reflects controversy about the definition of tardive dyskinesia and the difficulty of differential diagnosis, as well as variation in populations studied. Movements similar to those of tardive dyskinesia appear in certain naturally occurring disorders, in reactions to other types of medication, and in other neuroleptic-related movement disorders.

Tardive dyskinesia may be the manifestation of drug-induced hypersensitivity of dopamine receptors; in this case dopaminergic response overrides the normal balance between dopaminergic and cholinergic function in the basal ganglia. Cholinergic receptor hypersensitivity might also be involved in tardive dyskinesia. Prolonged exposure to anticholinergic agents or large doses of neuroleptics intrinsically high in anticholinergic properties (e.g., thioridazine) may ultimately alter cholinergic receptors.

It is possible that the symptoms comprising the tardive dyskinesia syndrome actually derive from heterogeneous etiologies. The implication is that at least two separate but clinically similar hyperkinetic dyskinesias that are pharmacologically opposite can occur with neuroleptic therapy. One dyskinesia is pharmacologically similar to the acute neuroleptic-induced extrapyramidal dyskinesias that are characterized by relative dopaminergic hypofunction or cholinergic hyperfunction; the other is related to the traditional pharmacology of tardive dyskinesia, characterized by relative dopaminergic hyperfunction or cholinergic hypofunction.

Treating tardive dyskinesia by augmenting central nervous system ACh logically derives from the theory of counterbalancing striatal dopaminergic–cholinergic influences. Many pharmacological agents that have been tested to correct this imbalance have shown unsatisfactory results. These include compounds that block the action of dopamine, prevent its synthesis, deplete its stores, or inhibit dopaminergic neurotransmission.

Choline and lecithin have been employed as alternative experimental treatments for the disorder. Limited clinical trials indicate that the administration of choline or lecithin is accompanied by improved course of tardive dyskinesia in some but not all patients.

Davis et al.[10] reported reduction in choreiform movements in a patient given 16 g/day of choline chloride. The effects persisted for 3 days after the treatment was stopped. Subsequently, similar results were obtained with three or four additional patients studied under double-blind conditions. Growdon et al.[11] performed a double-blind crossover study of choline administration to 20 chronic patients with tardive dyskinesia in a state hospital; blood choline levels increased significantly in every patient, and 9 of the 20 were rated as significantly improved. Because all patients had achieved adequate increases (around 170 percent) in serum choline levels, the differences in response were thought to reflect the heterogeneity of this syndrome.

In subsequent studies Barbeau[12] reported suppression of tardive dyskinesia in two patients and Yahr[13] reported similar experience, confirming the efficacy of choline therapy. Barbeau conducted a single-blind study in which 33 g/day of lecithin was given to four patients for 20 weeks.[14] Choreiform movements were reduced an average of 52 percent. In an independent study, Tamminga and colleagues confirmed these observations.[15]

2-Dimethylaminoethanol (deanol) has been used to treat tardive dyskinesia because it has been reported to increase brain ACh content and perhaps cholinergic activity. Deanol has an interesting history in that it was first proposed as a central stimulant and ACh precursor by Pfeiffer et al.[16] It was originally expected to enter the brain freely (which it does) and be converted there to choline and ACh.

Deanol has been employed in the treatment of chorea on the basis of laboratory and theoretical evidence that it may serve as a cholinergic precursor and may elevate central ACh. Early reports suggested a good therapeutic response among patients with tardive dyskinesia.

Casey, after reviewing available data, concluded that the effectiveness of deanol in treatment of tardive dyskinesia is currently unresolved.[17] Of 161 patients treated with deanol in 28 investigations, 59 (37 percent) improved, 1 worsened, and 101 (63 percent) showed only a mild response or no change. The dosage range for deanol was 800 to 2000 mg/day, with upper limits determined by side effects. It was noted that a deanol response, when present, occurred within the first week, and further dosage increases only had small additive effects.

The lack of reports on any depressogenic effect of deanol, which on the contrary may relieve anxiety in depressed patients, may also raise some doubt that depression would result from an increase in central cholinergic activity.

Mood Change

Robert Christison was the first to describe the toxic effects of physostigmine in 1855 when performing an experiment on himself with the calabar bean: he found that "volition is inoperative." It is well known that anticholinergics with central effects, notably scopolamine in doses of 10 μg/kg or more, induce auditory and visual hallucinations. These symptoms, which are characteristic of the anticholinergic syndrome, are promptly reversed by administration of physostigmine. However, this rather clear antagonistic effect of cholinesterase inhibitors on hallucinations precipitated by central anticholinergics is somewhat obscured by the observation that, after long-term exposure to irreversible cholinesterase inhibitors (notably organophosphorus insecticides), schizophrenic reactions with hallucinations may occur.

Analgesia

For almost 40 years it has been known that cholinergic agonists (particularly muscarinic agonists) and anticholinesterases exert analgesic actions; these compounds potentiate the analgesic actions of morphine and codeine.

It is a matter of controversy whether the cholinergic effect is exerted via morphine sites and/or enkephalins. Interestingly, naloxone antagonizes cholinergic analgesia. The finding that choline may antagonize morphine analgesia may also indicate that morphine and cholinergic agonists affect similar receptors.

Down's Syndrome

Phosphatidylcholine has been used successfully in the treatment of Down's syndrome. Cantor et al. conducted a preliminary study with a two-year-old Down's child treated with 150 mg/kg of a phosphatide complex over a 7-month period.[18] Using computerized EEG as a dependent variable, rather than behavioral findings, the investigators found marked normalization in neurological readings. Following discontinuance of this supplementation program, the patient experienced a minor regression toward pretreatment levels. It is interesting to note that the majority of Down's patients exhibit characteristics of Alzheimer's disease sometime in adulthood, and that morphological similarity has been observed in autopsy studies.

CONCLUSION

ACh remains a fruitful subject for investigation. Most clinicians recognize that a large number of pharmaceutical preparations, including certain antidepressants, antipsychotics, antihistamines, antispasmodics, antiparkinsonism agents, and certain gastric ulcer medications, are capable of producing the anticholinergic syndrome. Placing greater attention on the clinical use of choline and other phosphatides as cholinergic agonists may reveal these nontoxic nutrients as major therapeutic resources in the treatment of neurological diseases.

REFERENCES

1. Kunstscherova J: Effect of short-term starvation and choline on the acetylcholine content of organs of albino rats. *Physiol Bohemoslov* 1972; 21: 655–660.

2. Cohen EL, Wurtman RJ: Brain acetylcholine: increase after systemic choline administration. *Life Sci* 1975; 16: 1095–1102.

3. Haubrich DR, Wang PF, Chippendale T, et al.: Choline and acetylcholine in rats: effect of dietary choline. *J Neurochem* 1976; 27: 1305–1313.

4. Papavasiliou PS, Rosal V: Effects of choline in patients with levodopa-induced dyskinesia, in Barbeau A, Growdon JH, Wurtman RJ (eds): *Choline and Lecithin in Brain Disorders.* New York, Raven, 1979.

5. Deutsch JA: The cholinergic synapse and the site of memory. *Science* 1971; 174: 788–794.

6. Deutsch JA: Physiology of acetylcholine in learning and memory, in Barbeau A, Growdon JH, Wurtman RJ (eds.): *Choline and Lecithin in Brain Disorders.* New York, Raven, 1979, pp 343–350.

7. Etienne P, Gauthier S, Johnson G, et al.: Clinical effects of choline in Alzheimer's disease. *Lancet* 1978; 1: 508–509.

8. Christie JE, Blackburn IM, Glen AIM, et al.: Effects of choline and lecithin on CSF choline levels and on cognitive function in patients with presenile dementia of the Alzheimer's type, in Barbeau A, Growdon JH, Wurtman RJ (eds): *Choline and Lecithin in Brain Disorders.* New York, Raven, 1979, pp 377–387.

9. Peters BH, Levin HS: Effects of physostigmine and lecithin on memory in Alzheimer's disease. *Ann Neurol* 1979; 6: 219–221.

10. Davis KL, Hollister LE, Vento AL, et al.: Cholinergic aspects of tardive dyskinesia: human and animal studies, in Fann WE, Smith RC, Davis JM, et al. (eds): *Tardive Dyskinesia: Research and Treatment.* New York, SP Medical and Scientific Books, 1980, pp 395–403.

11. Growdon JH, Hirsch MJ, Wurtman RJ, et al.: Oral choline administration to patients with tardive dyskinesia. *N Engl J Med* 1977; 297: 524–527.

12. Barbeau A: Lecithin in neurologic disorders. *N Engl J Med* 1978; 299: 200–201.

13. Yahr M: Choline and lecithin administration to patients with tardive dyskinesia. *Trans Am Neurol Assoc* 1978; 103: 98–99.

14. Barbeau A: Lecithin in movement disorders, in Barbeau A, Growdon JH, Wurtman RJ (eds): *Choline and Lecithin in Brain Disorders.* New York, Raven, 1979, pp 263–271.

15. Tamminga CA, Smith RC, Ericksen SE, et al.: Cholinergic influences in tardive dyskinesia. *Am J Psych* 1977; 134: 769–774.

16. Pfeiffer CC, Jenney EH, Gallagher W, et al.: Stimulant effect of 2-dimethylaminoethanol: a possible precursor of brain acetylcholine. *Science* 1957; 126: 610–611.

17. Casey DE: Deanol in the management of involuntary movement disorders: a review. *Dis Nerv Syst* 1977; 38(12): 7–15.

18. Cantor DS, Thatcher RW, Ozand P, et al.: A report on phosphatidyl choline therapy in a Down's syndrome child. *Psychol Reports* 1985; (in press).

PART III

THE SCIENTIST AS CITIZEN

CHAPTER FOURTEEN

THE EVOLUTION OF A SCIENTIST'S SOCIAL CONSCIENCE

JOHN F. CATCHPOOL, MD

Bertrand Russell, a close friend of Linus Pauling, opened his autobiography with these words: "Three passions, simple but overwhelmingly strong, have governed my life . . . the longing for love . . . the search for knowledge . . . and unbearable pity for the suffering of mankind."

Linus Pauling's scientific and political life has been governed by a single unifying Einsteinian principle. This principle—the logical rightness or wrongness of any course of action—appears to have developed at an early age. He told me how, in a one-room schoolhouse in Congdon (a small inland town in Oregon), he developed the conviction that things should be done right. "None of this 70 percent stuff," he said. He illustrated his point with a joke:

> "Tommy," asked the teacher, "what does two and two make?"
> "Four," answered Tommy.
> "Very good, Tommy," the teacher commented.
> "Heck, Teacher," replied Tommy, "that's not very good . . . that's *perfect.*"

Pauling's life-long fascination with chemistry and mathematics began in high school. It evolved because in both subjects problems correctly solved end with a number that is 100 percent right—none of this 70 percent stuff. He admits that he did not like Latin, but Greek was tolerable because it was more esoteric.

At Oregon State Agricultural College he met two young men who had flunked out of the California Institute of Technology. They seemed to be fairly intelligent, so he assumed that Caltech's standards were high. He immediately applied there for a graduate fellowship, as well as to Harvard and the University of California, Berkeley. Although Berkeley was his first choice, he ended up at Caltech. A few years ago the Berkeley chemistry department questioned how they had let him slip through their fingers. Apparently the embarrassing oversight can be blamed on the eminent chemist G. N. Lewis: when reviewing Pauling's application, Lewis remarked, "Oregon State Agricultural College? Never heard of it!"

By 1931 Linus Pauling was on his way to becoming one of the world's greatest chemists. He recalls that in that year he became the first recipient of a prize in pure science offered by the American Chemical Society (ACS) to a promising scientist under 30 years old. It created quite a stir. In an article in *Time* magazine his professor, A. A. Noyes, was quoted as saying that some day Pauling would probably earn the Nobel Prize in chemistry. After 1932, the ACS Prize Committee raised the age limit to 35 years because they couldn't find a deserving chemist under 30.

By 1940, Pauling had completed most of the work that in 1954 would bring him the Nobel Prize in chemistry. His pursuit of the 100 percent correct, whole truth had led him through many crystal structures to an almost perfect understanding of the amino acids. His understanding was so perfect, in fact, that he could assemble in his mind's eye parts of the helical protein molecules—the famous alpha helix prediction.

The actual synthesis took place when Pauling was enduring a brief enforced confinement in a house in Oxford. In these pre-vitamin C days Pauling had a severe head cold. He was lying in bed feeling utterly miserable; he had completed all his crossword puzzles and read all the available mystery novels, so he pulled out a piece of paper and sketched amino acids on it. When he tried rolling the paper and folding it, he found that by rolling it over he could form hydrogen bonds between the amino acids. From this came his great understanding of the alpha helix, the beginning of one of the greatest discoveries in chemistry. This early prediction was later proved down to the last Ångström unit. Like all of Pauling's undertakings, it was perfect.

Some time later, these understandings of the chemical bonds and amino acid structures would lead him to suspect that a small error in the amino acid sequence of the hemoglobin molecule was responsible for the complex symptoms of sickle cell disease, which he then called a *molecular disease*. Molecular disease studies are now an important branch of medicine and there are institutes for the exclusive study of these problems. Work at these institutions already is yielding useful insights on diagnosis and therapy. This work one day may lead to cures for many of the inborn errors in metabolism that cause pain and early death.

When asked when he first began speaking publicly on social issues, Pauling recalled that it was not until the 1940 presidential election. At that time, Caltech students were organizing a mock election debate, and they could not find a professor who would take the side of Roosevelt against Willkie. Pauling volunteered, and in so espousing the Democratic cause (the liberal cause, at that time) was marked as a political radical in conservative Pasadena.

At the beginning of World War II, Pauling and his wife Ava Helen were both active in the movement called Union Now, devoted to bringing British children to the United States to escape the threatened invasion of Britain. (Coincidentally, I was one of those children who came to the United States in 1940. I returned in 1944.)

The war changed everything. Robert Oppenheimer asked Linus Pauling to head the chemistry division of the Los Alamos atomic bomb studies. Pauling declined, citing his commitment to 18 other military research projects, including the development of the world's first oxygen meter. He invented this meter on the train ride from Washington to Pasadena. Within 1 week of his arrival home he had a working model of the oxygen meter, so vital then for submarines and other war-time projects, and was back on the train to Washington carrying the model with him. Later, he was awarded the Presidential Medal for his outstanding contributions to the war effort.

After Pearl Harbor came the infamous executive order for the internment of all West Coast United States citizens of Japanese ancestry. Ava Helen Pauling was looking for a gardener to work on their Altadena home. The employment agency offered her a nisei Japanese man who had just been inducted into the U.S. Army and was awaiting orders. The day after he started work, she received anonymous threatening calls and found the garage door defaced with "Jap lover" slogans. She called the sheriff and the sheriff told her she should be more careful. "Sheriff," she replied candidly and typically, "I'm counting on you to protect me."

After Hiroshima, chemists and physicists with a knowledge of atomic physics were much sought after by service groups, colleges, and other organizations to explain the awesome atomic weapon that had been unleashed over Japan. Pauling, like many other scientists, gave speeches in which he referred to Einstein's famous equations. Ava Helen apparently attended several of these lectures, and she criticized his use of other people's opinions and quotations. "You must use your own," she chided. From then on, Pauling spent half his time reading and pondering world affairs. He found himself in accord with what Einstein was saying: "A new thinking is essential if mankind is to survive and move to higher levels. We must abandon competition and secure cooperation. Past thinking did not prevent wars, but future thinking must."

Pauling had been a founding member of the Emergency Committee of Atomic Scientists. Other members of this illustrious group included Einstein, Howard Urey, Hans Bethe, Leo Szilard, and Victor Wyskoff.

Another pivotal decision in Pauling's career occurred as he was sailing to Europe on the Queen Mary. At one point during the cruise he wrote this pledge on a piece of cardboard (which he still has): "I swear that I will make some mention of world peace in every speech I make." The next speech he made was at the F.D.R. Club, and a reporter was so inspired by it that he recorded the speech verbatim. The reporter was later fired for his efforts.

From 1945 to 1957 Linus Pauling made many speeches for world peace, for the prohibition of nuclear warfare and nuclear weapons, and for a nuclear test ban treaty. The famous Pauling–Teller debates on nuclear testing were broadcast over KQED in San Francisco. Pauling spoke at peace rallies all over the United States. He spoke about fallout, carbon 14, iodine 131, and other present dangers. He wrote a marvelous book which is about to be reissued; it should be a handbook for anyone who wants complete information on the dangers of nuclear power and continued nuclear weapons proliferation. In 1955, together with 50 other Nobel laureates, he wrote the Maynow declaration, named for the conference held at Maynow at Lake Constance in Switzerland.

In January 1958, the Paulings presented a written appeal to the United Nations that all nations of the world stop the spread of nuclear weapons. It was signed by 9235 scientists from 44 countries, including 40 Nobel laureates. Later 2000 more signatures were added. The significance of these numbers was not overlooked by the Senate Subcommittee on Internal Security, the successor to the infamous McCarthy subcommittee. Obviously, they reasoned, large numbers of communists and much Soviet money must be employed to collect so many signatures. These appeals were a direct threat to the military industrial complex—a threat to Teller's theme of ever-bigger H-bombs and a rebuff to Herman Kahn and others at the Rand Corporation who were already thinking the unthinkable. In the face of such opposition, no single person has ever been so devastatingly logical and marvelously articulate as Linus Pauling.

Pauling was ordered by the subcommittee to appear and bring all the signatures. He pointed out that these signatures had already been submitted to the United Nations. However, he suggested, he could bring copies of the signatures. The transcript of the hearings show Pauling to be a strikingly able and articulate defender of his position. This is a typical exchange:

"Dr. Pauling, did you know that Hayakawa, with whom you corresponded, had been given the Lenin Peace Prize?"

"No," replied Pauling, "but I did know that he had the Nobel Prize for physics." It is all recorded in *The Congressional Record* (86th Congress, 2nd session, June 21, 1960).

Pauling answered all questions until asked to reveal the names of those who distributed and collected signatures, especially those who collected the most signatures. As he said later, "I assumed that they were going to be singled out for some special attention from the FBI and others." He could see that if he did reveal their names, all these idealistic workers for peace would suffer reprisals and probably blacklisting when applying for university appointments and grants. He could not, he said, as a matter of conscience, morality, and justice, do that. He was reminded that his refusal would result in a contempt of Congress citation and imprisonment. Fifty or sixty people had already been sentenced to prison and a dozen or so were still in prison. I have heard Pauling say more than once that he was miserable at this prospect. He only hoped that he could persuade Ava Helen and the children to go to jail with him so that he could have the entire family around him.

Unlike others, Pauling had not taken the Fifth Amendment, but he supported his position as a matter of personal conscience, morality, and justice. At this point peace workers, writers, lawyers, and clear-thinking citizens of the world held their breath. This was to be the classic western showdown, with the honest scientist pitted against the big guns of the McCarthy-type tribunal. Senator Dodd, the congressional committee chairman, was one of the leading congressional opponents of the test ban treaty, and he was attempting to silence and discredit Pauling, who was at that time the leading spokesman for the treaty. President Kennedy was leaning toward a ban on atmospheric testing, since atmospheric testing could be easily detected and would reveal any cheating on the part of the Soviets. Dodd appeared to want to suppress Pauling's freedom to criticize government policy. He was threatening to use criminal sanctions against him for showing contempt of Congress. Lawyers call this type of argument seditious libel, and they consider it to be the hallmark of tyranny. When later the subcommittee backed down and failed to cite Linus for contempt, some legal observers were disappointed because they were losing such a good test case.

The criticism went on, however. Because Pauling dared question the wisdom of the generals who did not understand the scientific or doomsday consequences of nuclear war, the implication was that he was somehow un-American. After all, his neighbors in Pasadena were digging fallout shelters. A rumor ran around Caltech, at one point, that a million dollar bequest to the institution was contingent upon the dismissal of the renegade professor who had spent more than 40 years of his life there.

I remember well a day in 1959 when Albert Schweitzer, for whom I was working in Gabon, announced after dinner that Linus Pauling would be arriving in Lambaréné. "An American colleague is coming," he said, "and I want you to come with me to greet him when his canoe arrives." Schweitzer was a bit surprised that I knew so much about Pauling. Although I only knew of him from magazines, I had already adopted him as my ideal.

We had many famous visitors at Lambaréné: writers, movie stars, and presidential candidates like Adlai Stevenson. Usually Schweitzer sat at one side of the table. I sat opposite him with guests on either side of me. It was often my job to translate for the non-French- or non-German-speaking visitors. Schweitzer liked to pretend that he did not understand English, perhaps because it gave him more time to come up with a witty retort. If my translation was not accurate, it could be blamed for the lack of a suitable retort. Pauling, however, had no need of my services; he spoke excellent German.

After one of those dinners by lamplight at Lambaréné, Linus gave a marvelous discourse on the recently unraveled molecular explanation of sickle cell anemia. This was a great revelation to me because I had not learned of it in medical school.

In Africa I was treating sickle cell anemia every day, but Pauling knew more about it than I did. A number of things began to make sense. I remember every word of the conversations we had. I was asking him about thalassemia and I pronounced the word incorrectly. He turned sharply to me and said, "Why do you use the wrong pronunciation?" I told him that I had never heard it pronounced before; I had only read about it.

Of all the visitors who came to Lambaréné, Linus Pauling was the most at home. He seemed unaffected by the noise, the filth, and the confusion of an African bush hospital. To me, he was a new species of scientist: not an effete European or an Ivy League, ivory-tower type, but a native son of the western frontier who had grown up in a country town lacking even paved streets; a man who had worked his way through high school and college chopping firewood and carving up sides of beef.

During our conversations in Lambaréné, Pauling mentioned that there was a great revolution in biology and medicine taking place. He hinted that many medical doctors were going to be ignorant of these new developments. He also suggested that if I had time and wanted a break he would see if he could get me a postdoctoral fellowship at Caltech. I explained that chemistry was by far the worst of my subjects and that I had gotten through only by selecting the physical chemistry questions that had a numerical answer and could therefore be graded as correct or incorrect. That response prompted Pauling to recall a story about when he was 16 years old and holding down a summer job as a surveyor for road builders. While living in a tent and doing his homework by lamplight, he worked out all the answers to the chemistry problems in A. A. Noyes's book. One of the problems did not work out to a given answer. Pauling wrote to Noyes suggesting that his answer was wrong. Noyes wrote an irate reply pointing out that Pauling had misinterpreted the question. Perhaps Noyes was right; but if he was, then it was one of the few times that Pauling has ever been wrong about chemistry.

Pauling had come to Lambaréné to get Schweitzer's signature on a petition to ban atmospheric nuclear testing and to help him write his Declaration of Conscience, a document that Schweitzer, then 82 years old, labored over. There were connections between all of the petition signers. Schweitzer had actually shared rooms with Einstein in Zurich at about the time that Einstein was proposing the theory of relativity, and he knew many of the other scientists including the Berlin scientists who had originally proposed that an atomic weapon was possible. Although Schweitzer had four doctorates in religion, philosophy, music, and finally in medicine, he was not really steeped in modern sciences. He put his mind to it, however, and produced sound statements about fallout and the dangers of iodine 131. He recalled from his youth the ashy sunsets that followed the explosion of Krakatoa, and he envisioned how radiation could be carried around the globe. It became everyone's concern that a weapon exploded in Bikini could contaminate the world. Schweitzer's petition was released by the Nobel committee. It was circulated around the world and broadcast in every country, with the exception of the United States.

In January 1960, I started a postdoctorate at Caltech in the Department of Chemistry. I remember marching with Linus and Ava Helen Pauling through the streets of Los Angeles and being indelibly impressed by the catcalls and jeers of the onlookers and by the roughness of the police. I also remember conversations with acquaintances at Caltech who would say, "Oh, so you work with Linus now. We used to be friendly with the Paulings, but we do not see them since they became so political."

These were difficult days for Pauling and his family. I was called to the chemistry department because of a minor problem with a grant. The secretary, a longtime friend of Linus, remarked that if he would only spend more time on his chemistry and less on his political crusades, he would be much better off. Nobody was listening to him, she said. Part of this conversation got back to him. He was understandably furious and went right down to the office to point out that the error in the grant was a bookkeeping error and not due to his lack of attention. He was right, of course.

Then came that wonderful day in 1963 when it was announced that the Nobel Peace Prize was to be awarded to Linus Pauling. I happened to hear the announcement on my car radio as I was driving to Caltech. A professor passed me as I sat in my car. "Listen!" I shouted to him. The announcement was repeated.

"My God," he said, with tears rolling down his cheeks, "what shall we do?"

"Let's celebrate," I answered, "Caltech has always celebrated Nobel awards."

I had heard stories of the wild parties that followed the Nobel award for chemistry in 1954. Linus had always been popular with the students. He was homegrown, having spent his entire academic life at Caltech. But this time there were not any bonfires or skyrockets, as there had been in 1954; just a few handshakes, hugs, and warm congratulations. Three weeks later, Max Delbrück of the biology department asked me what the chemistry department was planning to do, because they, the biologists, wanted to honor him.

A few days later reporters from *Time* and *Life* magazines came to the campus to interview Pauling. He knew that editorially they leaned toward bigger and better bombs, so he asked for their promise that the articles would not be derogatory. Pauling sat in my little research room while the reporters phoned their editors. A few minutes later they came in and said that the editorial had already been written and it was derogatory. I found that editorial in my files the other day. A large headline read, "A Weird Insult from Norway."

One month later, Pauling dropped a bomb of sorts on Caltech. He called a press conference to announce that he was leaving the university after 40 years to join Robert Maynard Hutchins's Center for the Study of Democratic Institutions in

Santa Barbara. At one point during his time at the center, he asked me to join him in a seminar to discuss his proposal for a set of basic, ethical principals that could be acceptable to all people and all religions of the world. Just as Einstein had sought to unify all the forces of the universe, Linus Pauling sought to unify all the people of the world. This grand unifying principle, a personal testament, sums up admirably the man himself. It reads in part:

> I accept, as one of the basic ethical principles, the principle of the minimization of the amount of suffering in the world.
>
> I do not accept the contention that we cannot measure the suffering of other human beings, that we do not know what is good and what is evil.
>
> Even though my relationship to myself is subjective and that to other human beings is objective, I accept the evidence of my senses that I am a man, like other men; I am "fed with the same food, hurt with the same weapons, subject to the same diseases, healed by the same means, warmed and cooled by the same summer and winter" . . . I cannot in good faith argue that I deserve a better fate than other men; and I am forced by logic to accept as the fundamental ethical principle the Golden Rule: "As ye would that men should do unto you, do ye also unto them likewise." (Luke)

CHAPTER FIFTEEN

THE LYSENKO-PAULING-SAKHAROV FILE

IRVING S. BENGELSDORF, PhD

An old Chinese curse says, "May you live in interesting times." We now certainly do live in interesting times, just as there have been other interesting times. Consider the late 1940s, the years immediately following the end of World War II. The invention of the electronic digital computer and the semiconductor followed shortly after we learned how to make nuclear bombs. These three inventions have had, and will continue to have, profound effects on human societies and civilization. Inventions, like the flow of time, follow a progressive course. Once invented, they cannot be disinvented; we have no choice but to live with them.

Immediately after World War II was a time of rapid social upheaval. This period marked the abrupt dissolution of western imperialism and colonialism. The British and French empires quickly disappeared and set the stage for the postwar confrontation of the two new superpowers—the United States of America and the Union of Soviet Socialist Republics.

The feelings of good will and sympathy that had temporarily developed between the two countries as they had battled the common Nazi German enemy gave way to the distrust and antagonism of the cold war. That mutual hostility still exists today.

This period marked the last years of Josef Stalin, the Soviet premier who died on March 5, 1953, slightly more than 30 years ago. In his waning years, his paranoia and irascibility led to extremely strange behavior. Out of his many wild delusions grew his support, which reached a climax in 1948, of an incompetent agronomist named Trofim Denisovitch Lysenko. Stalin's support of Lysenko indirectly led some Soviet chemists and philosophers to attack Linus Pauling and his theory of resonance.

Meanwhile, in the United States, the people of Wisconsin in 1946 had elected a senator named Joseph R. McCarthy. He remained totally unknown for his first 4 years in office, but in February 1950 he suddenly became famous (or infamous, depending on your point of view) with a speech he delivered in Wheeling, West Virginia. In that speech the senator accused the U.S. Department of State of being infiltrated by hundreds of communists. Any challenge to Senator McCarthy to produce evidence for his claims was ignored, and only met with further accusations concerning communist influence in the United States.

Throughout history, intellectuals have always been easy prey for demagogic rabble rousers, and Senator McCarthy soon announced that American universities were infiltrated by communist faculties. So Dr. Pauling, an outspoken proponent of a global social outlook, came under attack. It was a terrible time during which academic careers were ruined by unsubstantiated accusations based on the flimsiest of evidence.

It is no surprise that the name McCarthy, like other notorious names, was converted into a new word in the English language: McCarthyism. One dictionary definition of McCarthyism is "public accusation of disloyalty to one's country, especially through procommunist activity, in many instances unsupported by proof or based on slight, doubtful, or irrelevant evidence."[1]

So, in 1951, when I obtained my doctorate in chemistry from the University of Chicago and came to Pasadena to carry out postdoctoral research with Dr. Pauling at the California Institute of Technology, he was faced with a paradox. Attacked in the Soviet Union as the idealistic, reactionary bourgeois author of the erroneous and vicious theory of resonance, he was at the same time under investigation by a U.S. congressional committee as a possible communist. As a graduate student at the University of Chicago, I had learned to read Russian. I already knew about the Soviet attacks on Dr. Pauling, and when I arrived at Caltech, I began to translate additional Russian papers on this subject.

To understand the Soviet position, we must go back to August 7, 1948. Trofim Denisovitch Lysenko, an agronomist with little training in biology, had called a meeting of the All-Union Lenin Academy of Agricultural Sciences. The purpose of the gathering supposedly was to discuss his ideas that the heredity of plants and animals did not depend on genetics, but could be changed by manipulation of the environment. According to Lysenko, genes played little role in a creature's inherited characteristics.

In the 1930s, Lysenko had teamed up with a lawyer named I. I. Prezent, who became his mouthpiece and speech writer. Prezent wrote, "The assertion that there are in an organism some minute particles, genes, responsible for the transmission of hereditary traits is pure fantasy without any basis in science."

Lysenko was more confused when he wrote, "Is heredity transmitted through the chromosomes during the sexual process? Of course, how could it be otherwise! We recognize chromosomes and do not deny their presence. But we do not recognize the chromosome theory of heredity. We do not recognize Mendelism-Morganism."

This illustrates a favorite form of argumentation in the Soviet Union: personification. One invokes the name of someone who has been selected as either a friend or as an enemy of the people. Thus, Lenin and Leninism are good; he was a friend of the people. But both Mendel, an Augustinian monk in Moravia who first worked out the details of genetic transmission, and Morgan, an American biologist who applied the genetic theory to a study of heredity in animals (fruit flies), are bad. Both were bourgeois reactionary enemies of the people. During Lysenko's reign of anti-intellectualism linked to Stalinism, railing against Mendelism or Morganism was proper. There was no need to explain what it meant; its obnoxious connotation was all that was needed.

Actually, the meeting that Lysenko chaired was a trap set to flush out and expose Lysenko's opponents. The affair's conclusion was determined before the meeting began. Stalin looked with favor on Lysenko, and the Central Committee of the Communist party had decided beforehand that Lysenko was correct, and his opponents were misled by alien reactionary ideas of bourgeois science.

As the last speaker of the meeting, Lysenko sounded the death knell for the science of genetics in the Soviet Union when he announced, "Comrades! I have been asked . . . as to the attitude of the Central Committee. . . . I answer, the Central Committee of the party has examined my report and approved it." Lysenko's words were greeted with a standing ovation.

What happened after Lysenko administered the coup de grace to genetics represents some of the more bizarre events in the almost 400 years of modern science. Scientists went up to the podium and recanted the views they had espoused only hours before. A letter of praise to Stalin was adopted unanimously; laboratories dealing with genetics were closed, and the professors dismissed. For 16 years, until Lysenko finally was ousted in 1964, genetics ceased to exist in the Soviet Union. For 16 years, Soviet biology students completed university courses without any instructions in genetics. And for 16 years, Soviet agriculture went from bad to worse under Lysenko's charlatanistic innovations.

The day after the meeting, August 8, 1948, *Pravda*'s report of the meeting was exultant: "As if moved by a single impulse, all those present arose from their seats and started a stormy, prolonged ovation in honor of the Central Committee of the Lenin-Stalin party, in honor of the wise leader and teacher of the Soviet people, the greatest scientist of our era, Comrade Stalin."

Lysenko's triumphant defeat of Soviet geneticists, achieved not through scientific debate but through political assault, did not go unnoticed. The thinking was that if one could debase geneticists by such tactics, why not use the same methods to eliminate scientists in other disciplines? Thus, immediately following Lysenko's triumph party philosophers teamed up with opportunistic scientists to attack other sciences. A flood of papers appeared to discredit the physics of Albert Einstein and Niels Bohr. Chemistry was not spared; in 1949, a determined attack was launched against Linus Pauling's theory of resonance.

To explain this particular argument, it is necessary to consider certain fundamental aspects of the science of chemistry. There now are 107 different types of atoms known, and these atoms form combinations called molecules. By universal agreement, chemists describe and represent molecules by simple, two-dimensional pictures called structures. A structure consists of the symbols of the various atoms making up the molecule. The atomic symbols are interconnected by straight lines, with each line representing a pair of bonding electrons. Consider the simple structures for methane (natural gas) and methyl alcohol (wood alcohol):

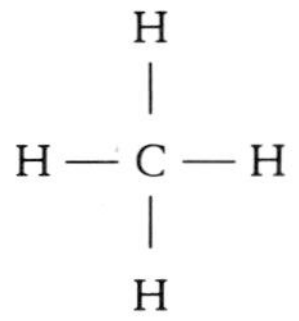

Methane

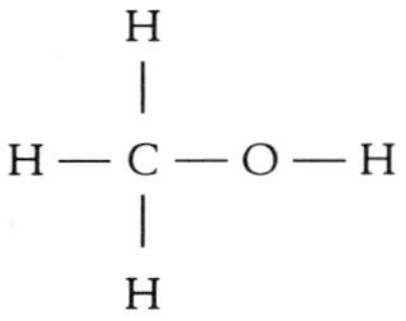

Methyl alcohol

Most of the more than six million molecules now known are adequately described by these pictorial structures, with one structure representing one molecule. However, there are four exceptions, as follows:

1. *Some structures can be written, but correspond to no known substance.* All attempts to produce a material called vinyl alcohol, for which a perfectly valid structure can be written, result instead in the production of acetaldehyde. Vinyl alcohol, although structurally legitimate, does not exist.
2. *Some structures that can be written do not represent a single substance, but two or more different substances.* Glucose, the sugar that fuels our bodily activities, exists in both an *alpha* and *beta* form. Such substances are examples of molecules called *isomers.* To explain them required a fundamental broadening of the structural theory.
3. *Some single substances behave as if they had two or more different structures.* Ethyl acetoacetate is a single substance, yet it sometimes behaves as if it were a ketone and sometimes as if it were an unsaturated alcohol. It is an example of what is called keto-enol tautomerism.
4. *There is a substance for which no single structure can be written.* The coal-tar hydrocarbon, benzene, does exist. It is a real substance. According to Marxist and Leninist dialectical materialism, therefore, benzene must have a structure. Yet, all attempts to write a single structure for benzene have been inadequate. In 1865, August von Kekulé proposed two closely related structures to represent benzene, neither of which could explain benzene's behavior. In spite of this shortcoming, chemists used one or the other of the Kekulé structures to describe benzene.

To get around this problem, Dr. Pauling combined the mathematics and concepts of quantum mechanics with the accepted chemical structures to develop his resonance theory. His theory successfully explained benzene's stability, its hexagonal symmetry, its planarity, and its carbon-to-carbon bond length. The resonance theory said that benzene was a hybrid molecule made up of contributions from the two Kekulé structures. Benzene was not one Kekulé structure part of the time, and the other Kekulé structure the rest of the time, but was a hybrid molecule all of the time.

The late George W. Wheland was one of my teachers at the University of Chicago. He was a former student of Dr. Pauling who helped develop the theory of resonance, and he also was bitterly attacked during the Soviet controversy. His analogy about the resonance theory and the two Kekulé structures of benzene is worth repeating. Wheland wrote,

> The statement that a mule is a hybrid between a horse and a donkey does not imply that a given mule is a horse part of the time and a donkey the rest of the time; neither does it imply that, at any given time, some mules are horses and the rest are donkeys. Instead, it implies that a mule is neither a horse nor a donkey but is a single kind of animal, intermediate at all times between the two extremes; and that all mules are the same kind of animal. In a similar sense, the structure of benzene is considered to be a hybrid [of the two Kekulé structures].[2]

The Soviet argument against Pauling was that his theory was contrived, a made-up convenience, an economy of thought that bore no relationship to reality. Such thought-constructs bore a strong resemblance to the philosophy of Ernst Mach, the Austrian physicist and philosopher who now is best remembered for the number that gives the ratio of the velocity of an aircraft to the velocity of sound. Mach's world outlook was severely criticized by Lenin, the deified first leader of the Soviet Union. Thus, to call anyone a Machist propagandist in the Soviet Union is an extremely derogatory accusation. And because of his resonance theory, Pauling was vilified by that label. Although Dr. Pauling now is no longer attacked by Soviet chemists, his resonance theory is still avoided as not the best way to describe molecules.

Thus far, I have given you the intellectual flavor of the so-called Pauling resonance controversy. But what really was behind it? In retrospect, the attack on Dr. Pauling was an indirect offshoot of the wave of anti-Semitism that swept the Soviet Union in Stalin's declining years.

Dr. Pauling had written an outstanding book entitled *The Nature of the Chemical Bond.* In turn, two Russian chemists, Ya. K. Syrkin and M. E. Dyatkina—both Jewish—had used Pauling's approach to write a book called *The Chemical Bond and the Structure of Molecules.* The attacks on Pauling were incidental to diatribes against Syrkin and Dyatkina. The anti-Semitism was revealed through the repetition of a unique word, *cosmopolite.* This is the official Soviet code word for Jew, as described by both Aleksandr I. Solzhenitsyn in his powerful novel *The First Circle,*[3] and by Roy A. Medvedev, brother of the exiled biologist Zhores Medvedev, in his Soviet history book entitled *Let History Judge.*[4]

Thus, an article I translated from the journal *Problems in Philosophy* states:

> The line of Ya. K. Syrkin and M. E. Dyatkina is a line of slavish grovelling before bourgeois science and culture, of the suppression of the achievements of Soviet science; it is the line of the cosmopolites exposed by our party. The cosmopolites do not fail to exalt the most insignificant achievement of any bourgeois flunky, to quote him dozens of times. To slight, to impoverish, to rob the progressive science of the socialistic state, to humiliate this science, to conceal its enormous progress and glorious tradition, not only from progressive people of foreign countries, but also from the Soviet people—this is the purpose of the cosmopolites.
>
> Thus, it is quite obvious that Ya. K. Syrkin and M. E. Dyatkina have appeared before the Soviet public in the unenviable role of propagandists for the avowedly erroneous and vicious theory of the American chemist, Pauling. It is not difficult to see that the line carried in the textbook by Syrkin and Dyatkina coincides to a considerable extent with the antiscientific line of Pauling, Wheland, and other bourgeois scientists directed towards the suppression of the achievements of Soviet science.[5]

The attack on Pauling's resonance theory obviously was motivated by opportunistic chemists who wanted to oust Syrkin and Dyatkina. As Zhores A. Medvedev, the exiled Soviet biologist, has put it, "making political accusations was the easiest and most tempting method of vanquishing opponents who could not be subdued by the force of scientific argumentation."[6] Thus, Lysenkoism, which started in biology, also claimed some victims among Soviet chemists.

At this time in the Soviet Union, following the attack on Dr. Pauling, Stalin had died and Lysenko now had become a favorite of Soviet Premier Nikita Khrushchev. But it was becoming more and more difficult to defend his antigenetic views. More than 30 years ago, on April 25, 1953, Watson and Crick in Britain had proposed a structure for DNA, the material of heredity comprising the genes. And in 1961, Nirenberg in America had worked out the first "word" in the cracking of the genetic code, thus opening the door to our possible understanding of how genes work.

In spite of these developments, Khrushchev had vigorously supported Lysenko at the February 10, 1964, meeting of the Central Committee. The showdown came in June 1964 at the election of scientists who had been proposed as new members of the Academy of Sciences. Khrushchev demanded that three new positions be created in genetics, and that one of these posts should go to N. Y. Nuzhdin, a Lysenko supporter.

The academy's biology section voted to admit Nuzhdin. But before any scientist can become an academician of the academy, the entire academy has to approve. Until June 1964 there never had been a case of a scientist who had been approved by an academy section, who then was turned down by the entire academy. But it happened with Nuzhdin.

Andrei D. Sakharov, a brilliant physicist who had been made an academician at the previously unheard of young age of 32, led the fight against Nuzhdin's appointment. He said, "I call on all those present to vote so that the only 'ayes' will be those who, together with Nuzhdin, together with Lysenko, bear the responsibility for the infamous, painful pages in the development of Soviet science, which fortunately are now coming to an end."

Khrushchev flew into a rage when he heard of Nuzhdin's rejection and Sakharov's opposition. He demanded an explanation from Sakharov and the physicist wrote a blunt, sharply worded memo. This further irritated Khrushchev, who then accused the Academy of Sciences of entering politics and threatened to restructure the entire academy—to convert it into an insignificant "Committee on Science." He also instigated a full investigation of Sakharov's career to try to find some compromising material.

But the Lysenko controversy was all over. Khrushchev, for other reasons, was removed from the Soviet premiership on October 15, 1964, and in February 1965 Lysenko was dismissed from his post as the director of the Institute of Genetics of the Academy of Sciences.

Partly because of Sakharov's courage, 16 years of Russian scientific nightmare had come to an end. But the damage had been done: although difficult to conceive in this day and age, there now is a generation of physicians in the Soviet Union who because of Lysenko received no training in genetics during their medical schooling.

Can a Lysenko return? Probably not. But in his book, *Fat Sasha and the Urban Guerrilla,* David Bonavia, a British correspondent who was expelled from the Soviet Union because he wrote about dissenters, says, "No thinking person can become well acquainted with a sizeable number of Soviet citizens, who dare to speak their minds to him, without experiencing a sense of loss and wastage. He will mentally contrast the courage, frankness, and sincerity of the people whom Soviet society casts aside, with the callousness and instinctive mendacity of those whom it raises up."[7] Among those callous and mendacious individuals elevated in Soviet society, there is always the possibility of another Lysenko. In our society, there is always the possibility of another McCarthy.

The spirit of Lysenko and McCarthy is everywhere. Consider the 10 years from 1966 to 1976 during the so-called Cultural Revolution in the People's Republic of China. Ten years of intellectual harassment led to stagnation of badly needed national development of scientific and technological goals. China still is trying to recover from that social fiasco.

As Dr. Conway Zirkle, a famous American geneticist, wrote in 1949 in his book, *Death of a Science in Russia:* "Unfortunately, we have learned during the last few years that the mere fact that an event is preposterous does not mean that it cannot occur."[8] That sentence sounds as if it were written only yesterday.

REFERENCES

1. *The Random House Dictionary of the English Language,* unabridged edition. New York, Random House, 1966.

2. Wheland GW: *Advanced Organic Chemistry.* New York, Wiley, 1949, p 392.

3. Solzhenitsyn AI: *The First Circle.* New York, Bantam Books, 1972, p 488.

4. Medvedev, RA: *Let History Judge: The Origins and Consequences of Stalinism.* Washington, Vintage Books, 1973, p 483.

5. Tatevskii SM, Shakhparanov MI: *Voprosi Filosofii* (Problems in Philosophy) No. 3. 1976 (1949). (A partial translation by Irving S. Bengelsdorf appeared in *J Chem Ed* 1952; 29: 13.)

6. Medvedev ZA: *The Rise and Fall of TD Lysenko.* New York, Columbia Univ. Press, 1969, p 6.

7. Bonavia D: *Fat Sasha and the Urban Guerrilla.* New York, Athenaeum, 1973.

8. Zirkle C: *Death of a Science in Russia.* Philadelphia, Univ. of Pennsylvania Press, 1949.

CHAPTER SIXTEEN

LINUS PAULING AND THE MEDICAL REVOLUTION

RICHARD P. HUEMER, MD

Historians have disagreed among themselves about the "great man" theory, some championing it and others believing that events unfold naturally through a process of historical necessity. An analogous debate has entered the field of evolutionary biology in recent years, where formerly the gradual processes of point-mutation and natural selection held undisputed sway, being a form of historical necessity. Now scientists acknowledge the importance of quantum-leap genetic transformations—a "great organism" arising unexpectedly to deflect the current of evolution. Both controversies seem to be variations of the perplexing heredity-versus-environment problem. I shall have more to say about this problem later, in the context of a disease model.

Similarly, people might spend lengthy although unproductive hours debating whether Linus Pauling is largely responsible for the modern revolution in medical science, or whether it would all have come to pass anyway. I happen to believe that we could have progressed without Pauling, albeit at a much slower pace. As a chemist, Linus Pauling has been a catalyst of awesome potency.

I do not know how much of Pauling's genius derived from his environment—particularly the intellectual ambience at the California Institute of Technology—and how much sprang from inner necessity. At any rate, I set forth here the bare outlines of his career as I have learned them from his associates and his publications. The external details may not reveal what we really need to know, but perhaps they will inspire younger men and women to follow his lead.

Linus Pauling was born on February 28, 1901, in Portland, Oregon, and grew up in that town and in a neighboring community. His father, a pharmacist, died when Linus was 9 years old. Linus attended the Oregon Agricultural College in Corvallis, majoring in chemical engineering. He dropped out of college for a year to help support his mother and sisters and worked during that time as a teaching assistant. He met his future wife, Ava Helen Miller, in a chemistry class that he was teaching.

The year 1922 proved to be a fateful one for young Linus Pauling. In that year the diffraction of X rays by crystals was discovered, and also in that year Linus arrived at the California Institute of Technology to begin graduate studies in the institute's active young chemistry department. At the suggestion of department chairman A. A. Noyes he began work on the structure of crystals as elucidated by X rays.

After a few years of work, the crystallographers succeeded in determining crystal structures of many elements and simple compounds, but some problems had become apparent. In dealing with complex crystals, it was no simple matter to determine which of many possible structures was most likely to be the actual structure, and thus worth the labor of experimental verification. In a landmark paper in 1928, Pauling formulated a set of five rules relating to crystal structure, which considerably simplified the task. He referred to this as the "coordination theory of the structure of ionic crystals."[1]

Linus Pauling turned his attention to the chemical bonds between atoms, and in 1931 he published a paper titled "The Nature of the Chemical Bond."[2] Using the principles of quantum mechanics, Pauling formulated six rules for the electron-pair bond. This led to his important work on resonance in molecular structures such as benzene.

The body of Pauling's earlier work was concerned with molecular structure and the nature of the chemical bond. By the mid 1930s his intellectual curiosity had begun to probe the applicability of this earlier work to molecules of biological importance. His work with R. B. Corey during the 1940s on X-ray diffraction of amino acids and small peptides led ultimately to the description of the alpha-helix structure in protein molecules.[3] His theoretical papers on antibodies in 1940 did not successfully explain antibody formation, but they embodied the crucial concept of molecular complementarity. The lineage of the double-helix model for DNA can be traced back unequivocally to Pauling's concepts of complementarity and the alpha helix.

Pauling had published on hemoglobin as early as 1936, but his major contribution in hemoglobin chemistry came in the late 1940s. On hearing a lecture by William Castle on sickle cell anemia, Pauling began to wonder whether there might be an abnormal region on the surface of the globin molecule capable of combining under appropriate conditions with a complementary site elsewhere on the globin to cause an alignment of hemoglobin molecules sufficient to distort the cell. In a landmark paper with Itano, Singer, and Wells,[4] Pauling described electrophoretic and other physical measurements demonstrating the abnormal hemoglobin variant. Thus was born the modern concept of molecular disease. Pauling also made use of hemoglobin structure in his important studies with Zuckerkandl on the process of molecular evolution.[5]

As J. H. Sturdivant has noted in the earlier festschrift,[6] "Pauling's scientific work has unfolded with a strong, logical coherence and interdependence of the successive extensions." It is all of a piece and has an underlying unity. Pauling started with the particular and worked toward the general, building ever more encompassing structural theories to explain more complex phenomena. He moved from the properties of substances of limited general interest to properties of systems (including social systems!) vital to all. His more recent work includes a search for the chemical basis of mental disease, a molecular theory of general anesthesia, the concept and principles of orthomolecular medicine, and investigations of human health benefits of ascorbic acid.

And all of Pauling's work bears the imprint of his special style. "There is," as Alex Rich and Norman Davidson point out, "a boldness and audacity in [Pauling's] suggestion of new ideas that are often, at first blush, outrageous in the simplicity with which they explain complicated phenomena."[7]

Boldness, audacity, and outrageous simplicity are not tools that win the affection of the medical profession, especially when an outsider employs them on medical problems. Thus a certain irony prevails: Linus Pauling, a scientist whose discoveries in biological chemistry provide the foundation of much that is taught in medical schools, is hardly revered by that minority who speak the opinions of organized medicine. The revolution is over; the revolutionary is no longer needed and even has become something of a bother.

But the revolution in medicine is not over. It took a wrong turn somewhere; medicine became impersonal, narrowly specialized, reductionistic, and highly technological. Even medical journals have begun to question the value of the status quo.[8, 9] A host of "holistic" and "alternative" clinics, counterrevolutionaries all, have sprung up like lawn mushrooms. (I am tempted to extend the simile by pointing out that lawn mushrooms are not often wholesome.) Some have even abandoned normality in favor of the paranormal, thereby augmenting physic with metaphysics.[10] There is too much fermenting for one to say the revolution is over.

A fact of scientific life is reductionism. Modern medicine wishes to be scientific, in the same way that a person wishes to be virtuous, so it too is reductionistic. Medicine has aped the basic sciences by dividing into specialties within specialties, isolating single variables in clinical studies, and relying heavily on single-agent therapies. In science, reductionism has excellently served the pursuit of truth; in medicine, it has fragmented the field and led doctors away from a holistic perspective.

I have occasionally remarked in public that natural medicine is synthetic. By this I do not mean that it is especially artificial, but rather that it requires assembly; natural (read holistic) medicine is an inductive process. That is how reductionism can serve medicine: not as a model for its design, but as a source of scientific truths that physicians can employ in understanding people, their diseases, and therapies. The progress of the medical revolution will depend on technology employed in the service of a holistic, inductive approach to medical problems.

Enter Linus Pauling, once again. In 1968 he introduced the term *orthomolecular* to mean the provision of the optimum concentration of molecules normal to the body, for the treatment and prevention of disease.[11] Orthomolecular medicine and psychiatry had been practiced before Pauling, of course. They were called by various other names. What Pauling did was to provide an understanding of how that method could work. His 1968 paper in *Science*[11] is a brilliant work of theoretical induction from the facts of biology and biochemistry.

We know from genetics that nobody inherits a perfect set of genes (if indeed "perfection" can be defined in any but the most relative of ways); polymorphism is rampant.[12, 13] Each of us carries in the heterozygous state several genes that would cause serious illness if homozygous, and a large number that have no obvious phenotypic effects even in the homozygous state although they are deviations from the "wild" type. The latter deviant genes may be regarded as elements (minor molecular diseases, if you like) predisposing their host toward various illnesses.

Additional predisposing elements are environmental: deficiency of cofactors for enzymes, presence of enzyme poisons, viral alterations of genetic programming, and the like. We can apply the general term *molecular lesion* to all such predisposing factors, and assert that their accumulation leads to clinically manifest disease. The more molecular lesions there are, the worse are the symptoms, and the more the symptoms characterize a group of diseases or a particular disease. (Every clinician is familiar with the vague, ill-defined nature of the symptoms of early disease. I am convinced that not a few professors of medicine owe their reputations for diagnostic acumen to the natural tendency for symptoms to become more definite as the problem patient makes his way through the chain of referral to meet the ultimate authority.)

Thus diseases, which are conventionally defined as sets of symptoms and physical (including laboratory) findings, can also be defined as sets of molecular lesions. It is important to realize that such sets are not the ordinary sort. They seem to be what Sokal and Sneath have termed polythetic,[14] meaning that each member of a class possesses a large (but unspecified) number of the properties that characterize the class as a whole, and each property of the class is possessed by large numbers (but not all) of the class members. Diseases are probably for the most part polythetic sets, sharing molecular lesions among each other. Small sets would partially characterize and serve as predisposing factors for a restricted number of diseases into which the small sets could evolve by expansion. As a set became more filled, its alternative pathways of development would become progressively fewer. (I have presented this analysis in greater detail elsewhere.[15])

It follows that the art of diagnosis could be enhanced—could indeed become a true science of diagnosis—through a process of measuring numerous biochemical characteristics of the body in a reductionistic and highly technological fashion, and analyzing the resulting sets of molecular lesions in terms of their known relation to diseases. New (and sometimes vague sounding) diagnostic labels might need to be devised: hepatic dysfunction, mineral imbalances, neoplastic diathesis, for example. It does not necessarily follow, but it seems reasonable to expect, that orthomolecular therapy would be the treatment of choice in most cases if diseases were regarded as multifactorial deviations from optimal biochemical functioning of the body.

In orthomolecular medicine, as in conventional allopathic medicine, man is perceived as a biochemical system, as distinguished from, say, a spiritual entity or a system of energy fields. Orthomolecular medicine achieves a holistic perspective by considering the diagnostic whole as a mosaic of biochemical data and the therapeutic whole as a mosaic of corrective measures. Because each medical case is unique from this viewpoint, it follows that traditional methods of clinical investigation (such as the double-blind study) are unsuitable for the validation of orthomolecular concepts. To borrow the words of Howard Schneider[16]:

> in the instance wherein we perceive (and our investigations identify) multicausal sets of parameters, we are faced with the necessity of using a different grammar of biologic science, of abandoning the satisfying imagery of univalent concepts of causation and adopting the apparently necessary conventions and grammar of multivariance statistics. . . . We must learn to ask not questions but what can only be called a questionnaire.

That is the task remaining for the fulfillment of the medical revolution: the acquisition of a holistic perspective and of the methodology for analysis and verification of holistic therapeutics. That is part of Linus Pauling's legacy to those who pursue the ideal of health. Perhaps the story of Pauling's own intellectual journey over the past 60 years, in which he broadened so remarkably his own vision and understanding, can serve as model for what needs to be done.

REFERENCES

1. Pauling L: The coordination theory of the structure of ionic crystals, in *Festschrift zum 60. Geburtstage Arnold Sommerfelds.* Leipzig, Verlag Hirzel, 1928, pp 11–17.

2. Pauling L: The nature of the chemical bond. Application of results obtained from the quantum mechanics and from a theory of paramagnetic susceptibility to the structure of molecules. *J Am Chem Soc* 1931; 53: 1367.

3. Pauling L, Corey RB: Two hydrogen-bonded spiral configurations of the polypeptide chain. *J Am Chem Soc* 1950; 72: 5349.

4. Pauling L, Itano HA, Singer SJ, et al.: Sickle cell anemia, a molecular disease. *Science* 1949; 110: 543–548.

5. Zuckerkandl E, Pauling L: Evolutionary divergence and convergence in proteins, in Bryson V, Vogel HJ (eds): *Evolving Genes and Proteins.* New York, Academic, 1965, pp 97–166.

6. Sturdivant JH: The scientific work of Linus Pauling, in Rich A, Davidson N (eds): *Structural Chemistry and Molecular Biology.* San Francisco, Freeman, 1968, pp 3–11.

7. Rich A, Davidson N: *Structural Chemistry and Molecular Biology* (preface). San Francisco, Freeman, 1968.

8. Carlson RJ: Holism and reductionism as perspectives in medicine and patient care. *West J Med* 1979; 131: 466–470.

9. Lappe M: Holistic health: a valuable approach to medical care. *West J Med* 1979; 131: 475–478.

10. Joy WB: *Joy's Way.* Los Angeles, JP Tarcher, 1979.

11. Pauling L: Orthomolecular psychiatry. *Science* 1968; 160: 265–271.

12. Harris H: Enzyme and protein polymorphism in human populations. *Br Med Bull* 1969; 25: 5–13.

13. Lewontin RC, Hubby JL: A molecular approach to the study of genetic heterozygosity in natural populations. II. Amount of variation and degree of heterozygosity in natural populations of *Drosophila pseudoobscura. Genetics* 1966; 54: 595–609.

14. Sokal RR, Sneath PHA: *Principles of Numerical Taxonomy.* San Francisco, Freeman, 1963, p 14.

15. Huemer RP: A theory of diagnosis for orthomolecular medicine. *J Theoret Biol* 1977; 67: 625-635; reprinted in *Advances* 1984; 1(3): 53–59.

16. Schneider HA: Biologic setting of modern nutritional sciences, in Schneider HA, Anderson CE, Coursin DB (eds): *Nutritional Support of Medical Practice.* Hagerstown, Harper and Row, 1977, pp 1–8.

CHAPTER SEVENTEEN

THE FUTURE OF ORTHOMOLECULAR MEDICINE

LINUS PAULING, PhD

This has been a great day for me, and yesterday, too, especially to have so many of my former students and collaborators here saying nice things about me. I was not sure that they would, when I heard that they were coming. I can say nice things about them, too. I feel that I have been very fortunate in having been associated with them and with the others who are not here today. Much of the success of the work that we carried out was due to their contributions. Of course I am pleased also with the other participants in this fine program. I dedicated my book *Vitamin C and the Common Cold* to Irwin Stone and also to Albert Szent-Gyorgyi, who discovered vitamin C long ago, when he was trying to find out what kept some fruits and vegetables from turning brown when they were exposed to light. Of course, it was an antioxidant, and it turned out to be vitamin C.

Since my former students and former associates have talked about my past life, I thought that I should also talk a bit about my past life. Three days ago I gave two speeches in Italy. I was able to live up to the pledge I made in December 1947, which Dr. Catchpool mentioned, that I would mention the need for world peace in every talk that I gave. One of my talks in Italy was about the need for peace in the world, about the path to world peace. I mentioned that it was hard to understand why the American people are willing that the government should have the policy of spending 1.6 trillion dollars on militarism in the next 5 years, and that I thought that the answer was that the American people were misled about the missile crisis, about nuclear vulnerability, about the Soviet Union having more missiles than we have or nuclear warheads with greater destructive power, so that we have to catch up. I think that I even quoted the statement that Senator Christopher Dodd and Senator Paul Tsongas made last year, which was, "The President of the United States lies. This was unthinkable 20 years ago." It was a shock to me to read this statement made by two senators here in the United States.

Then I got a letter from a psychologist friend who wrote that he had reached the conclusion that President Reagan is unable to distinguish between reality and fantasy. He quoted President Reagan's fantasy that the Soviet Union has far greater nuclear destructive power than the United States, and then he quoted from the Pentagon report of the Department of Defense of 1982 that there is an approximate equality of destructive power in the arsenals of the Soviet Union and the United States. Then—fantasy again—President Reagan says that the campaign for a nuclear freeze is being orchestrated and led by communists.

In fact, the State Department says that there is no evidence that communists are involved in any serious way in the campaign for nuclear disarmament. It is just good sense—good sense to stop wasting so much money on militarism, if we are going to solve the problems of the world. We have to cooperate, all the people and all the nations in the world.

The reason that I spend time thinking about medical problems, about vitamin C, for example, is that I believe that we are going to solve this problem of finding out how to keep the world from being destroyed in a nuclear war, and that it is worthwhile to be thinking of making the world a better place for the coming generations of human beings.

One way in which this can be done is by improving the health of people, by cutting down on the amount of suffering caused by hypoascorbemia, as Irwin Stone says, from which essentially everybody in the world is suffering. Only a few enlightened persons, who take 10 or 12 g a day of vitamin C, are in the fortunate position of not suffering from this genetic disease that we have learned to control, but only just barely, by getting a diet that contains enough ascorbate to keep us from dying, but not enough, it has turned out, to put us in the best of health. That can be done only with supplementary vitamin C.

The other talk that I gave to the symposium that I was attending was on the role of the physical sciences in modern biology. I talked about one aspect of this, and in fact it is quite pertinent to what we have all been talking about: about vectors of disease and about the human body and how it functions.

I doubt that I thought much about the nature of life until 1929. I was then carrying on research on the structure of minerals and other inorganic substances. Then in 1929 Thomas Hunt Morgan came from Columbia University, bringing with him Sturdivant and Bridges and Emerson and Tyler. Sturdivant and Bridges were two of the three students who had cooperated with Morgan in developing the theory of the gene, in discovering the gene. It was not known, of course, that it consists of polynucleotides, but they knew a lot about it even though they did not know its chemical composition. They kept talking about the *specificity* characteristic of life. One example of this specificity is that parents have children who resemble them. This resemblance we now know even goes so far as the amino-acid sequences of the polypeptides that constitute the specific proteins in their bodies, and their specificity in the action of enzymes as catalysts.

Morgan was working on self-sterility of *Ciona,* the sea squirt. In 1935 and 1936 I was working on diamagnetic oxygen as well as triplet oxygen, the normal state, with the idea that we could tell something about how oxygen molecules are held by hemoglobin molecules in the red cells of the blood. The idea was that we could distinguish between two kinds of combination, one involving a mainly physical force that would leave the oxygen in the triplet state, leave it paramagnetic, and the other chemical combination, the forming of chemical bonds that would make the oxygen molecule diamagnetic. We measured the magnetic susceptibility of venous blood and arterial blood, and found that the oxygen molecules were held in the hemoglobin molecule by forming chemical bonds. We also found a remarkable change in magnetic properties of the iron atoms when the hemoglobin in the red cells is oxygenated.

I was giving a talk in New York in 1936 at the Rockefeller Institute for Medical Research, a seminar on this subject, and Karl Landsteiner asked me to talk with him. Karl Landsteiner had discovered the A, B, and O blood groups in 1900, and others, L and M and Rhesus factor, later on. He had been carrying out experiments in the field of immunology (immunochemistry) and he asked if I could explain his observations. I could not explain them, but he told me a great deal in several days of discussion; he told me a great deal about immunology. I kept thinking about what he had said, and finally I reached a decision as to what I thought was going on that permitted antibodies to show such remarkable specificity in their interaction with antigens. Landsteiner was making azoproteins, using simple chemical substances such as para-aminobenzoic acid taken off the shelf, got out of the stock room, diazotizing these amines, coupling them with proteins, using these azoproteins as antigens, then making antibodies that would combine specifically with the simple chemical substance that had been attached to the original protein. This appealed to me, in that I felt that I knew a lot about the simple chemical substances such as benzoic acid or parachlorobenzoic acid, metachlorobenzoic acid, orthochlorobenzoic acid or toluic acid, and hundreds of other substituted benzoic acids as well as other substances you could use instead of the benzoic acid.

By 1940, I had reached the conclusion that I knew the answer to the question of the molecular basis of biological specificity, the molecular basis of life. There were two ideas that had been discussed. A German physicist named Pascual Jordan published a paper in 1940, about the time that I had published my paper about the structure of antibodies and the nature of serological reactions. He advocated one of these ideas, which is that identical molecules attract one another more strongly than nonidentical molecules because of the phenomenon of quantum mechanical resonance. Max Delbrück brought this paper to my attention, and I said I did not believe that the extra energy of attraction that you get from quantum mechanical resonance between identical molecules could possibly be the explanation, because this extra energy is less than the energy of thermal agitation. It just would not work. But if—and this was in my paper on antibodies—the antibody has a combining region that is complementary in the arrangement of its atoms to the haptenic group of the antigen, you get strong and highly selective interaction. So we wrote a paper in 1940 saying that biological specificity in general results from the detailed molecular complementariness of the interacting groups, and that Jordan was wrong about his idea of quantum mechanical resonance. We also said the gene consists of two mutually complementary molecules, each of which, when they are separated, can act as a template for the synthesis of a replica of the other one, so that gene duplication occurs that way, using one half of the gene for the template for the other half because of its complementariness.

Of course, some years later examples of complementariness began to show up. The alpha helix and the pleated sheet are arrangements of polypeptide chains in which there are two complementary groups which interact, the NH— group of a peptide interacting with the oxygen atom of the carbonyl groups of another peptide, and that is a highly directed interaction. You can achieve these hydrogen bonds by coiling the polypeptide chain in the helix or by arranging it in a somewhat staggered linear arrangement coming back on itself to make the pleated sheet where the hydrogen bonds are formed laterally. And then, of course, Watson and Crick discovered the double helix 13 years later, in 1953, when they were able to show that two nucleotides—a purine and a pyrimidine—form two hydrogen bonds with one another, and two other nucleotides—another purine and another pyrimidine—form three hydrogen bonds with one another, and that the gene consists of two polynucleotides which are mutually complementary, adenine combining with thymine and guanine combining with cytosine.

By 1948, my students and my associates Dan Campbell and David Pressman, who worked for several years on this project, had carried out studies of the interaction of antibodies with haptenic groups, hundreds of experiments, a thousand perhaps, determining equilibrium constants. By 1948 we had tied down these ideas, so far as they are concerned with antibodies and antigens, so tightly that there was no possibility of saying that we were wrong.

So, molecular complementariness, this tight fit of the complex of atoms of one molecule onto the complex of atoms of another molecule, is the basis of life. Biology now is developing; molecular biology is going along strongly, also genetic engineering. We are going to get more control of ourselves, with a better understanding of the nature of our own bodies and the way in which these bodies function. I am not going to make an effort to predict in detail what the future of orthomolecular medicine will be. I think that it has been done already, by the participants in this seminar; but I might make a quantitative statement. Someone sent to me a clipping saying that Dr. Pauling says that we can live to be 100 years old, and in fact I had said that; that by proper use of supplementary nutrients and other health practices, people in general could live 25 years longer than they do now, live to be 100 years old, and lead good lives too, not have a long period of debility as the body begins to fail.

Well, Irwin Stone said that he believed that I could live for another 50 years; it was 15 years ago when he made that statement, so he would say that he thinks that we can live 35 years more than presently accepted. It may well be that in a generation or two we shall have enough knowledge, especially in the orthomolecular field, to permit people to live to be 110 years old. I think that this is worthwhile. If we can extend the period of well-being, then we shall have extended the ratio of well-being to suffering, and I think that will be quite worthwhile.

I have enjoyed myself for many years, after I got through the initial period of not understanding the world very well. I have enjoyed myself, and it has been a special pleasure for me to have been here today and yesterday. Thank you.

Dr. Pauling's extemporaneous talk was presented at the conclusion of the Orthomolecular Medical Society Conference held in his honor, May 8, 1983, in San Francisco, California.

CHAPTER EIGHTEEN

THE TWENTY-FIVE MOST CITED PUBLICATIONS OF LINUS PAULING

ZELEK S. HERMAN, PhD

Linus Pauling is one of the most illustrious scientists of modern times. He has been awarded two unshared Nobel Prizes (Chemistry, 1954; Peace, 1962), some 50 honorary doctorates, and numerous honors, including the National Medal of Science (1974), the Lenin International Peace Prize (1970), and the Priestley Medal of the American Chemical Society (1984). During a career spanning over 60 years, Pauling has published more than 600 scientific articles and books in fields ranging from theoretical physics to medicine.[1] His research interests are catholic to an extent scarcely equalled by anyone since Leonardo da Vinci, owing largely to Pauling's having established a universal *Weltansicht.*

Therefore, it is of interest to analyze the number of citations in the *Science Citation Index* (Institute for Scientific Information, Philadelphia) to Pauling's most cited publications. This has been done from 1955, the year of inception of the *Science Citation Index,* through 1983. In order to make the search as accurate as possible, obvious mistakes by citing authors were taken into account and publications not having Pauling as first author were considered.

While a part of this search could have been performed with the computer online services of the *Science Citation Index,* it was decided to perform the search manually, because of the vagaries of some writers (*vide infra*).

The results are shown in Table 18.1. In this table the number of citations to the various editions and translations of *The Nature of the Chemical Bond* and of *General Chemistry* have been combined. On perusal of this table, it is clear that *The Nature of the Chemical Bond* has a significance far exceeding that of any of Pauling's other publications. The variety of citations indicates the breadth of Pauling's effect on many fields of science. Nevertheless, it is unwarranted to compare the significance of the publications listed in this table merely according to their numerical rankings, as the size of readership differs in different fields of science and medicine. Moreover, there exist many hundreds of citations to Pauling's publications in papers published before the inception of the *Science Citation Index* in 1955.

If Linus Pauling is not the most cited author in the *Science Citation Index,*[2] he is certainly one of the most miscited. For example, in the 1955 to 1964 cumulation of the *Science Citation Index,* citations to Linus Pauling's work can be found under Pauling, B. L. Pauling, C. L. Pauling, E. Pauling, I. Pauling, J. Pauling, K. Pauling, L. A. Pauling, L. B. Pauling, L. D. Pauling, L. J. Pauling, R. Pauling, R. C. Pauling, and Paulingbl.

During the period from 1955 to 1983 there were 31 citations to a paper[3] not even written by Pauling, although his name is mentioned in the text. Occasionally, the work of Linus Pauling is cited under the names of his sons, Crellin Pauling or Peter Pauling. Furthermore, there exist numerous mistakes by citing authors regarding the year, volume, or page number of a particular publication. Indeed, the present author is guilty of at least one error of this latter kind. Nevertheless, these types of error are well known to the users of the *Science Citation Index.** It is estimated that the error in the number of citations listed in Table 18.1 is less than 1 percent.

This research has been supported in part by a grant from the Japan Shipbuilding Industry Foundation.

REFERENCES

1. A list of Pauling's scientific publications from 1923 to 1968 was compiled by Gustav Albrecht and is published in *Structural Chemistry and Molecular Biology: A Volume Dedicated to Linus Pauling by his Students, Colleagues, and Friends,* A. Rich and N. Davidson (eds): San Francisco, Freeman, 1968, pp 887–907. A compilation of his publications from 1968 onward has been made by D. Munro and the author and is available on request from the Linus Pauling Institute.

2. The publication cited most often is probably Lowry OH, Rosebrough NJ, Farr AL, and Randall RJ: *J Biol Chem* 1951; 193: 265.

3. Schuch AF, Sturdivant JH: *J Chem Phys* 1950; 18: 145.

*Fortunately, there is only one scientist who publishes under the name of L. Pauling. Two scientists publish under the name of Z. S. Herman, and their citations are not distinguishable in the *Science Citation Index.*

Table 18.1 The twenty-five publications of Linus Pauling that are cited most often in *Science Citation Index* during the period 1955–1983

No. of citations	Numerical rank	Publication	Title	Co-authors
16,027	1	*The Nature of the Chemical Bond, and the Structure of Molecules and Crystals.* Ithaca, NY, Cornell Univ. Press, 1st ed 1939, 2nd ed 1940, 3rd ed 1960.	—	—
841	2	*Introduction to Quantum Mechanics, with Applications to Chemistry.* New York, McGraw-Hill, 1935.	—	E. Bright Wilson, Jr
617	3	*Science* 1949; 110: 543.	"Sickle cell anemia, a molecular disease."	H. A. Itano, S. J. Singer, and I. C. Wells
525	4	*Proc Natl Acad Sci (USA)* 1951; 37: 205.	"The structure of proteins: two hydrogen-bonded helical configurations of the polypeptide chain."	R. B. Corey and H. R. Branson
456	5	*J Am Chem Soc* 1947; 69: 542.	"Atomic radii and interatomic distances in metals."	—
434	6	*Proc Roy Soc (London)* 1927; A114: 181.	"The theoretical prediction of the physical properties of many-electron atoms and ions. Mole refraction, diamagnetic susceptibility, and extension in space."	—

349	7	*Science* 1961; 134: 15.	"A molecular theory of general anesthesia."	—
266	8	*J Am Chem Soc* 1931; 53: 1367.	"The nature of the chemical bond. Application of results obtained from the quantum mechanics and from a theory of paramagnetic susceptibility to the structure of molecules."	—
264	9	*J Am Chem Soc* 1940; 62: 2643.	"A theory of the structure and process of formation of antibodies."	—
256	10	*Vitamin C and the Common Cold.* San Francisco, Freeman, 1970. *Vitamin C, the Common Cold, and the Flu.* San Francisco, Freeman, 1976.	—	—
235	11	*J Am Chem Soc* 1939; 61: 1769.	"The electron diffraction investigation of the structure of benzene, pyridine, pyrazine, butadiene-1,3,-cyclopentadine, furan, pyrrole, and thiophene."	V. Schomaker
228	12	*Proc Roy Soc (London)* 1953; B141: 21.	"Stable configurations of polypeptide chains."	R. B. Corey
227	13	*J Am Chem Soc* 1935; 57: 2680.	"The structure and entropy of ice and of other crystals with some randomness of atomic arrangement."	—
225	14	*General Chemistry.* San Francisco, Freeman, 1st ed 1947, 2nd ed 1953, 3rd ed 1970.	—	—

No. of citations	Numerical rank	Publication	Title	Co-authors
223	15	*Phys Rev* 1930; 36: 430.	"The rotational motion of molecules in crystals."	—
218	16	*Evolving Genes and Proteins,* V Bryson and HJ Vogel, eds. NY, Academic, 1965, pp 97–166.	"Evolutionary divergence and convergence in proteins."	E. Zuckerkandl
211	17	*Proc Roy Soc (London)* 1949; A196: 343.	"A resonating valence-bond theory of metals and intermetallic compounds."	—
206	18	*Proc Natl Acad Sci (USA)* 1951; 37: 235.	"Atomic coordinates and structure factors for two helical configurations of polypeptide chains."	R. B. Corey
201	19/20	*J Am Chem Soc* 1935; 57: 2086.	"A quantum mechanical discussion of orientation of substituents in aromatic molecules."	G. W. Wheland
201	19/20	*J Chem Phys* 1936; 4: 673.	"The diamagnetic anisotropy of aromatic molecules."	—
199	21	*Proc Natl Acad Sci (USA)* 1951; 37: 729.	"Configurations of polypeptide chains with favored orientations around single bonds: two new pleated sheets."	R. B. Corey
181	22	*Nature* 1964; 203: 182.	"Nature of the iron-oxygen bond in oxyhaemoglobin."	—

180	23	*Nature* 1953; 171: 59.	"Compound helical configurations of polypeptide chains: structure of proteins of the α-keratin type."	R. B. Corey
168	24	*J Am Chem Soc* 1929; 51: 1010.	"The principles determining the structure of complex ionic crystals."	—
156	25	*J Am Chem Soc* 1932; 54: 3570.	"The nature of the chemical bond. IV. The energy of single bonds and the relative electronegativity of atoms."	—

THE AUTHORS

Emile Zuckerkandl ("Toward a Molecular Biology of Predisposition to Disease") is an eminent molecular biologist and is president of the Linus Pauling Institute of Science and Medicine. After receiving his PhD at the Sorbonne in 1959, he accomplished his postdoctoral studies at the California Institute of Technology. He served as research director of the CNRS in Montpellier, France, for 10 years, beginning in 1965. Dr. Zuckerkandl edits the *Journal of Molecular Evolution* and has written books on protein evolution and on population genetics. He is a recipient of the Order of Merit from the French government.

Richard T. Jones ("Functional Properties of Abnormal Human Hemoglobins") is professor of biochemistry and chairman of the Department of Biochemistry in the School of Medicine of the Oregon Health Sciences University in Portland, Oregon. Dr. Jones received his MD from Oregon in 1956 and his PhD from the California Institute of Technology in 1961, where he worked with Walter Schroeder and Linus Pauling. He returned to the medical school in Oregon in 1961 and established a laboratory for structural studies of hemoglobin. In 1974 he spent a sabbatical with Max Perutz in Cambridge, England, where he studied the functional properties of chemically altered and mutant human hemoglobins. Except for a 14-month term in 1977 and 1978 as the acting president of the University of Oregon Health Sciences Center, he has taught biochemistry, directed a research team, and chaired the Department of Biochemistry since 1967. He and his research associates are interested in mapping the functionally important parts of the hemoglobin molecule by studying chemically modified and mutant hemoglobins.

Daniel T.-b. Shih ("Functional Properties of Abnormal Human Hemoglobins") is a research assistant professor in the Department of Biochemistry of the School of Medicine of the

Oregon Health Sciences University in Portland, Oregon. Shih received his BS in pharmaceutical sciences from Taipei Medical College in 1970 and his PhD in medical basic sciences from Osaka University School of Medicine, Osaka, Japan, where he studied with Kiyohiro Imai. He has been a member of the faculty at Oregon since 1984. His research focuses on the function of chemically modified and mutant hemoglobin and on the interaction between hemoglobin and other chemical compounds.

Irwin Stone ("Scurvy, the Cosmic Connection") had a long and distinguished career in chemistry. After studying chemical engineering at City College of New York, Dr. Stone spent 37 years with the Wallerstein Company, retiring in 1971 as head chemist responsible for all research in the fermentation and enzyme laboratories. He is listed as inventor in 26 U.S. patents in the brewing, food, pharmaceutical, nutrition, and medical fields. He was awarded two honorary doctorates, and in 1983 he received the highest award of the International Forum for Human Development, the Statuette with Pedestal, for "outstanding work in the field of human nutrition." Dr. Stone died on May 4, 1984, a few hours before a meeting of the Orthomolecular Medical Society and Academy of Orthomolecular Psychiatry at which he was to have received three additional awards. The awards were presented posthumously in gratitude for a career of service to mankind.

Jeffrey S. Bland ("Lipid Peroxidation-Induced Diseases") is the director of the Nutritional Supplement Analysis Laboratory at the Linus Pauling Institute of Science and Medicine. He is on leave from the University of Puget Sound, where he is a professor of nutritional biochemistry. Dr. Bland studied biology as an undergraduate at the University of California, Irvine, and obtained his PhD in chemistry from the University of Oregon. He has been actively involved for the past dozen years in nutrition-related research, with particular emphasis on the role of biological antioxidants in retardation of lipid peroxidation in vivo and in vitro, the relation between hair mineral levels and blood chemical parameters, and the effects of essential fatty acids on the arachidonic acid cascade. Dr. Bland's other professional interests include computer applications in health promotion and the development of methods for early assessment of nutritional inadequacies. At the Linus Pauling Institute he is developing a technique of metabolite profiling of urine with the use of field ionization mass spectrometry.

Denham Harman ("The Aging Process") is Millard Professor of Medicine and professor of biochemistry at the University of Nebraska College of Medicine. He did his undergraduate and graduate work in chemistry at the University of California, Berkeley, receiving his PhD in 1943. After 7 years at Shell Development Company in the Reaction Kinetics Department, he left to enter Stanford Medical School. Upon completing an internship in 1954 he joined the Donner Laboratory of Medical Physics on the University of California, Berkeley campus. In 1956 he left the Donner Laboratory to complete a residency in internal medicine. He joined the faculty of the University of Nebraska College of Medicine 2 years later. Dr. Harmon is executive director of the American Aging Association.

Stephen A. Levine ("Antioxidant Biochemical Adaptation: A Unified Disease Theory") received his training at the University of California, Berkeley in molecular genetics and biochemistry. After receiving his PhD, he worked in an agricultural biochemistry laboratory, which led to his exposure to carbon monoxide and other toxic chemicals. Within 6 months he developed severe food and chemical allergies and was told by experts at major allergy clinics that he would never lead a normal life. Calling on his scientific background and intuition he discovered that supplementation of key antioxidant nutrients reversed his symptoms, results since repeated in clinical trials by physicians. As a result of these findings Dr. Levine founded the Allergy Research Group, Nutri-Cology, Inc., a company dedicated to producing hypoallergenic nutritional supplements, where he is director of research. Dr. Levine has lectured across the United States and Canada, has published extensively in the medical literature, and has held editorial positions with the *International Clinical Nutrition Review, Orthomedicine,* and the *Allergy Research Review.* He is conducting research in his unified disease theory of antioxidant adaptation.

Parris M. Kidd ("Antioxidant Biochemical Adaptation: A Unified Disease Theory") is a biomedical consultant. He received his PhD in cellular and developmental biology at the University of California, Berkeley. His postdoctoral training was completed at the University of California, San Francisco, in the Department of Anatomy and the Cardiovascular Research Institute. Dr. Kidd has received a number of honors including the Kirkwood Memorial Award from the San Francisco Heart Association for the best postdoctoral performance in 1977. He has considerable research experience and has published numerous peer-reviewed full articles in the medical literature. Dr. Kidd recently collaborated on a book, *Antioxidant Adaptation: Its Role in Free Radical Pathology,* with Stephen A. Levine.

Jerzy W. Meduski, Jerzy D. Meduski, Khashayar Khakmahd, Akbar Azad, and **Claude Cruz** ("Photon Counting in Nutritional Biochemistry") prepared their study at the Department of Neurology of the University of Southern California School of Medicine in Los Angeles, where J. W. Meduski heads a nutritional research laboratory. In addition to his experimental and theoretical work in nutritional biochemistry, J. W. Meduski continues his life-long studies of intermediary metabolism, of the effects of nutrition on pharmacological responses of organisms, and of toxinology. Educated in Poland (medical degree in Warsaw, 1946, and PhD in biochemistry and animal physiology in Lodz, 1951), Holland, Scotland, and Moscow, J. W. Meduski spent the first half of his professional life in Poland and now resides and works in the United States. His closest coworker is his son, J. D. Meduski, who has cooperated with his father since his teens. Educated at the University of Southern California, J. D. Meduski received a BS in biology in 1978 and a BS in chemistry in 1979. His main interest is the application of physical chemistry methods to studies of biological phenomena, especially nutritional biochemistry. He discovered the principle of the oligodynamic activity of silver. Khashayar Khakmahd, Akbar Azad, and Claude Cruz are former students of J. W. Meduski, presently active in bioengineering and scientific medicine, in nutrition, and in the theoretical study of the design of computers and the mathematical modeling of biological phenomena, respectively.

Ewan Cameron ("Vitamin C and Cancer Cachexia") is a research professor at the Linus Pauling Institute. Dr. Cameron was educated at the University of Glasgow and the Royal College of Surgeons in Edinburgh and Glasgow and took his medical degree at the University of Glasgow in 1944. He served for 3 years as a medical officer (Lt. Col. senior surgical specialist) with the British armed services in Burma before becoming a general surgeon. He retired from his post as senior consultant surgeon in Vale of Leven Hospital, Loch Lomondside, Scotland, in 1982, when he assumed his present position. He is the civil consultant in general surgery to the Royal Navy in

Scotland and a Lister medallist in pathology. Dr. Cameron has published many scientific papers concerned with the treatment of cancer, and he has authored two books: *Hyaluronidase and Cancer,* Pergamon, 1966, and with Linus Pauling, *Cancer and Vitamin C,* Linus Pauling Institute, 1979; Warner Books, 1981.

Melvin Greenblatt, MD ("Nitrites, Nitrosamines, and Vitamin C") is a fellow of the College of American Pathologists and clinical professor of pathology at the University of Southern California. His major research activity has been in experimental chemical carcinogenesis. He is the author of many research articles on nitrosamine formation in vivo. Currently he is director of laboratories, Westlake Community Hospital and vice chairman of the Environmental and Iatrogenic Committee of the College of American Pathologists, which deals primarily with environmental problems in the clinical laboratory.

Michael Rosenbaum ("Nutrients and the Immune System") has been engaged in the private practice of medicine and clinical nutrition for 10 years in Mill Valley, California. His interest in nutrition began while doing research in clinical biochemistry at the Hebrew University in Jerusalem, for which he earned an MS in clinical biochemistry in 1966. He returned to the United States to complete his MD in 1968 at the Albert Einstein College of Medicine. Subsequently, he completed a psychiatry residency at the University of California, San Francisco, and practiced psychiatry for several years. Since 1979, Dr. Rosenbaum has been a vice president and board member of the Orthomolecular Medical Society and has served as editor of the society's official newsletter, *Orthomedicine.*

John E. Morley and **Allen S. Levine** ("Hormones, Formones, and Gormones") have collaborated for the past 5 years on research related to the central regulation of food intake as well as gastric acid secretion. Dr. Morley is currently director of the Geriatric Research, Education and Clinical Center at the Sepulveda Veterans Administration Medical

Center in Sepulveda, California, and professor of medicine at the University of California, Los Angeles. His current work focuses on the role of neuroregulatory substances in aging with an emphasis on memory and feeding. Born in South Africa, he was educated at the University of Witwatersrand where he obtained his MB, BCh in 1972. He then completed an endocrine fellowship at the University of California, Los Angeles and moved to the Minneapolis Veterans Administration Medical Center where he resided from 1980 to 1984. Dr. Morley is on the editorial board of *Peptides* and the *American Journal of Physiology.* Dr. Levine is a research chemist with the Minneapolis Veterans Administration Medical Center and an associate professor in the Department of Food Science and Nutrition at the University of Minnesota. Levine received his PhD in nutrition from the University of Minnesota in 1977 and completed a fellowship in the Department of Medicine at the University of Minnesota. Drs. Morley and Levine were recently presented the Mead Johnson Award from the American Institute of Nutrition.

Richard A. Kunin ("Orthomolecular Psychiatry") is in the private practice of psychiatry and orthomolecular medicine in San Francisco. Dr. Kunin is a graduate of the University of Minnesota Medical School. He took his residency training in psychiatry at the New York Hospital Payne Whitney Clinic and his postdoctoral fellowship in neurology and neurophysiology at Stanford University. He has written and lectured extensively on orthomolecular medicine and psychiatry and is the author of two books: *Mega-Nutrition* and *Mega-Nutrition for Women,* both published by McGraw-Hill. Dr. Kunin is a founder and past president of the Orthomolecular Medical Society.

Jonathan E. Rothschild ("The Role of Phospholipids in Neurological Function") is on the technical staff of Cardiovascular Research, Ltd., Concord, California, where he conducts clinical research in conjunction with various university medical centers in the field of nutritional pharmacology. Foremost among these studies are the use of cholinergic agonists in the treatment of Alzheimer's disease and of memory defects due to cerebral arteriosclerosis. He has a BS from Rutgers University and an MA from San Francisco State University. In recent years his research has focused on nutritional modulation of immunodeficiencies.

John F. Catchpool ("The Evolution of a Scientist's Social Conscience") is a family practitioner in Marin County, California. Dr. Catchpool was born and educated in London, where he earned his medical degree at Kings College Hospital. His postdoctoral training included residency at the Albert Schweitzer Hospital in Lambaréné, Gabon (where he later became chief of medical service) and fellowship at the California Institute of Technology. At the latter institution, he studied molecular mechanisms of anesthesia under the direction of Linus Pauling. In 1969 he served as medical director of Aid to Biafran Children in Africa. His wide-ranging interests include famine relief, rural health care delivery in developing countries, edible protein from the water hyacinth, epidemiology of malnutrition, and tropical medicine.

Irving S. Bengelsdorf ("The Lysenko-Pauling-Sakharov File") is a technical writer-specialist at the Jet Propulsion Laboratory/California Institute of Technology. He did his undergraduate work at the University of Illinois, Champaign-Urbana, and received his PhD in chemistry from the University of Chicago in 1951. Following postdoctoral research with Linus Pauling at Caltech, he has taught chemistry at the University of California, Los Angeles; journalism and general science at the University of Southern California; science writing at the California Institute of Technology; and has worked in industry at the General Electric Research Laboratory, Schenectady, New York; TEXUS Research Center, Parsippany, New Jersey; and U.S. Borax Research Corporation, Anaheim, California. In 1963, he switched careers to become an award-winning science writer for the *Los Angeles Times.* He now writes a weekly science news column for the *Los Angeles Herald.*

Richard Peter Huemer ("Linus Pauling and the Medical Revolution") received his medical degree from the University of California at Los Angeles, and spent 3 postdoctoral years at the California Institute of Technology in developmental biology. Subsequently he headed investigations in cancer immunology and experimental gerontology at the Sepulveda, California, Veterans Administration Hospital. Departing that facility as a result of his opposition to the Vietnam conflict, he entered private medical practice and soon became intrigued by the potential of orthomolecular medicine. He has published and lectured extensively on that subject, and served a term as president of the Orthomolecular Medical Society. In addition to editing this symposium volume, Dr. Huemer has performed editorial duties for *Mechanisms of Ageing and Development* and the *Journal of the International Academy of Preventive Medicine.* He has also authored newspaper and magazine columns, technical and popular articles, and a comic strip. He serves on the Los Angeles County Task Force on Nutrition.

Zelek S. Herman ("The Twenty-Five Most Cited Publications of Linus Pauling") is a research associate at the Linus Pauling Institute of Science and Medicine, where he has served as Linus Pauling's assistant since 1980. Prior to that he held research positions at the University of Denver, Stanford University, and the Rockefeller University. A native of Denver, he took his undergraduate training at Case Institute of Technology, and he received a number of advanced degrees at the University of Uppsala, Sweden, culminating with a PhD in quantum chemistry in 1975. His scientific research is concerned mainly with theoretical chemistry and physics, and he has published some 25 scholarly articles in these fields. He is an accomplished singer and guitarist, specializing in the Jacobite music of Scotland and the songs of the Swedish poet Dan Andersson. He has translated a book about Finland's greatest poet, *Johan Ludvig Runeberg* (Twayne Publishers). He recently returned from Zagreb, Yugoslavia, where he was a Fulbright guest professor at the Rudjer Bošković Institute.

INDEX

Absorption of nutrients, 106
Academy of Orthomolecular Psychiatry, xii, 99, 261
Academy of Sciences of U.S.S.R., 240, 241
Acetaldehyde, 238
Acetyl coenzyme A, 215
Acetylcholine, 196, 202, 214–217, 220–221
Acetylkynurenine, 193
Acrodermatitis enteropathica, 154
Actin, 9, 14, 15
Activated oxygen species, 108
Addiction, 180, 189
Adenine, 252
Adenomatosis of colon and rectum, 10, 13
Adenosine, 202
S-Adenosylmethionine, 199
Adipose tissue, 93
Adolescence, 12
Adrenal cortical extract, 206
Adrenal glands, 92, 191
Adrenaline, 99, 182, 194, 195, 199
Adrenochrome, 99, 182, 194, 195
Adrenolutin, 182
Adulthood, 12
Aerobic environments, 89
Affective syndrome, 182
Age, 59
Age pigment, 77. *See also* Lipofuscin
Aging, 18, 67, 75, 92, 96, 98, 144, 218
Aging of surfaces, 123
Agoraphobia, 202
Agricultural chemicals, 141
Air pollution, 49, 70, 91, 105
Albumin, 152
Alcohol abuse, 155
Alcohol intoxication, 203
Alcoholic hepatitis, 70
Alcoholics, 197
Alcoholism, 181
Alcohols, 59, 62, 93, 94
Alfalfa, 173
Alkalosis, 203
All-Union Lenin Academy of Agricultural Sciences, 236
Allantoin, 51*n*.
Allergens, 147
Allergic reaction, 147
Allergy, 68, 149
Allergy to food, 148. *See also* Food and chemical sensitivities
Allograft rejection, 167, 169. *See also* Homograft rejection
Allografts of brain tissue, 206
Allopathic psychiatry, 207
Allosteric activation, 96, 98
Alopecia, 154
Alpha helix, 228, 244, 252
Alveolar air, 92
Alveolar macrophages, 147
Alzheimer's disease (senile dementia), 13, 79, 80, 98, 219, 222
American Chemical Society, 228, 254
American Psychiatric Association Task Force Report, xii, 184, 187
Amine intermediates, 193
Amines, secondary, 140
Amines, tertiary, 141
Amino acid sequence, 5, 250
Amino acid transport, 206
Amino acids, 20, 75, 108, 151, 152, 180, 207, 228, 244
Amino acids, branched chain, 152
Aminochromes, 194–195
o-Aminohippuric acid, 193
Amnesia, 218

Amnion cells, 17
Amphetamine, 189
Amphibians, 50
Amyloidosis, 80
Anaerobes, 58, 76, 88
Analgesia, 189, 222
Anchorage of cultured cells, 8, 17
5-Androst-16-ene-3-ol, 172
Anemia, 152. *See also* Sickle cell anemia; Thalessemia; Fanconi's anemia; Hemolytic anemia; Megaloblastic anemia
Anergy, 148, 154, 155
Anesthesia, 161*n.*, 245
Angiopathy, 102
Anorexia, 137, 152
Anorexia nervosa, 154
Anthropoidea, 51
Antibodies (immunoglobulins), 148–150, 153–154, 166, 244, 251–252
Antibodies, IgA, 148–149, 153, 154
Antibodies, IgD, 148
Antibodies, IgE, 148–149
Antibodies, IgG, 148
Antibodies, IgM, 148
Antibodies, secretory, 148
Antibody formation, 156, 157
Antibody level, 150
Antibody response, 156–157, 164, 167
Antibody structure, 148
Anticholinergic, 217, 220–221
Anticholinesterase, 218
Antidepressant, 200, 222
Antigen, 155, 251, 252
Antigens, non-self-, 106
Antigens, oncodevelopmental, 8
Antihistamine, 222
Anti-intellectualism, 237
Antineoplastic drug, 62
Antioxidant adaptation, 88, 96, 100, 104
Antioxidant defenses, 64–65, 88, 104–108
Antioxidant enzyme adaptation, 98
Antioxidant enzymes, 107, 194–195
Antioxidant nutrients, 65
Antioxidant protection, 67
Antioxidants, 59, 67, 70, 80, 91–92, 99, 146, 161, 249
Antipsychotic drugs, 220, 222
Anti-Semitism, 239
Antiviral effect, 160
Anxiety, 180, 202, 205, 206, 221
Aorta, 102
Appetite, 184
Appetite regulation, 174
Arachidonate catabolism, 108
Arachidonic acid, 68, 69 (*fig.*), 167
Arachidonic acid cascade, 68, 106, 261
Arecoline, 196
Aristotle, 114
Arrythmias, 138
Arterial blood, 94, 251
Arterial wall, 61
Arteries, 61
Arteriosclerosis, 182
Arthritis, 68, 70, 190
Ascorbate. *See* Vitamin C
Ascorbate spillover, urinary, 53
Ascorbic acid. *See* Vitamin C
isoascorbic acid, 142
site of synthesis, 50
Asparagine, 115
Asparaginyl residue, 46, 73
Asparagus, 69
Aspartate, 202
Aspartic acid, 195
Aspartyl residue, 39, 41, 45, 46
Aspirin, 160, 167, 190
Asteroid, 51
Ataxia telangiectasia, 2
Atherogenesis, 64
Atherosclerosis, 57, 59, 60, 65, 79
Atherosclerotic plaques, 101
Athletic performance, 139, 205
Atmosphere, oxidizing, 49, 58, 76
Atmosphere, reducing, 49, 75
Atomic bomb, 229
Atopic dermatitis, 97
Atopic reactions to foods, 106, 148
ATP (adenosine triphosphate), 78, 89, 114, 193
Atropine, 218

Attention deficit disorders, 204
Autacoid tissue regulators, 108
Autism, 100, 203
Autoimmune disorders, 57, 68, 80, 106, 148
Autoimmunity, 80, 106, 108
Autooxidative degradation, 107
Avitaminosis, 182
Azoproteins, 251

B-cells, 147, 149
Bacteria, 68, 157, 161, 167
Bactericide, 159, 160
Barbiturates, 182, 198
Basal metabolic rate, 80
Basophils, 146, 196
Batten's disease, 67, 79
Behavior, stereotyped, 100
Benditt model, 60
Benzene, 238, 244
Benzodiazepines, 189, 202
Benzoic acid, 251
Beriberi, 192
Beta-carotene. *See* Carotene
Betaine, 194
Betel nuts, 162, 196
Bethe, Hans, 229
Betting odds, 187
Bicarbonate ion, 203
Bikini, 232
Bile salts, 62
Bioassays, 174
Bioflavonoids, 198
Biogenic amines, 198–200
Biological clock, 78
Birds, 50
Blackburn, George, 152
Blastocyst, 7, 81
Blastogenesis, 150
Bleomycin, 62
Blood, 90 (*table*), 93, 181
Blood, arterial, 94, 251
Blood, venous, 251
Blood-brain barrier, 181, 200, 216
Blood cells, 65
Blood count, complete, 151
Blood groups, 251
Blood pressure, 61
Blood sugar, 206
Blood vessels, wall of, 77
Bloom's syndrome, 79
Blue-green algae, 76 (*table*)
Bohr, Neils, 237
Bohr effect, 43
Bombesin, 175
Bond, chemical, 244
Bond, hydrogen. *See* Hydrogen bond
Bonding electrons, 238
Bond length, 238
Bonds, double, 117, 167
Bone marrow, 145, 147, 152
Bourgeois science, 237, 240
Bowel infections of infancy, 164
Bowel transit time, 62, 174
Boyle, Robert, 114
Brain, 65, 98, 119–121, 191, 216
Brainstem, 205
Brain tissue grafts, 180, 206
Bran, 155
Breakfast, 205
Breast, 62
Breast milk, 164
Bridges, Calvin, 250
Bronchitis, 92
Bronchopulmonary dysplasia, 65
Brussels sprouts, 69
Buffer, phosphate, 118
Bufotenin, 193
Building blocks, 75
Burns, 156
Butylated hydroxytoluene, 123
γ-Butyrobetaine, 136

Cabbage, 69
Cadmium, 155, 165–166
Caerulein, 175
Calcium, 165, 195, 196, 198, 203, 205
California Institute of Technology, 28, 227, 232, 233, 236, 243, 244
Calories, 151

Campbell, Dan, 252
Canadian Mental Health Collaborative Study, 184, 186
Cancer, 1, 57, 62–64, 69, 70, 79, 97, 137, 138, 155, 160, 167, 189
Cancer cachexia, 133, 137–138
Cancer plus cancer-treatment syndrome, 133, 137
Cancers
    bladder, 141
    cervical, 18
    childhood cancers, 18
    colon, 134, 141
    epidermoid, 7
    esophageal, 141–142
    gastric, 141–142
    head and neck, 97
    hepatocarcinoma, 141
    Hodgkin's disease, 155
    lung, 69
    mammary, 21, 79
    oral, 162
    pancreatic, 11, 134
    renal carcinoma, 134
    squamous cell, 97
    teratocarcinoma, 7
Candida, 146, 148, 150, 155–157
Carbohydrate, 145, 203, 205
Carbohydrate metabolism, 174
Carbohydrate titration, 205–206
Carbohydrates, complex, 205
Carbon dioxide, 49, 76, 200
Carbon dioxide rebreathing, 203
Carbon-monoxy hemoglobin, 30, 32
Carbon tetrachloride, 62, 101
Carbonyl group of peptide, 252
Carcinoembryonic antigen, 8
Carcinogen, 2, 6, 18, 62, 141, 142
Carcinogenesis, 2, 63–64, 142
Carcinogenicity, 64, 140, 141
Cardiac muscle, 77, 135
Cardiac toxicity, 61
Cardiogenic shock, 138
Cardiovascular disease, 64, 104, 138
Carnitine, 135–138
Carotene, 63–65, 77, 90 (*table*), 144, 162
Casein, 173–174
Case studies, 187
β-Casomorphins, 174
Casopeptone, 174
Castle, William, 244
Catabolism, 152
Cataracts, 98
Catecholamines, 59, 62, 193–195, 200
Catecholamines, oxidized, 99
Cell division, 6, 8
Cell-mediated immunity, 80, 152–168
Cell membranes, 77, 90 (*table*), 106, 162
Cell morphology, 17
Cellular regulation, 59
Center for the Study of Democratic Institutions, 233
Central nervous system, 67, 79, 219
Cerebellum, 205
Cerebral cortex, 205
Cerebral hemorrhage, 103
Cerebral ischemia, 103
Cerebrospinal fluid, 67, 181, 182
Ceroid, 59, 77
Ceruloplasmin, 90 (*table*), 156
Cetiedil, 21
Chain-carrying sequences, 58
Chediak-Higashi syndrome, 159
Chemical food additives, 205
Chemical messengers, 172
Chemicals, exposure to, 96–97, 103
Chemiluminescence, 114–128
Chemistry panel, 201
Chemotaxic chamber, 151
Chemotaxis, 146, 156–157, 159
Chemotherapy, 133
Childhood, 12
Children, 152
Chimeras, 7
China, 241
Chloramines, 104
Chlorine, 194
Chlorine dioxide, 104
Chlorophyll, 49
Chlorpromazine, 189

Cholecalciferol, 163
Cholecystokinin, 175
Cholesterol, 61 (*table*), 144, 166, 173
Cholesterol hydroperoxides, 61
Choline, 196, 202, 214–216, 219–222
Cholinergic activity, 217
Cholinergic effects, 216
Cholinergic function, 214
Cholinergic memory synapses, 218
Cholinergic neurons, 202, 215, 219
Cholinergic receptors, 13
Choreiform movements, 217, 220
Choroid plexus, 195
Chromatin, 4*n*.
Chromatography, 173, 197
Chromium, 117, 204
Chromosome 21, trisomy of, 98
Chromosome breaks, 162
Chromosomes, 77, 236
Chromosomes, translocations, 4
Chronic schizophrenia, 187
Cidal capacity of phagocytes, 146, 153, 157, 164, 166
Cigarette smoke, 91
Cilia, function of, 153
Ciona, 251
Cirrhosis, 70
Clinical nutrition, 169, 201
Clinical studies, 245
Clofibrate, 62
Cobalamin. *See* Vitimin B_{12}
Cobalt, 204
Codeine, 222
Coenzyme Q, 64
Cofactors, 144, 151, 191, 215
Cognition, 218
Cognitive function, 217
Cold, common, 54, 158, 228
Cold-blooded animals, 50, 78
Cold war, 235
Collagen, 77
Colon, 62, 175
Colonialism, 235
Communist Party Central Committee, 237
Communists, 236, 250
Complement, 80, 150, 161
Complement system, 149–150
Complementarity, molecular, 244
Computer, 28, 33, 116, 124, 235
Concanavalin-A, 150
Congress, contempt of, 230–231
Congressional Record, 230
Connective tissue, 161
Constant, equilibrium, 252
Coordination theory of crystal structure, 244
Copper, 12, 13, 62, 65, 68, 77, 98, 195, 196–198
Copper deficiency, 62
Copulation, 52
Corn oil, 191
Coronary arteries, 60
Coronary atherosclerosis, 62
Coronary heart disease, 57, 60, 121
Cortisol, 174, 206
Cortisone, 195
Cosmic connection, 51, 54–55
Cosmopolite, 239–240
Courage, 241
Crosslinking of membrane proteins, 108
Cross-tolerance to oxidants, 90
Crystallography, 244
Crystals, structure of, 244
Crystal surface, analogy to cell surface, 123
CSS syndrome. *See* Scurvy, subclinical
Cultural Revolution, 241
Cyclic AMP, 159
Cyclic GMP, 159
Cysteine, 91
Cystic fibrosis, 70
Cytolysis, 167
Cytromembranes, 118, 122–123
Cytomembrane systems, 117
Cytoplasmic factors, 6
Cytosine, 252
Cytotoxic quinones, 195

Deanol, 196, 221
Decarboxylation, 215

Declaration of Conscience, 232
Dedifferentiation, 8
Deficiency disease, 52, 181
Degenerative diseases, 68, 70, 80, 98, 103–108
Dehydroascorbic acid, 49
Delayed hypersensitivity, 148, 150–157, 164, 166, 167
Delbrück, Max, 233, 251
Dementia, 98, 99, 181, 219. *See also* Alzheimer's disease
Dendritic spines, 67
Deoxyhemoglobin, 30–31, 35, 37, 39, 41, 46
Deoxypyridoxine, 157
Department of Defense, 250
Depression, 173, 180, 182, 190, 196, 198–200, 205, 206
Depressogenic effect, 221
Dermatitis herpetiformis, 97
Dermones, 175
Detoxification, 89
Development of plants, 172
Developmental disabilities, 203
Developmental pathways, 6, 10, 246
Diabetes, 79, 98, 102–103
Diagnosis, 246–247
Dialectical materialism, 238
Diarrhea, 151, 152, 175
Diazotization, 251
1,2:5,6-Dibenzanthracene, 114
Diet, standard American, 65
Dietary deficiency, 48
Dietary fiber, 62, 63 (*table*)
Dietary supplements, 219
Differential diagnosis, 201, 220
Differential equations, 125
Differentiation, 6, 8, 147
Dimethoxyphenylethylamine, 193
2,6-Dimethyl-3,5-diethycarbonyl-1,4-dihydropyridine, 78
2-Dimethylaminoethanol, 196, 221
Dimethylated indoles, 194
Dimethylnitrosamine, 141
Dimethyltryptamine, 193
Dinosaurs, 50, 51
Dioxygen, 120, 122–123
1,2-Diphosphoglycerate, 31
Disease, chronic, 152
Disease, degenerative. *See* Degenerative diseases
Disease, mental. *See* Mental disorders
Disease, predisposition to, 1
Disease, systemic, 97
Diseases, viral, 54
Disulfide bonds, 148
DNA, 2–6, 9–11, 62, 63, 69, 240
  excision repair, 76 (*table*)
  junk DNA, 5
  noncoding sequences, 3
  recombinantional repair, 76 (*table*)
  repair mechanisms, 2, 76 (*table*), 77
  sequence, 2–4
  transcription, 6
Dopa, 195, 214, 217
Dopamine, 189, 193–195, 202, 214, 220
Dopaminergic activity, 173, 217
Dopaminergic receptors, 206, 220
Double-blind studies, 182, 183, 186–188, 198, 207, 221, 247
Double helix, 252
Down's syndrome, 67, 98–100, 204, 222
Doxorubicin, 61
Dreams, 197, 206
Drinking water, 104
Drosophila, 78
Drugs, 141
Duodenal mucosa, 172
Dutch black cattle, 154
Dynorphin, 174
Dyskinesia, 202
Dysperception, 205

Ecological illness, 106
Ecosphere, 105
Ectoderm, 11
Eczema, 97
Edema, 152
EDTA, 203
Egg yolks, 215

Ehrlich reagent, 196
Eicosapentaenoic acid, 68
Einstein, Albert, 229, 232, 233, 237
Elastin, 77
Elderly people, 167–169, 219
Electrocardiogram, 201
Electroconvulsive therapy, 182–184, 187, 189
Electroencephalogram (EEG), 173, 201, 222
Electron acceptor, 88
Electron density, 58
Electron exchange, 115
Electronically excited states, 115
Electron microscopy, 102
Electrons, 94, 118
Electrons, unpaired, 115
Electron transfer, 94
Electron transport, 58
Electrophiles, 58, 64
Electrophilic addition, 69
Electrophilic peroxidizing species, 60
Electrophoresis, 19, 148, 244
Embryo, 7, 8
Emerson, Sterling, 250
Emesis. *See* Vomiting
Emphysema, 92
Encephalitis virus, 162
Encephalopathy, 198
Endocrine dysfunction, 98
Endocrine system, 163
Endoderm, 11
Endorphins, 173, 174
Endothelium, vascular, 102, 103
Energy, human, 205
Energy fields, 247
Energy of stabilization, 41
Energy of thermal agitation, 251
Energy requirements of muscle, 135
Energy transfer acceptor, 115 (*fig.*)
Engulfment by phagocytes, 146, 153, 167
Enkephalins, 174, 222
Enteritis, 191
Environmental effects, 7–10, 18, 19, 70, 246, 247
Enzyme, 20, 49, 58, 181, 192, 250
  alcohol dehydrogenase, 155
  alkaline phosphatase, 155
  antioxidant, 89
  aromatic hydrocarbon hydroxylase, 69
  arylsulfatase, 147
  carbonic anhydrase, 155
  carboxypeptidase, 155
  catalase, 64, 67, 90 (*table*)
  catechol-*o*-methyltransferase, 194, 199, 200
  choline acetyltransferase, 202, 215, 218, 219
  CPK, 65
  cytochrome C, 117
  cytochrome P-450, 77, 120*n.*, 198
  dehydrogenase, 89
  δ-6-desaturase, 191
  DNA and RNA polymerase, 155
  fatty acid ligases, 100
  gastrointestinal, 173
  glucose-6-phosphate dehydrogenase, 81, 91*n.*, 94–96, 104
  glutamic acid decarboxylase, 194
  glutathione peroxidase, 59, 64, 67 (*fig.*), 77, 81, 90 (*table*), 91–101, 104
  glutathione reductase, 90 (*table*), 91*n.*, 92–93
  glutathione synthetase, 67
  glutathione-S-transferases, 90 (*table*)
  GOT, 65
  GPT, 65
  gulonolactone oxidase, 51, 52
  heme-containing peroxidases, 77
  histaminase, 147
  3-hydroxyanthranilase, 193, 194
  3-hydroxyanthranilate oxidase, 192
  lactate dehydrogenase, 117
  lysozymes, 153
  monamine oxidase, 193–195, 200
  myeloperoxidase, 146, 160
  N-methyltransferase, 193, 200
  organ-specific, 102

Enzyme (*cont.*)
ornithine decarboxylase, 8
oxidase, 51, 89, 100
oxidative, 79
peptidases, 174
peroxidase, 64, 67
phospholipase, 69 (*fig.*)
prostacyclin synthetase, 79
reductase, 64
respiratory chain, 77
serine esterase, 69 (*fig.*)
superoxide dismutase, 63–64, 67–68, 77, 90 (*table*), 94, 99, 155
transaminase, 65, 204
transketolase, 203
tryptophan pyrrolase, 198
uricase, 51
xanthine oxidase, 68
Enzyme activation, 96
Enzyme cofactors, 247
Enzyme poisons, 246
Eosinophilia, 165
Eosinophils, 146, 147, 151, 195
Epidermoid carcinoma, 7
Epinephrine. *See* Adrenaline
Epithelium, 161
Epoxides, 69
Equilibrium constants, 252
Erythrocytes. *See* Red blood cells
Erythrocytosis, 38
Escherischia coli, 162
Esculin, 115
Essential fatty acids, 117–118, 121–124, 180, 191. *See also* Polyunsaturated fatty acids
Essential fatty acyls, 123
Essential nutrients, 89
Estrogen, 198
Estrogenic activity, 172
Estrogen receptors, 62
Ethane, 101
Ethanolamine, 69 (*fig.*)
Ethoxyquin, 78, 80
Ethyl acetoacetate, 238
2-Ethyl-6-methyl-3-hydroxypyridine, 78
Eukaryotes, 76
Eukaryotic cells, 117
Euler-Cauchy method, 124–125
Evening primrose oil, 191
Evil, 233
Evolution, 49, 75–77, 88, 243–244, 246
Exercise, 205
Exhaustion, 133
Exorphins, 174–175, 190
Extracellular fluid, 172
Eye, 65

Fabry's disease, 57
Facilitated diffusion, 122
Fallout, 230–232
Fallout shelters, 231
Family support, 201
Fanconi's anemia, 79
Fasting, 198
Fatigue, 133, 136–138, 152, 205
Fatty acid peroxides, 89
Fatty acids, 119, 202, 215. *See also* Essential fatty acids; Long-chain fatty acids; Polyunsaturated fatty acids
Fatty liver, 70
Federal Bureau of Investigation, 230
Feldman, Richard J., 28, 47
Females, longevity of, 80
Ferredoxin, 75
Ferritin, 5, 117
Ferrous ammonium sulfate, 118
Fertility, 162
Fertilized egg, 11
α-Fetoprotein, 8
Fetus, 8
Fiber, dietary, 62, 63 (*table*)
Fibroblasts, 5, 8, 9, 11, 13, 14, 16, 17, 61
Fibronectin, 8, 9, 14, 15
Fibrosis, 77, 92
Fifth Amendment, 231
Fingernail bed, 65, 197
Firefly, 114
Fish, 50
Fluorescence, 114
Folate, 144, 151, 152, 157, 158, 168,

197–198, 203
Food additives, 205
Food allergens, 149
Food allergy, 148. *See also* Food and chemical sensitivities
Food and chemical sensitivities, 106, 262
Food restriction, 80
Foreign cells, 149
Formone, 173, 175
Free-radical damage, 81, 89
Free-radical intermediates, 89
Free-radical reactions, 75, 77, 80, 81, 198
Free radicals, ix, 62, 70, 75, 88, 89, 115, 146, 147, 162, 194, 195
Free-radical stress, 93
Free-radical theory of aging, 75
Frequency distribution, 187
Fried foods, 167
Frog skin, 175
Fructose, 206
Fruit flies, 78
Fungal infections, 169
Fungi, 161. *See also Candida*
Fungicide, 160
Funk, Casimir, 52

GABA (γ-aminobutyric acid), 194, 202, 205
Gamma globulin, 148. *See also* Antibodies
Garlic, 69
Gas chromatography, 119, 197
Gas heating system, 105
Gastric acid, 173
Gastric inhibitory peptide, 175
Gastrin, 175
Gastrointestinal tract, 93, 148, 173, 215
Gaucher's disease, 57
Gene, 1, 240, 252
- ACR, 13, 14
- β-actin, 15
- coding sequences, 4, 5
- complementation groups, 14
- controller gene, 5
- duplication, 4
- expression, 15
- multiplication, 4
- mutation rate, 9*n.*
- noncoding sequences, 4, 5
- polygenes, 5
- promoter sequences, 3
- rate of expression, 3, 15
- regulation, 20
- sequences, 3–5
- structural, 2–3
- suppressor, 4
- theory of, 250
- transcription, 3, 9*n.*

Genetic code, 240
Genetic defects, 9. *See also* Inborn errors of metabolism; Molecular disease
Genetic disease, 250
Genetic engineering, 252
Genetic predisposition, 1, 3, 103–105, 246
Genetic program, viral alteration of, 246
Genetics, 236–237, 241, 246
Genetic switches, 15, 16
Genitourinary tract, 148
Genome, 2, 4, 6
Genome, viral, 5
Genotoxicity, 6, 7
Germ cells, 2
Gliadin, 173, 174
Glowworms, 114
Glucagon, 174, 206
Glucose, 49, 117, 238
Glutamic acid, 42, 194, 202, 205
Glutamine, 195, 202, 205
Glutaminyl residue, 41
Glutathione, 59, 60 (*fig.*), 64 (*table*), 90 (*table*), 91, 92, 101, 142, 146, 195
Gluten, 173
Glycine, 194, 202
Glycyl residue, 41
Golden Rule, 234
Gormone, 175
Gout, 68
Grains, 151
Granulovascular degeneration, 219
Ground state, 114
Ground-state product, 115

Growth, 204
Growth hormone, 206
Growth inhibition, 17
Growth retardation, 154
Guanine, 252
Guilt, theorized, 201
Guinea pigs, 136

Hair, 191
Hair mineral analysis, 202, 204–205
Hallucinations, 196, 200, 222
Hallucinogen, 99, 182, 194, 199
Halogenated hydrocarbons, 107
Haloperidol, 189
Haplotype, 12
Hapten, 252
Heart disease, 167
Heart, 65, 92, 119–121
Heart, atria, 216
Heinz bodies, 95
Hematin, 117
Hematocrit, 95
Heme, 29, 33, 35, 36, 198
Hemoglobin, 63, 94, 117, 244, 251, 260
  α chains, 29–30, 32, 39
  β chains, 21, 29–30, 39, 46, 95
  $\alpha_1\beta_2$ contact region, 39, 41
  C-terminal residue, 31, 42, 45
  globin chains, 96
  half saturation point, 35–36
  mutant, Alberta, 41
  mutant, British Columbia, 41
  mutant, Cowtown, 42–46
  mutant, Korle-Bu, 46
  mutant, Milwaukee, 37
  mutant, Mobile, 46
  mutant, Potomac, 41
  mutant, Rush, 41
  mutant, sickle-cell, 46, 96
  mutant, Vancouver, 46
  mutant, Vanderbilt, 36–37
  mutant, Yakima, 38–41
  oxygen affinity, 36–37, 41, 43, 46
  oxygenated, 251. *See also* Oxyhemoglobin
  saturation curve, 33, 38, 41
Hemoglobin A, 41, 43, 46
Hemoglobin diseases, 96
Hemolysis, 59, 65, 95, 96
Hemolytic anemia, 95
Hemorrhage, 136
Hepatitis B, 5
Hepatomegaly, 152
Hepatotoxicity, 204
Herpes virus, 14
Heterogeneity of schizophrenias, 187, 197–198
Hexose monophosphate shunt, 91*n*., 95, 98, 99, 146, 160
High-density lipoprotein, 61 (*table*), 62
Hill plot, 35–37, 43
Hip dysplasia, 70
Hippocampus, 206
Hiroshima, 229
Histadelia, 197–198
Histamine, 106, 147, 149, 151, 165, 196–200
Histapenia, 197–198
Histidyl residue, 39, 41, 45, 99
Historical necessity, 243
Hodgkin's disease, 155
Hoffer, Abram, xi–xii, 99, 182–184, 187, 194–197, 207
Holistic medicine, 245–247
Homeostasis, 164
Homograft rejection, 153, 155, 158, 163. *See also* Allograft rejection
Homolytic oxidations, 115
Homo sapiens ascorbicus, 48
Hormone, 172
Horse chestnut, 115
Hospital, 184, 201
Humoral immunity, 150, 153, 156–157, 161–162, 166, 168
Huntington's chorea, 13, 79, 195
Hutchins, Robert Maynard, 233
Hybrid molecule, 239
Hydrocarbon exhalation, 101
Hydrocortisone, 8
Hydrogen, 76

Hydrogen bond, 40, 41, 228, 252
Hydrogen peroxide, 58, 62, 67, 81, 94, 96, 98–100, 117, 146, 160
Hydrogen sulfide, 76
Hydroperoxides, 63, 64, 81, 122 (*fig.*)
5-Hydroxy-indole acetic acid, 194, 203
Hydroxykynurenine, 193
Hydroxylation, 136
Hydroxyl radical, 58, 62
5-Hydroxytryptamine. *See* Serotonin
Hyoscine, 218
Hyperactivity, 194, 204
Hyperbaric oxygen, 91, 99
Hyperestronism, 62, 63 (*table*)
Hyperinsulinemia, 100
Hyperkinesis, 220
Hyperlipidemia, 138
Hyperlipoproteinemia, 60
Hypersegmentation of nuclei, 157
Hypersensitivity, 68
Hypertension, 79
Hyperthermia, 191
Hyperuricemia, 68
Hyperventilation syndrome, 203
Hypoascorbemia, 250
Hypochondriasis, 180
Hypoglycemia, 100, 206
Hypothalamus, 162, 206
Hypoxanthine, 117

Imipramine, 200
Immortalization, 14
Immune competence, 154, 158
Immune complexes, 80, 147, 149, 151, 161
Immune deficiency, 79
Immune deficiency, acquired, 151
Immune dysfunction, 164
Immune dysregulation, 104, 107
Immune function, 166
Immune profile, 149
Immune reactions, 149
Immune regulation, 158
Immune response, 144, 147, 158
Immune responsiveness, 145
Immune system, 2, 10, 19, 52, 92, 98, 144–145, 147, 156, 158, 163, 191
Immunity, cell-mediated. *See* Cell-mediated immunity
Immunity, humoral. *See* Humoral immunity
Immunochemistry, 251
Immunocompetence, 144, 151
Immunodeficiencies, 2, 144
Immunodepressant, 168
Immunoglobulin. *See* Antibodies
Immunology, 144, 169
Immunomodulation, 158
Immunostimulant, 161, 162, 168
Immunosuppression, 2, 156, 161, 162, 163, 167
Immunotoxicity, 166
Imperialism, 235
Inborn errors of metabolism, 96, 192, 228
Indoles, 193, 195, 199
Industrial chemicals, 141
Infant development psychoses, 100
Infection, 69, 89, 103, 104, 148, 152–154, 156, 162, 164, 166, 169
Inflammation, 68, 104, 156
Inflammatory/degenerative symptomatologies, 88, 103
Inflammatory mediators, 89, 149
Inflammatory reaction, 149
Influenza virus, 160
Informational macromolecules, 10, 18
Ingestion by phagocytes, 159
Inhibition of growth, 17
Initiator of tumors, 7, 8, 14
Inositol, 202
Insulin, 100, 174, 206
Interferon, 150, 160, 166
Interleukin-2, 150, 163
Intermediary metabolism, 89
Internment of Japanese, 229
Intestinal bacteria, 215
Intestinal transit time, 62, 174
Intestine, 93, 164, 216
Intima of aorta, 102
Intimal cell, 60

Ion-radical reactions, 115
Ionic bond, 45
IQ (intelligence quotient), 98–99, 188, 204
Iron, 90 (*table*), 94, 96, 125–128, 152, 156, 163–166, 169, 205
Iron-binding capacity, 165
Irritability, 152, 205
Irritable colon, 175
Isoascorbic acid, 142
Isoleucine, 194
Isomer, 238
Isozymes, 8, 12

Jimson weed, 218

Kekulé structures, 238, 239
Kennedy, John F., 231
Ketene, 90
Keto-enol tautomerism, 238
Ketosis, 205
Khrushchev, Nikita, 240, 241
Kidney, 50, 65, 92, 102, 107, 119–121, 136
Kidney disease, 80
Kinetics, first-order, 116
Kinins, 106
Klenner, Frederick R., 54
Knowledge, 227
Krakatoa, 232
Kryptopyrrole (mauve factor), 196–197
Kupffer cells, 147
Kwashiorkor, 151, 152
Kynurenic acid, 193
Kynurenine, 193

Laboratory animals, 161, 162, 167, 168
Laboratory findings, 246
Lactate, 203
Lactobacilli, 164
Lactoferrin, 164
Lambaréné, 231–232
Landsteiner, Karl, 251
Lassitude, 133, 136, 137
Lead, 165–166, 169, 198, 204–205
Learning, 218
Learning disability, 180, 203, 204
Learning tests, 206
Lecithin, 202, 215, 217, 219–221
Lectins, 150
Legumes, 151
Lenin, 237, 239
Lenin Peace Prize, 230, 254
Leonardo da Vinci, 254
Leucine, 194
Leucyl residue, C-terminal, 45
Leukemia, 98
Leukocyte endogenous mediator, 156, 164
Leukocytes, 80, 137, 156
Leukocytosis, 165
Leukotriene C, 68, 69 (*fig.*)
Leukotrienes, 68, 89, 147, 151
Levodopa, 195, 214, 217
Lexotype of protein, 20
Lexotypes, 21
Lexotypic change, 19
Liberal cause, 228
Life, molecular basis of, 251, 252
Life, origin of, 49
Life span, 75, 77–78, 80
  average, 78, 80, 81
  maximum, 78, 81
Lifestyle, 70
Light, 63
Light production, 124, 127–128
Lind, James, 52
Linoleic acid, 102, 167, 191
Linoleic acid hydroperoxide, 102
Linolenic acid, 190–192
Linseed oil, 192
Linus Pauling Institute of Science and Medicine, 137, 139
Lipid membranes, 59
Lipid peroxidation, 57–61, 64–65, 67–68, 70, 77, 100–103, 162
Lipid peroxide determination, 118
Lipid peroxide initiators, 70
Lipid peroxides, 59, 93, 117
Lipid peroxides, serum level, 100–101
Lipids, unsaturated, 59, 70, 77. *See also* Polyunsaturated fatty acids
Lipofuscin, 59, 79, 98, 99

Lipoproteins, 61, 62
Liquid scintillation counters, 116
Lithium, 168, 204
Liver, 50, 62, 65, 92, 93, 102, 105, 107, 119–121, 124, 135, 141, 147, 164, 191, 215
Lobotomy, 184
Long-chain fatty acids, 135, 138
Lophine, 115
Los Alamos project, 229
Love, 227
Low-density lipoprotein, 60, 62
Lucigenin, 115
Luminescence, 114
Luminogenic reagent, 116
Luminol, 115
Luminometers, 116
Lung, 17, 65, 89, 90, 92, 102, 104, 105, 119–121, 147
Lung tumor acceleration, 92
Lupus. *See* Systemic lupus erythematosus
Luteinizing hormone-releasing hormone, 172–173
Lymph nodes, 92, 148, 152
Lymphocytes, 13, 68, 145, 147, 149, 150, 152, 163. *See also* T-cells
Lymphocyte transformation, 158, 160, 164
Lymphoid atrophy, 164
Lymphoid tissues, 145, 147, 148, 158
Lymphokines, 150, 153, 155, 167
Lymphopenia, 157, 161
Lysenko, Trofim D., 235–239, 241
Lysenkoism, 240
Lysine, 136, 138
Lysosomes, 77
Lysozymes, 161
Lysyl residue, 41

McCarthy, Joseph, 230, 235, 236, 241
McCarthyism, 236
Mach, Ernst, 239
Macromolecular constituents, 94
Macrophage activating factor, 150
Macrophage inhibition factor, 153
Macrophages, 2, 8, 89, 150, 156, 158, 159, 160, 166, 167
Macular degeneration, 79
Magnesium, 114, 165, 195, 203
Maimonides, xi
Malabsorption, 151
Malignancy, 59, 69
test for, 20
threshold of, 4, 13, 18, 20
Malignant transformation, 6, 8, 15–17
viral, 14
Malignant tumors, 141. *See also* Cancer
Malnutrition, 144, 145, 148, 151–155, 163, 165, 168, 180, 201
Malnutrition in hospitals, 152
Malondialdehyde, 96, 101, 103
Malpractice litigation, 188
Malvaria, 196–197
Mammalian cell, 117
Mammals, 50, 58, 88, 191, 216
Manganese, 65, 90 (*table*), 195, 196, 198, 201, 202, 204
Mania, 180, 190, 199
Manic-depressive psychosis, 188, 192
Marasmus, 151
Marine oils, 191
Marxism, 238
Mass spectrometry, 197, 261
Mast cells, 68, 149, 151
Master switch, 15
Mathematical modeling, 127 (*fig.*)
Mauve factor (kryptopyrrole), 196–197
Maynow declaration, 230
Meat, as source of carnitine, 135
Medical model, 180, 201
Medvedev, Roy A., 239
Medvedev, Zhores A., 239, 240
Megadoses, 158, 161, 168, 183, 189, 203
Megaloblastic anemia, 157
Megavitamins, 185, 204, 207
Megavitamin therapy, xi–xii, 180, 181, 184, 186–187
Meiosis, 76 (*table*)
Melanocyte inhibitory factor, 172
Melanocyte stimulating hormone, 173
Mellaril (thioridazine), 185, 203, 220

Membrane lipids, 58, 192
Memory, 217, 218, 265
Mendacity, 241
Mendel, Gregor, 237
Mendelism-Morganism, 236–237
Menopause, 12
Mental disorders, 98, 180, 188, 219, 245
Mental retardation, 204
2-Mercaptoethylamine, 78, 80
Mercury, 165–166, 169
Mesoderm, 11
Metabolic defect, 96
Metabolic diseases, 108
Metabolism, aerobic, 88
Metabolism, inborn errors, 96, 192, 228
Metabolism, intermediary, 263
Metabolism, oxidative, 13
Metachlorobenzoic acid, 251
Metaphysics, 245
Methane, 238
Methemoglobin, 96
Methionine, 90 (*table*), 91, 101, 136, 157, 192, 194, 195, 198, 199, 215
5-Methoxy-*NN*-dimethyltryptamine, 193
Methyl alcohol, 238
Methylation, 193, 194, 198–200, 215
Methyl donor, 194, 199, 215
L-α-Methyldopa hydrazide, 217
Methylindoles, 195, 199
Methylnicotinamide, 182
α-Methyl-1-paratyrosine, 200
Methyltryptamine, 199
Michaelis-Menten equation, 181
Microprocessors, 116
Microsomes, 117, 118, 124
Militarism, 249, 250
Milk, 164, 174, 190
  breast, 164
  powdered, 167
Mineral deficiency, 164
Minerals, 145, 152, 180, 188, 194, 197, 202
Mitochondria, 77, 78, 90 (*table*), 117, 118, 124, 135, 193
Mitogen, 150, 153, 157, 160, 161, 163, 166
Mitogen response, 154–155
Molecular biology, 252
Molecular disease, 5, 57, 70, 228, 244, 246. *See also* Inborn errors of metabolism
Monamine oxidase inhibitors, 193, 199
Monoclonal antibody, 150
Monoclonal theory, 60, 61
Monocytes, 147, 151, 161, 163
Monosodium glutamate, 202
Morgan, Thomas Hunt, 237, 250
Morphine, 222
Morphine receptor, 174, 190
Morphology of cells, 9, 15
Motilin, 175
Motility of gastrointestinal tract, 137, 173–175
Motility of macrophages, 160
Motility of phagocytes, 146, 151, 156–157, 159
Mucopolysaccharides, 77
Mucosa, integrity of, 153
Mucosal fluids, 148
Mucous membranes, 161
Mucus, 68
Multivariance statistics, 247
Muscarinic agonists, 222
Muscle, cardiac, 77, 135
Muscle, skeletal, 92, 119–121, 135
Muscle atrophy, 136, 137
Muscle necrosis, 65
Muscular dystrophy, 70
Mutagen, 60–62
Mutagenesis, 63
Mutant, temperature sensitive, 15
Mutation, 2, 9, 11, 14, 16, 17
  conditional-lethal, 51
  reverse, 17
  somatic, 2, 18
Mutational distance, 15, 16 (*fig.*)
Mutational state, 2
Myasthenia gravis, 68
Mycosis fungoides, 97
Myeloid cells, 146
Myeloid leukemia, 7
Myocardial contractile efficiency, 138

Myocardial infarction, 59, 138
Myocardium, 77, 135
Myoglobin, 33, 117
Myosin, 9

N-terminal amino acid sequence, 174
NAD (nicotinamide adenine dinucleotide), 193, 194
NADH, 99, 117
NADP, 60 (*fig.*), 193
NADPH, 60 (*fig.*), 81, 91*n.*, 92, 94–96, 99, 104
Naloxone, 174, 222
Narcotic addiction, 189
Nascent surface of biomembranes, 123
National Medal of Science, 254
Natural killer cells, 2, 166
Natural selection, 243
Nature of the Chemical Bond, The, 239, 254
Nausea, 137, 175, 198
Nazi Germany, 235
Needleman, Herbert, 205
Negative charge, 39
Negative nitrogen balance, 152, 168
Nematodes, 78
Nerve damage, 158
Nervous system, 70, 105, 158
Neural tissue, 99
Neurasthenia, 180
Neurochemistry, 202
Neurofibrillary tangles, 219
Neuroleptic drugs, 185, 220
Neuromelanin, 79
Neuromodulators, 202
Neuronal ceroid lipofuscinoses, 67
Neuron damage, 198
Neurons, 8, 79–80, 98, 99, 219
Neurospora, 78
Neurotransmitter replacement, 214
Neurotransmitters, 98, 100, 202, 214, 217
Neutrophils (polymorphonuclear leukocytes), 60, 67, 89, 145, 146, 151–159, 167
NH-terminal group of peptide, 252
Niacin (nicotinic acid, vitamin B_3), xii, 182, 184–186, 190, 192–194, 198, 203
Niacinamide (nicotinamide, vitamin B_3), 183, 199, 202–204
Niacinamide receptors, 189
Nirenberg, Marshall W., 240
Nitrite ion, 140, 141
Nitrogen dioxide, 90
Nitrosamines, 140–142, 264
Nitrosation, 140, 142
Nitrosoguanidine, 15
Nitrosohemoglobin, 141
Nitrosomyoglobin, 141
Nitrosopyrrolidine, 142
Nitrosyl chloride, 90
Nitrous acid, 140
Nitrous anhydride intermediary, 140
Nobel Prize, 228, 230, 233, 254
Noradnamine, 200
Noradrenaline (norepinephrine), 182, 199, 200, 202
Noyes, A. A., 228, 232, 244
Nuclear disarmament, 250
Nuclear family, 105
Nuclear freeze, 250
Nuclear material, 80
Nuclear test ban, 230
Nuclear testing, 231
Nuclear warfare, 230
Nuclear weapons, 230, 235, 249
Nucleic acids, 58, 68
Nucleic acid synthesis, 150, 156
Nucleotides, 75, 252
Nucleus basalis of Meynert, 80
Nutrient deficiency, 145, 146
Nutritional assessment, 145
Nutritional biochemistry, 263
Nutritional deficiencies, 2, 107
Nutritional pharmacology, 265
Nutritional supplements, 204
Nystagmus, 203
NZB mice, 80

Obsessive-compulsive neuroses, 196
Old age, 12
Olive oil, 167

Oncodevelopmental antigens, 8
Oncogenes, 3, 9, 14, 18
    c-*fos*, 17
    c-Ha-*ras*, 14
    myc, 4
    N-*myc*, 4
Opiate, 191
Opiate receptor, 174, 190
Opioid peptide-like substances, 172
Opioid peptides, 174
Oppenheimer, Robert, 229
Opsonization, 146, 159
Oral contraceptives, 199
Oregon State Agricultural College, 227–228, 243
Organic brain disorders, 180
Organic psychoses, 182
Organized medicine, 245
Organ meat, 68
Orgotein, 70
Origin of life, 75
Orthochlorobenzoic acid, 251
Orthomolecular doses, 145
Orthomolecular Medical Society, viii–x, xii, 253
Orthomolecular medicine, ix, xi, 55, 138, 180, 245–247, 252–253
Orthomolecular practitioners, 158
Orthomolecular psychiatry, 180, 201, 202, 207
Orthomolecular substances, 21
Orthomolecular therapy, 186–188, 201–204
Osmond, Humphry, xi-xii, 182–184, 187, 196–197
Osteoarthritis, 79
Overarousal, 196
Oxidant/antioxidant balance, 88
Oxidant attack, 105, 107
Oxidant exposure, 108
Oxidant gases, 92
Oxidants, 60 (*fig.*), 61, 107
Oxidant stress, 59, 89, 90, 97, 104–105
    adaptation to, 97
Oxidation, 58, 194
Oxidation-reduction potential, 49
Oxidative damage, 69
Oxidative degradation, 77
Oxidative metabolism, 62, 98
Oxidative phosphorylation, 58, 88, 89
Oxidative polymerization, 79
Oxidative stress, 88–89, 94–96, 99–108
Oxidized adrenaline, 182
Oxidized cholesterol, 167
Oxygen, 49, 65, 67, 88, 94, 114, 117, 124, 164
    binding, 43
    biradical, 115
    concentration, 94, 124
    diamagnetic, 251
    dioxygen, 117
    electrode, 33, 118
    hyperbaric, 91, 99
    meter, 229
    paramagnetic, 115, 251
    partial pressure, 33, 35
    radicals, 89, 96
    saturation curve, 33, 38, 41
    singlet, 58, 123
    tension, 33
    toxicity, 88
    triplet, 123, 251
    uptake assays, 118
Oxyhemoglobin, 29–33, 35, 37, 39, 46
Oxyl radicals, 115
Oxyradicals, 80
Oxytetracycline, 142
Ozone, 58, 76 (*table*), 89, 91, 92, 101, 104, 105

Pain, 68, 151
Palliative treatments, 9
Pancreas, 92, 172, 173
Pancreatic secretion, 172
Pantothenic acid, 107, 157, 203, 204
Para-aminobenzoic acid, 251
Parachlorobenzoic acid, 251
Paranoid symptoms, 188, 196
Parasites, 147, 149
Parietal cells, 175

Parkinson's disease, 13, 79, 195, 214, 217, 220
Pathogens, 147, 159
Pauling, Ava Helen, 229, 231, 233, 243
Pauling, Crellin, ix, 255
Pauling, Linus, viii–xii, 28, 35, 46, 54–55, 57, 113–114, 134, 137–138, 140, 158, 160, 181, 227–234, 236–240, 243–247, 253–259
Pauling–Teller debates, 230
Peace, ix, 229, 249
Peanut oil, 167
Pearl Harbor, 229
Peer review, 188
Pellagra, 181, 192, 206, 207
Pellagra, cerebral, 181, 182
Penicillin, 191
Pentamer, 148
Pentane, 101
Perceptual disorders, 197
Peristalsis, 137, 173–175
Permeability of membranes, 59
Pernicious anemia, 158, 181
Peroxidation of membrane lipids, 108
Peroxidative crosslinking, 96, 98
Peroxidative damage, 94–95, 98, 99, 106
Peroxide assays, 118
Peroxides, 65, 101, 115
Peroxidized corn oil, 93
Perutz, Max, 28
Pesticides, 105
Pfeiffer, Carl, 195–198, 207
Phagocyte motility, 146, 151, 156–157, 159
Phagocytes, 146, 147, 153, 165
Phagocytic index, 146
Phagocytosis, 77, 89, 156–158, 164, 169
Phenobarbitone, 62
Phenocopies, 8
Phenols, 194
Phenothiazines, 182–184, 186, 189, 191, 194, 201
Phenotypic effects, 246, 247
Phenylalanine, 21, 199
Phenytoin, 62, 198
Pheromone, 172
Phobic neurosis, 192
Phorbol esters, 7, 9, 15
Phosgene, 90
Phosphatides, 222
Phosphatidylcholine, 69 (*fig.*), 214–215, 217, 222
Phosphatidylethanolamine, 215
Phosphatidylserine, 215
Phospholipids, 68
Phosphorylcholine, 215
Photochemical decomposition, 115
Photochemical event
  accumulation period, 118
  depletion period, 118, 127
  steady-state, 118
  time-to-peak, 118, 127
Photochemical quenching, 63
Photochemical smog, 91. *See also* Air pollution
Photodynamic action, 58 (*table*), 63
Photolytic reactions, 115
Photometry, astronomical, 116
Photomultiplier, 117
Photon, 115
Photon counting, 116–128
Photosensitizer, 63
Photosynthesis, 49, 76
Physical examination, 180, 201
Physics, atomic, 229
Physostigmine, 219, 221
Phytate, 155
Phytohemagglutinin, 150, 153. *See also* Mitogen
Pituitary gland, 163
Placebo, 183, 187, 204, 219
Plants, green-leaf, 77
Plasma cells, 148
Plasma membrane, 95
Plasminogen activator, 8
Platelet aggregation, 79
Platelets, 61, 102, 151
Pleated sheet, 252
Pneumococcus, 162
Poikilotherms, 50, 78

Point mutation, 2, 3, 243
Pollution, 48, 155, 204–205
of air, 49, 70, 91, 103–105
of atmosphere, 58 (*table*)
chemical, 104, 105
Polycythemia, 38
Polygenes, 5
Poly-IC, 160
Polymorphism, 246
Polymorphonuclear leukocytes. *See* Neutrophils
Polynucleotides, 250
Polypeptides, 3, 5, 29, 250
Polythetic classes, 246
Polyunsaturated fatty acids, 96, 117, 167, 168. *See also* Essential fatty acids
Polyunsaturated lipids, 77
Porphyria, 198
Postmitotic cells, 77
Postpartum depression, 182
Postsynaptic neurons, 189
Pravda, 237
Precursor therapy, 202, 207, 214
Predisposition to disease, 1, 10–11, 246, 247
Pregnancy, 22, 155
Premenstrual syndrome, 163
Premorbid adjustment, 186
Pressman, David, 252
Preventive medicine, 169
Primates, 76 (*table*), 77, 191
Prison, 230–231
Processed antigens, 160
Processed foods, 141
Progesterone, 163
Prolactin, 173, 190
Promoters of tumors, 7–9, 14, 167
Pro-oxidant drugs, 62, 63 (*table*)
Prosimiae, 51
Prostaglandins, 69 (*fig.*), 77, 89, 108, 123, 151, 167, 168, 190–192
Protein, 145, 205
lexotype, 20
metabolism, 144
profiling, 19, 21
synthesis, 6, 156
Protein-calorie malnutrition, 148, 151–153
Protein–DNA complexes, 6
Psoriasis, 97
Psychiatric disturbance, 198
Psychiatry, 180, 183, 215
Psychosis, 182, 200
Psychotomimetic compounds, 193
Psychotropic medications, 185
Public health, 70
Pulmonary artery, 102
Pulmonary infections, 92, 98
Pulse counting, 116
Purine, 68, 252
Pyridine, 78
Pyridone, 193, 194
Pryidoxal 5-phosphate, 157, 194, 197, 198, 203, 205
Pyridoxine. *See* Vitamin B_6
Pyrimidine, 252
Pyrogallol, 115, 199
Pyrogen, 164
Pyrroluria, 197–198

Quantum leap, 243
Quantum mechanical resonance, 251–252
Quantum mechanics, 238, 244
Quantum yield, 115
Quaternary ammonium compounds, 216
Quenchers of lipid peroxides, 69
Quenching of free radicals, 67, 70

Radiation, 51, 58, 65, 75, 114, 133
Radiation, ultraviolet (uv), 77, 81
Rand Corporation, 230
Random damage, 77
Rate of synthesis, 3
Reagan, Ronald, 250
Reagin antibody, 149
Receptor assays, 174
Recommended daily allowance (RDA), 48, 137–139, 162
Recorder, 33, 116
Red blood cells (erythrocytes), 13, 63, 65, 92, 94–97, 99, 100, 104, 156, 251

deformability of, 95
membrane of, 96
Redox-active metal, 94
Redox activity, 96
Redox balance, 88, 89
Reducing equivalents, 94, 99, 104, 107
Reduction, 58 (*table*)
Reductionism, 245, 247
Regulator molecules, 3, 5
Rejuvenation of surfaces, 123
Relaxed conformation, 36–37, 41, 45, 46
Reptiles, 50
Resistance to disease, 106
Resonance, 235–238, 244
Respiration, 78, 89
Respiratory burst, 89
Respiratory center, 77
Respiratory distress syndrome, neonatal, 65
Respiratory tract, 148
Reticuloendothelial system, 147 (*fig.*), 165
Retina, 102
Retinoblastoma, 4, 10
Retrolental fibroplasia, 65
Retrovirus, 3
Revolution, medical, 245
Reye's syndrome, 160
Rheumatoid arthritis, 65, 190
Riboflavin. *See* Vitamin B_2
Ritalin, 203
RNA, 3, 19, 11
Roosevelt, Franklin D., 228
Rotifers, 78
Russell, Bertrand, 227

Sakharov, Andrei D., 241
Salicylates, 194. *See also* Aspirin
Saliva, 148
Salt bridges, 45
Sampling period, 118
Santavuori-Halti disease, 67
Sardines, 68
Saturated fat, 61
Saturation curve of hemoglobin, 33
Sauna, 191
Schizophrenia, xi, 99–101, 173, 180–202
Schizophrenia, chronic, 100, 187
Schizophrenias, classification, 197–198
Schweitzer, Albert, 231–233
Sciara, 2
Science Citation Index, 254–255
Scleroderma, 68
Scopolamine, 218
Scurvy, 48, 50–53, 133, 136, 138, 158, 181
subclinical, 48, 53, 206
Sea, 77
Seborrheic dermatitis, 97
Secondary amines, 141
Secondary structure, 148
Secretin, 175
Sedation, 186
Sedative, 200
Seditious libel, 231
Selenite, 165
Selenium, 59, 61, 63 (*table*), 65, 68, 77, 79, 90–93, 96, 97, 101, 104, 107, 108, 144, 162, 165, 169
Self-mutilation, 191
Semiconductor, 235
Senate Internal Security Subcommittee, 230
Senescence, 15, 81, 98
Senile plaques, 219
Sepsis, 165
Serine, 215
Serotonergic neurotransmission, 203
Serotonin, 106, 151, 195, 198–200, 202, 214
Serum lipids, 108
Sexual behavior, feminine, 206
Sexual maturity, 12
Sexual roles, 105
Shock, 53
Sickle cell anemia, 21, 57, 70, 95, 228, 231–232, 244
Sickle cell hemoglobin, 46
Siderophores, 164
Signal-to-noise ratio, 116
Silver, 195, 196
Simplicity, 245

Singlet oxygen, 63, 115
Skin, 103, 107, 136, 148, 154, 161, 191
Skin burn injury, 103
Skin diseases, 97
Skin peptides, 175
Sleep, 184, 203, 206
Sleep, rapid-eye-movement, 206
Sleep, slow wave, 206
Sleep disturbance, 203
Smoke, cigarette, 89
Smokers, 97
Smoking, 61, 62, 63 (*table*), 69
Smooth-muscle spasm, 151
Social systems, 245
Solvents, 107
Solzhenitsyn, Aleksandr I., 239
Somatic cells, 2
Somatic mutation, 2, 18
Somatostatin, 174, 175
Sonneborn, Tracy, 10
Southern Californians, 91
Soviet science, 113, 240
Soviet Union, 235–237, 239–243, 249
Soybeans, 215
Specialization, 245
Specificity, 148, 250, 251
Spectral response, 117
Spectrin, 95
Spectrophotometer, 33
Spleen, 80, 92, 102, 148, 152
Stalin, Josef, 235
Stalinism, 237
Starvation, 206
State Department, 235, 250
Steady state, 118
Stem cells, 8, 145, 147
Steroid hormones, 162, 163, 172
Stevenson, Adlai, 231
Stomach, 140. *See also* Gastrointestinal tract
Stone, Irwin, ix, 249, 253
Stress, 2, 7, 48, 50, 61–63, 103, 105, 106, 133, 161*n.*, 162, 168
Stroke, 102–103
Structure of crystals, 228
Sturdivant, Alfred H., 245, 250
Subclinical deficiency, 206
Substance P, 175
Substantia nigra, 195, 206
Substrate concentration, 181
Sudden infant death syndrome, 51–52
Suffering, 227, 233
Sugars, 205
Suicide, 183
Sulfur amino acids, 64 (*table*), 90 (*table*), 101, 104, 148
Supernova, 51
Superoxide, 62, 67, 98
Superoxide anion, 58, 60–63, 68, 70, 94, 96, 146
Superoxide dismutase. *See* Enzyme
Surgery, 133, 152, 156, 161, 168
Symmetry, 33
Synapses, 217
Synaptic poisons, 99
Syphilis, 182
Systemic lupus erythematosus, 68, 79, 80
Szent-Gyorgyi, Albert, x, 48, 249
Szilard, Leo, 229

T-cell function, 160
T-cells, 147–150, 152–157, 160, 161, 166, 167
  cytolytic or effector, 147, 148, 150, 153
  helper, 147, 148, 150, 153, 156, 158, 161, 167
  helper/suppressor ratio, 148–150, 153, 155
  killer, 160, 166
  null, 149, 152, 155
  suppressor, 2, 147, 148, 153, 158, 161, 167
Tannic acid, 142
Tardive dyskinesia, 201–202, 220, 221
Target cells, 148
Taurine, 202
Tay-Sachs disease, 57
Technology, 142, 145, 147
Teller, Edward, 230

Template, 252
Tense conformation, 36–37, 41, 45, 46
Teratocarcinoma, 7
Tertiary structure, 148
Tetanus toxoid, 162
Tetradecanoylphorbol acetate, 14
Tetrahedron, 32
Thalassemia, 95, 232
Therapeutics of optimization, 207
Thiamin. *See* Vitamin B_1
Thiobarbituric acid assay, 101, 103
Thioridizine, 185, 203, 220
Third world countries, 152, 165
Threonyl residue, 41
Thrombi, 60
Thromboembolic disorders, 162
Thromboxanes, 69 (*fig.*), 89
Thymic involution, 154, 155, 167
Thymidine, 150
Thymosin, 151, 152, 155
Thymus, 92, 145, 147, 151–152, 157–158, 161, 168
Thymus, hormones of, 151
Thyroid, 93
Thyrotrophin-releasing hormone, 172–173
Thyroxine, 173
Time magazine, 228, 233
Tissue culture, 8, 14
Tissue injury, 101
Tobacco, 162
Tocopherol. *See* Vitamin E
Tolerance to oxidants, 89, 92
Toluic acid, 251
Total parenteral nutrition, 155
Toxic chemicals, 262
Toxicity, 93, 102, 133, 141, 155, 165–166, 195, 204–205
Toximolecular principle, 201, 202, 207
Tranquillizers, 185
Transconformational protein, 4*n.*
Transfer factor, 150
Transference, 201
Transferrin, 152, 164
Transformation, malignant, 6
Transformation of lymphocytes, 167
Transmethylation, 193
Transnitrosation, 141
Transport proteins, 97
Trauma, 53, 68, 69, 89, 103
Treaty, nuclear test ban, 230, 231
Tremor, 186
Triglycerides, 65, 138
Trimethylamine, 215
Trisomy of chromosome 21, 98
Truffles, 172
Tryptamine, 193
Tryptophan, 192–194, 198, 199, 202, 203, 206
Tryptophan load test, 194, 203
Tuberculin, purified protein derivative, 150, 157
Tuberculosis, 155
Tumor, benign, 60
Tumor initiators, 7, 8, 14
Tumor promoters, 7–9, 14, 167
Tumors, Ehrlich ascites, 68
Turkel, Henry, 204
Twilight sleep, 218
Tyler, Albert, 250
Type A behavior, 62
Tyrosine, 152, 199, 202
Tyrosyl residue, 46, 73

Ubiquinone (coenzyme Q), 64, 78
Ultraviolet radiation, 77, 81
Unhygienic living conditions, 152
Union Now, 229
United Nations, 230
Unsaturated fatty acids, 144, 167
Unsaturated linkages, 58
Unsaturated lipids, 59, 70, 77
    dietary, 79
Urethane, 17
Urey, H., 229
Uric acid, 51*n.*, 77, 90 (*table*), 115, 117
Urinalysis, 201

Valyl residue, 46
Vascular endothelium, 101
Vascular system, 105

Vasculitis, 97
Vectors of disease, 250
Vegetable oils, 191
Veins, 61, 102
Venous blood, 94
Verbal communication, 100
Vertebrates, 49
Vigor, 134, 137, 139
Vinyl alcohol, 238
VIP, 175
Virus, 18, 19, 157, 161
Virus infections, 68, 148, 160
Viruses, oncogenic, 19
Viruses as mutagens, 18
Visceral protein, 154
Vision, 204
Vitamin A, 104, 107, 108, 144, 148, 161–162, 168. *See also* Carotene
Vitamin B_1 (thiamin), 189, 190, 203
Vitamin B_2 (riboflavin), 157, 193
Vitamin B_3. *See* Niacin; Niacinamide
Vitamin B_5. *See* Pantothenic acid
Vitamin B_6 (pyridoxine), 144, 145, 151, 156, 168, 184, 189, 190, 195, 197, 203, 204. *See also* Pyridoxal 5-phosphate
Vitamin B_{12} (cobalamin), 117, 157, 158, 181–182, 189, 190, 195, 203
Vitamin C (ascorbic acid)
    antioxidant, 64, 90 (*table*), 104, 108, 198, 249
    and cancer, 21, 63 (*table*), 70, 114
    in carnitine biosynthesis, 136–139
    deficiency, 52. *See also* Scurvy
    evolutionary history, 49
    in heavy metal intoxication, 165, 205
    human requirement, 48, 250
    in immunological function, 107, 146, 158–160, 168–169
    in mental illness, xi, 188, 198
    in mentally disabled children, 203–204
    in shock and trauma, 53
    site of synthesis, 50
    stabilization of kryptopyrrole, 197
    tissue saturation, 137
    urinary excretion, 53, 188
    in viral illness, 54, 144, 158, 160
Vitamin C and the Common Cold, 54, 249
Vitamin C, the Common Cold, and the Flu, 158
Vitamin D (cholecalciferol), 144, 162–163
Vitamin E (tocopherol), 59, 61–63, 65, 68, 77, 79, 93, 95, 97, 101, 104, 107, 142, 144, 162, 165, 168
Vitamin-enzyme testing, functional, 202–203
Vitamins, 145, 152, 180, 188, 193, 194, 202
Vomiting, 151, 152, 175

War, 114
Warm-blooded animals, 50
Watson and Crick, 240, 252
Weight gain, 93
Weight loss, 97, 137, 152
Wheat, 190
Wheland, George W., 239, 240
White blood cells, 98, 153. *See also* Leukocytes
Willkie, Wendell, 228
Wilson's disease, 12, 57
World peace, 229, 249
World War II, 229, 235
Wurtman, Richard, 206
Wyskoff, Victor, 229

X chromosome, inactivation of, 81
X rays, 13, 17, 244
x-y recorder, 33
Xanthurenic acid, 203
Xeroderma pigmentosum, 14

Yeast, 68. *See also Candida*

Zinc, 90 (*table*), 98, 107, 108, 144, 146, 148, 150, 151, 154–157, 166, 168, 169, 191, 195–198